Encyclopedia of the Animal World

8 *Enzymes—Follicle mites*

Printed exclusively for J & H International Corporation for distribution in the United States

ENZYMES, substances promoting chemical changes within living matter. Living organisms are able, by an immense network of chemical reactions, to incorporate matter from outside and use it to produce *energy or as materials for growth and reproduction. Enzymes can be justly described as the catalysts of life. Chemical catalysts are defined as substances which can accelerate reactions without themselves forming part of the product or being used up. Thus finely divided nickel will catalyze the adding of hydrogen atoms to double-bonded pairs of carbon atoms in the chains of fatty esters, a process which greatly raises the melting point, and in effect, converts an oil into a fat. Enzymes fulfil an analagous role in living systems. For example, they enable the body to utilize—or burn—fuel at a temperature of only 98·6°F (37°C).

The idea that digestion was brought about by 'ferments' in the gastric juices and that similar 'organized ferments' capable of converting sugar to alcohol were present in yeast cells, dates from the early 19th century. Such substances were named enzymes—meaning simply 'in yeast'—by the German physiologist Kühne in 1878. The first enzyme to be prepared in a crystalline, albeit impure, form was the plant enzyme, urease, in 1926.

All enzymes are proteins. They are rapidly destroyed at temperatures of 122°F (50°C) and over and their activities are greatly affected by changes in acidity. They have several other characteristics which distinguish them from inorganic catalysts. First, in the sense that they bring about a much greater lowering of the free-energy of activation, they are much more efficient—they have relatively a much greater influence on the speed of reactions. For example, the enzyme catalase is about 1,000 times as effective as platinum in decomposing hydrogen peroxide. Secondly, they show a much greater specificity, that is to say the scope of activity of any particular enzyme is more limited than that of inorganic catalysts which will often promote a whole range of reactions. Thirdly, enzymes are much less stable; their effectiveness decreases with time.

The material on which an enzyme acts is known as its substrate. Enzymes usually, though not invariably, include the suffix 'ase' in their names, and are named after their substrates. Thus, in general terms, enzymes which split proteins are called 'proteases' and, to give a more specific example, the enzyme which catalyses the conversion of succinic to fumaric acid in the citric acid cycle (see Kreb's cycle) is known as 'succinic dehydrogenase'.

Co-enzymes. For many reactions to proceed requires other substances in addition to the enzyme and substrate. Sometimes the activators are relatively unspecific; metallic ions, especially those of divalent metals such as zinc or magnesium, are examples of such cofactors. Important cofactors for a range of reactions in which hydrogen atoms are taken from or added to substrates were discovered during attempts to purify the enzyme, zymase, found in yeast, in 1904. It was found that when extracts of yeast were dialyzed, that is to say placed in a bag of parchment material bathed in running water to allow small molecules—but not proteins—to leach out, they lost the power to ferment glucose. The ability could be restored by adding boiled but undialyzed yeast

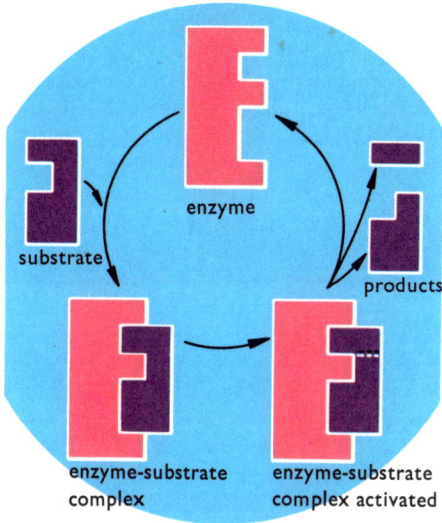

Diagram illustrating the action of an enzyme in a chemical reaction in which a substrate is broken down into its constituent products.

juice. It thus appeared that fermentation depended on two factors, a protein which could be destroyed by heat and a heat stable substance of low molecular weight. The cofactor was given the name 'co-zymase'.

Many years later, it was found that an enzyme present in red blood cells also required a co-enzyme and between 1930 and 1940 the structures of both this and of co-zymase were elucidated. The co-enzymes each contained pentose sugar, phosphoric acid and a purine, which is a nitrogenous organic base; compounds of this kind are called nucleotides, since they resemble the degradation products of nucleic acids. The co-enzymes also contain pyridine: co-zymase is diphospho-pyridine nucleotide or nicotinamide adenine dinucleotide (NAD) and the cofactor in red blood cells is triphospho-pyridine nucleotide or nicotinamide-adenine-dinucleotide phosphate (NADP).

The importance of NAD and NADP is that they act as hydrogen carriers in many metabolic reactions which involve the removal of a pair of hydrogen atoms and are thus, in effect, oxidative. The substrate molecule is acted upon by a specific dehydrogenase enzyme and the hydrogen atoms are removed and passed on to the nucleotide carrier. Ultimately the hydrogen may be used elsewhere in a reductive reaction or oxidized to water.

The action of enzymes

About 800 enzymes have now been identified and named. A very few may be considered to give some idea of the range of processes in animals which involve enzymes.

The realization that digestion was a chemical process in which food was made soluble by the gastric and other juices dates from the 17th century. Spallanzani (1729–1799) actually removed samples of the stomach juice and showed that if warmed, it could digest meat even outside of the body.

The stomach produces a protein-splitting enzyme known as pepsin, as well as secreting hydrochloric acid to provide the strongly acid medium necessary for the pepsin to work. Pepsin acts to break some of the peptide links which hold together the chains of amino-acid in the protein molecule. The chemical action is hydrolysis—the addition of water. But only the bonds at certain positions are affected, digestion of proteins being completed in the duodenum, under more neutral conditions, by two enzymes known as trypsin and chymotrypsin which are secreted by the pancreas. As a result of the action of these three enzymes, the proteins in the food are reduced to short polypeptide chains; the final solution to amino acid units is completed by another group of enzymes in the pancreatic and intestinal secretions.

The digestion of carbohydrates similarly involves a series of enzyme-catalysed reactions. So-called monosaccharide sugars, such as glucose or fructose need no digestion; they are absorbed without change. Disaccharide sugars, made up of two linked mono-saccharides, such as sucrose (or cane-sugar), of which glucose and fructose are the units, are hydrolyzed by enzymes in the duodenum. The breakdown of starch, an insoluble polysaccharide composed of repeatedly linked glucose units, starts in the mouth by the action of amylase in the saliva. The amylase breaks off double units of glucose—the disaccharide maltose—from the polysaccharide chain, though it does not entirely reduce it. The process is continued in the duodenum, where the disaccharide units are also split. Fats, too, which are esters of fatty acid and glycerol, are also hydrolysized to their constituents by lipases of which the most active occurs in the pancreatic secretion.

The products of digestion are used to supply energy, to make living materials and in the disposal of waste products. Some of the steps in intermediate metabolism are described elsewhere (see energy and Kreb's

Enzymes

cycle). All these reactions are carried out by enzymes. For example, the first step in the utilization of glucose, whether by yeast or animal muscle, is its conversion to glucose-6-phosphate. This involves the transfer of a phosphate group from adenosine triphosphate (ATP) and the action is promoted by an enzyme called 'hexokinase'. In effect, at the start of this series of changes known as glycolysis, energy in the form of the phosphate bond is actually added to the glucose molecule and, indeed, a further such bond is added at a later stage. But this energy, and more, is finally recovered in the resynthesis of ATP. Hexokinase is but the first of many enzymes involved in the metabolism of carbohydrates in the glycolytic sequence and subsequently in the citric acid cycle.

The nature of enzymes

Enzymes are proteins. Proteins are large molecules composed of a number of amino-acid units—or residues—linked together. The link is achieved by the elimination of a molecule of water between the amino (—NH$_2$) group of one amino-acid and the carboxyl (—COOH) group of another; the result is the peptide bond. About 20 different

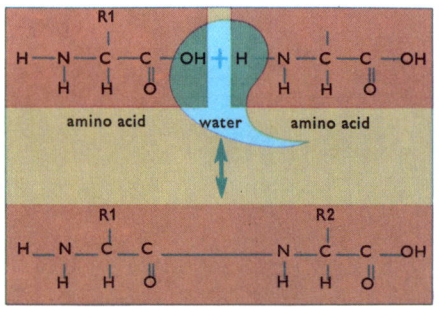

The peptide bond. Amino acids can be linked together by the elimination of a molecule of water between the carboxyl (COOH) and amino (NH$_2$) and groups. R$_1$ and R$_2$ represent different chains making up the respective amino acids. In the digestion of proteins the peptide bond is hydrolyzed.

amino-acids form the building bricks of all proteins. A protein may contain one or more polypeptide chains each comprising several hundred amino-acid units. Their sequence is known as the primary structure of the protein. The chains also have, however, a characteristic organization in three dimensions, the molecule holding its shape by the formation of cross linkages between adjacent pieces of chain. Such links are of various types; an important example is the disulphide bridge between adjacent molecules of the amino-acid cysteine, the 'double molecule' being known as cystine.

The shape of one enzyme, at least, has been worked out. Lysozyme is an enzyme, discovered by Sir Alexander Fleming in 1922, which can attack the polysaccharide cell wall of certain bacteria. It is found in nasal mucus and other places. It has 129 amino-acid residues arranged in a single polypeptide chain, giving a molecular weight of 14,400. The molecule has a somewhat globular shape, and it is formed by the folding of the chain into a complex and

Structure of glucose, and its reaction with ATP, catalyzed by the enzyme hexokinase, to form glucose-6-phosphate. Ⓟ = phosphate group.

characteristic shape, stabilized by four disulphide bridges. It can be compared to a ball, or irregular knot, of wire or chain, spot welded at four fixed points.

The most interesting feature, however, is that a cleft runs roughly through the middle of the molecule. It has been shown that units of the amino-sugars, which make-up the polysaccharide which is the substrate of the enzyme, attach to sites in the cleft. It seems that a six unit length of chain would just fill the cleft. The enzyme is then thought to act by breaking a single link between the fourth and fifth sugar molecule from the top of the cleft. Thus an enzyme can be likened to a complicated three dimensional key, into which the substrate—or a section of it— exactly fits. The result is that particular terminal groups of the enzyme are brought into close juxtaposition with specific groups of the substrate. In this sense, in the course of the chemical reaction, the enzyme combines with its substrate, a view of enzyme action favoured by earlier workers.

The synthesis of enzymes

The characteristic shape of protein molecules is believed to be determined by the amino-acid sequence. The main problem of enzyme synthesis, therefore, is how the amino-acid units are assembled in the right order by living cells. Clearly the cell must contain a store of necessary information to make enzymes, as well as the essential machinery. Whereas carbohydrates can be built up by successive addition of repeated units, protein synthesis seems to take place in a single operation. To withhold a single essential amino-acid from a growing organism prevents any protein synthesis whatever.

The information for the building of enzymes is now acknowledged to lie in the desoxyribonucleic acid (DNA) of the chromosomes within the nucleus of the cell. DNA is a macromolecule, consisting of a double spiral chain of sugar and phosphate groups, to which four organic bases are attached. Since any sample of DNA is always found to contain exactly equal amounts of the bases adenine (A) and thymine (T) and exactly equal amounts of cytosine (C) and guanine (G), it was proposed that along the double spiral the A of one strand is always paired with the T of the other, and C is always paired with G. Thus if the strands are separated, each can make a new partner by assembling the string of complementary bases. The genius of this proposal, for which Francis Crick and his associates gained a Nobel Prize, is that it provides a molecular basis for the replication of the hereditary material when the chromosomes divide.

How can the 20 different amino-acids in a polypeptide sequence be coded by four different nucleotides? Clearly a single nucleotide cannot stand for a single amino-acid. Two nucleotides per amino-acid would only give 16 combinations, which is not enough; three nucleotides would provide 64 possible arrangements, which is too many. So either the code must be degenerate in that each amino-acid is coded by more than one triplet, or some of the possible triplet configurations must make nonsense. These possibilities are by no means exhaustive on information theory. But it has now been shown that a specific sequence of three bases, known as a codon, does produce each amino-acid and, furthermore, the code has been cracked.

The DNA of the nucleus does not, however, directly act as a template for the assembly of the amino-acid units. The synthesis of proteins is carried out in the cytoplasm of cells. Enzyme-secreting cells, such as those of the pancreas, contain, in their basal regions, a prominent system of densely packed membranes known as the endoplasmic reticulum. These membranes bear granules, called ribosomes, about 150Å across, on one side, and enclose spaces or

Repeating units of glucose in the polysaccharide: starch.

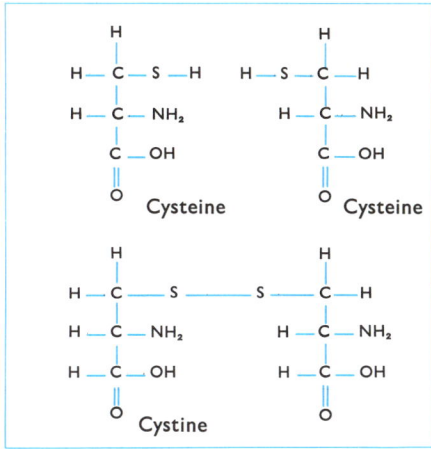

Formation of a molecule of cystine from two molecules of cysteine, showing how adjacent polypeptide chains can be joined by disulphide links.

cisternae between their smooth sides. The onset of enzyme synthesis is associated by the appearance of granules in the cisternae. These granules soon disappear, but concurrently so-called zymogen granules, which are associated with protease activity, are formed in the distal part of the cell. There is little doubt that the zymogen granules are formed from the intracisternal granules.

The ribosomes are mainly composed of ribonucleic acid (RNA) which differs from DNA in two respects, the possession of ribose instead of deoxyribose and of uracil instead of thymine. About 80% of the total RNA in the cell is ribosomal; the remainder is soluble. If enzymes are synthesized at the site of the ribosomes it might be supposed that the ribosomal RNA is a copy of the nuclear DNA and provides the templates. The view that each ribosome has the template for a single protein could not, however, account for the large number of different protein molecules synthesized by bacteria which possess only a few ribosomes. The hypothesis of Jacob and Monod is that the ribosomal RNA does not act in this way, but that the nuclear information is instead transferred to short lengths of messenger RNA, which move into the ribosomes and act as the templates. According to the hypothesis the amino-acids are then each attached to yet another type of nucleic acid, 'transfer' RNA, and then lined up by base pairing between the 'messenger' RNA and the 'transfer' RNA. Finally the lined up amino-acids are joined by peptide links.   F.J.G.E.

EPHEMERA, a word used for insects that live less than a day. It forms the basis for the name of an order of insects, the Ephemeroptera or mayflies, and also expresses the popular notion of the longevity of *mayflies: that they live 'less than a day, only a matter of a few hours'.

There are two ways in which this general idea can be falsified. In the first place the mayfly is an aquatic insect that goes through the usual stages of an incomplete metamorphosis. The full life-cycle may take a few weeks or months or, in many species, one, two or three years. At the end of this time the nymph climbs up the stem of a water plant and comes to rest, clinging with its legs. A split appears in the cuticle of the back and a winged insect emerges after a while to allow the wings to dry, and flies to a bush or a rock near the waterside. This is known as the subimago (or subadult), a stage in the life-history peculiar to mayflies. In some species the subimago stage lasts a few minutes, in others it may last 24 hours or more. The subimago, at the end of its time, comes to rest, the cuticle of its back splits and the perfect insect or imago frees itself of the old skin and flies off. The transformation from the nymph to the subimago to the imago takes place more or less simultaneously over the whole region, usually in May. After the emergence of the imagos the bushes, rocks and waterside vegetation are decorated with thousands of dried and empty skins of the subimagos.

The imago may die the same evening as it emerges from the subimago, the following

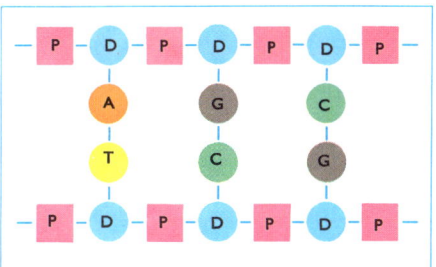

Diagrammatic structure, much simplified, of desoxyribonucleic acid (DNA). The two chains of sugar (D) and phosphate (P) groups are joined, in a ladder-like configuration, through pairs of bases. Adenine (A) is always paired with thymine (T) and guanine (G) with cytosine (C).

morning or evening, or it may live several days. Individuals under observation in captivity have lived as much as a week. The real way in which the dictionary definition can be shown to be false is that the mayfly as an individual—counting its life-span from the moment an egg is laid to the death of the imago resulting from it—lives for anything from a few months to three years.

The last stage, of adulthood, in the life of the mayfly is unusually brief. It is, in fact, no more than the final reproductive phase. The swarming of mayflies over rivers is a nuptial dance in which mating takes place. After this the females lay their eggs in water, each laying two batches as a rule, totalling up to four thousand eggs.

The reproductive potential of these insects is best emphasized by what happens when mayflies swarm. When mayflies are on the wing the air-space over the lakes, rivers and streams is crowded with their milling thousands. At times the swarms move farther from the water and around the Great Lakes and streets of towns and villages may be invaded by them.

The fishermen in France speak of the showers of mayflies falling into the rivers of the Great Lakes as fish manna. So far as Lake Erie is concerned, the manna has been seriously reduced as a result of pollution, by sewage, industrial effluent and what have been called other hazards of civilization.

The females die after laying their eggs and the males as the dance peters out, causing a shower of insect food onto the water. This forms food for the fish, linking the life-cycle of the mayflies with that of fishes and interference with it, by pollution or any other cause, means loss of sport to the fisherman and a reduction in the food supply to mankind generally.   M.B.

EPHYRA, the small *medusa released from a scyphistoma, which is the *polyp phase in the life-history of many jellyfishes. During the winter months the ephyra is budded off the scyphistoma by muscular action and is a minute, gelatinous animal only a few millimeters in diameter. It consists of a central disc region, the edges of which are drawn out into eight lobes. Each lobe is divided into two

Scyphistoma of *Aurelia aurita* hanging down from the underside of a rock, strobilating to produce ephyra larvae.

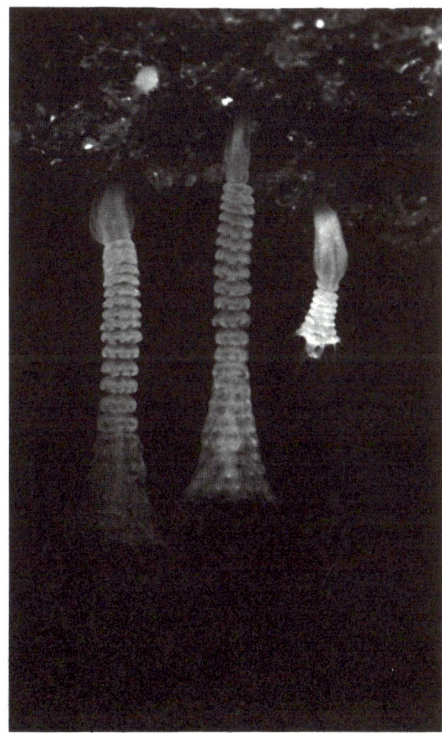

Epidermis

lappets with a central sense tentacle or rhopalium. In the centre of the disc on the under or sub-umbrella surface is a square mouth. The ephyra lives in the surface waters of the sea and feeds on small planktonic animals, which are caught by *nematocysts. These animals accumulate on the lappets which bend and convey this food to the mouth. As it grows the ephyra expands the edge of the disc so that it fills in the gaps between the lappets and gradually assumes the shape of the adult medusa. The corners of the mouth may enlarge into long, frilly arms and the canal system develops. By the summer, the medusa is adult and capable of sexual reproduction. Not all ephyrae develop from scyphistomae. In the genus *Pelagia*, which lives in the open oceans, the ciliated planula larva changes directly into an ephyra by flattening and pushing out eight bifid lobes. An ephyra may give rise to a scyphistoma instead of an adult medusa if the conditions are unfavourable. CLASS: Scyphozoa, PHYLUM: Cnidaria. S.E.H.

EPIDERMIS, the outer pavement layer of the body. In some aquatic invertebrates it consists of no more than a simple epithelium, but in all vertebrates it is a many layered, so-called stratified epithelium, which is either periodically moulted, as in reptiles, or continually lost at its surface and replaced by cell division at its base as, for example, in mammals. In vertebrates the epidermis itself rests upon a bed of connective tissue, the dermis, the two together forming the skin.

The epidermis performs important protective functions. In land vertebrates, for example, it controls loss of water by evaporation and also prevents the penetration of harmful ultra-violet radiation. This last property is due to the presence within the epidermal cells of a brown pigment, melanin, which is manufactured by and transferred from pigment cells in the basal layers of the epidermis. Derivatives of the epidermis, such as feathers and hairs are important as insulating materials to prevent heat loss in warm-blooded birds and mammals. Epidermal glands of various kinds may be concerned with such functions as mucus production (fishes and amphibians), poison manufacture (some amphibians), temperature regulation (sweat glands in mammals) or the production of chemical substances which act as markers of territory or sex attractants.

In the mammalian superficial epidermis, cell division is largely confined to the basal layer of cells—the stratum germinativum—in contact with the dermo-epidermal junction. As the cells get pushed outwards they build up within them an insoluble fibrous protein called keratin. Structures known as tonofilaments can be seen by electron microscopy even in the basal layer. As the cells move outwards they form successively the stratum spinosum, the stratum granulosum (or granular layer), and the stratum corneum. Ultimately, the cells, now cornified have no nuclei and contain only dead keratin; it is believed that this keratin arises from tonofilaments together with interfilamentous material from the granular layer.

The hair follicles may be regarded as tubular inpushings of epidermis, and the hair—a tough cylinder of keratin—is formed by division of cells at the base of the follicle in a region known as the matrix. Follicles do not produce hair continuously. Hairs are periodically shed and replaced by new ones, either in a pattern as in animal moulting, or in a continuous process as in the human scalp, which loses 50–100 hairs a day. Moulting of mammals, like reproduction, is controlled through the hormonal system by seasonal changes in the environment. Attached to each hair follicle is a sebaceous gland, which secretes the waxy sebum, and in some areas of the body (in man notably under the arms) an apocrine gland. The activity of sebaceous glands is under the control of hormones. Man and other primates also possess eccrine sweat glands which are separate from the hair follicles; they function to help control body temperature by evaporation.

The epidermis on human palms and soles or on mammalian foot-pads is of a different variety. It has neither hair follicles nor sebaceous glands. In human skin of this type the sweat gland openings are arranged on raised ridges, which form characteristic and individual patterns or dermatoglyphs. Thus finger prints can be exactly matched to their owners. See skin. J.E.

EPITHELIUM, a thin layer or sheet of cells. Epithelia form boundaries, either, like the epidermis, covering organs, or lining internal spaces, as in the ducts of various glands. They are classified according to the height of the cells, flattened cells forming pavement epithelia, tall cells forming columnar epithelia, and also according to whether they are only one cell thick (simple epithelia) or several cells thick (compound epithelia).

EQUIDAE, living equids, including the horse *Equus przewalskii*, ass *E. asinus*, Asiatic wild ass *E. hemionus*, Plains zebra *E. quagga*, Mountain zebra *E. zebra* and Grévy's zebra *E. grevyi* are all, apart from the stripe patterns of the zebras, very similar in appearance and in anatomy. All wild equids have erect manes and a dark stripe along their backs. The major differences are

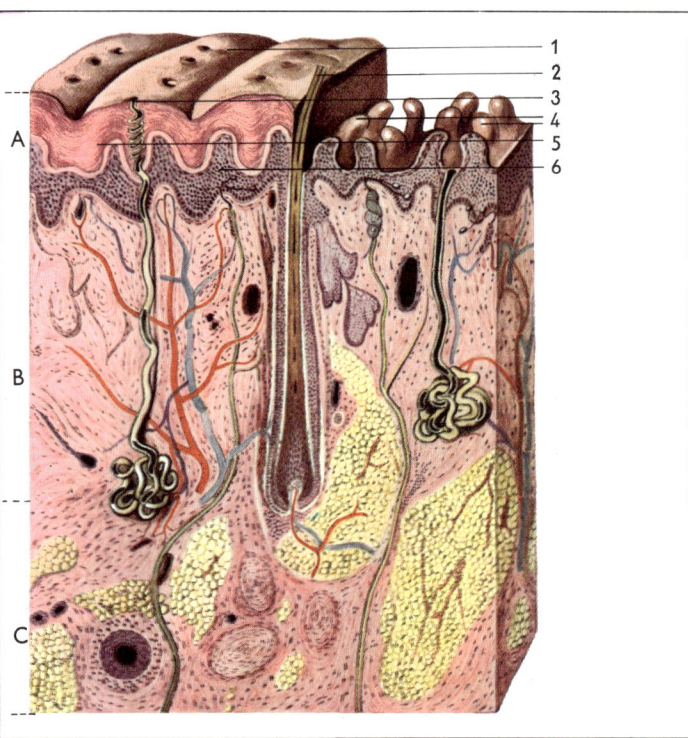

Section through the human skin (left).
A. Epidermis:
 1. outer layer of skin with grooves and the pores of sweat glands
 2. a hair
 3. exit from sweat gland
 4. papilla
 5. stratum corneum
 6. stratum granulosum.
B. Dermis or corium
C. Subdermis or subcuticle layer.
(Right) Fingerprints formed by the pattern of grooves and ridges in the outer layer of the epidermis.

Zebroids and horses, the former being hybrids from the mating of Grévy's zebra with horses.

in the size and shape of the ears, which are very long and pointed in the ass, long and round in the Grévy's zebra and short and pointed in the horse and in the other zebras. The ears of the Asiatic wild ass are intermediate between those of the horse and the ass.

All equids have the same tooth formula: three incisors, one canine, four premolars and three molars in each jaw. The first premolars, the 'wolf teeth', are vestigial and often absent as are the canines in females. Incisors, canines and premolars appear first as milk teeth and are shed and replaced by permanent teeth from the age of two and half to four years. Infundibula, the marks on the incisors of equids only, are present in both jaws in most species. The shapes of these marks which change with the wear of the teeth are the most reliable criteria for assessing the age of equids. For reasons of convenience the lower jaw is normally used for ageing the horse but it has to be the upper jaw in the Plains zebra, in which species there are marks in the upper jaw only.

Two species of equids have been domesticated: the ass and the horse. Members of the other species, onagers, one of the Asiatic wild asses, have been tamed, even in prehistoric times, by the Assyrians. However, no great success has been achieved with these and tame zebras, which are known to lack the stamina which is essential for a draught or riding animal.

Equids become sexually mature at the age of two years in females and three years in males. In captivity they may even breed at that age; in the wild, however, stallions are at least four or five years old when competing for mares with fully grown stallions. Captive animals are reported to have lived up to 40 years. At the age of about 20 years the teeth are usually worn down to the extent that the animals cannot survive on grass or hay

Naso-nasal contact during the greeting ceremony of Plains zebra stallions.

Equidae

alone. The oldest equids found in the wild are therefore rarely older than 20 years.

All equids can be interbred with each other and some of the hybrids are of practical importance as they are more suitable to specialized jobs than either parent species. One of these is the mule (donkey stallion × horse mare) another is the zebroid (Grévy's zebra × horse). Both are especially useful as pack or riding animals in high mountains. The latter are used for safaris on Mount Kenya. All the hybrids are normally infertile. No hybrids are known of wild equids in their overlapping ranges.

The gestation period of equids is about one year and apart from rare exceptions only one foal is born at a time. Most foals are born during the night or in the early morning, and the mares are able to delay birth for hours when disturbed. During parturition the mare lies on her side. She does not assist the foal and she does not eat the afterbirth, in contrast to many other animals. The foals are precocious and they start following their mothers within about 30 minutes of birth.

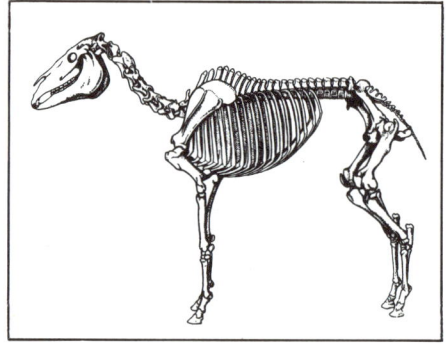

Skeleton of a domestic horse.

The equids are grazers but under especially hard conditions they browse to some extent.

The voices of the different equids are quite characteristic, and a number of different sounds can be distinguished in each species. In some species, e.g. in the horse and in the Plains zebra, the voices are individually so varied that the animals recognize each other by their calls.

Equids have a keen sense of sight, hearing and smell. They see colours as we do, but these are of little importance to them, whereas perception for motion is greatly refined. This is an adaptation which enables them to spot potential predators from far away. Captive animals recognize their keepers by sight, voice and smell.

Some behaviour patterns of the equids are so similar that they can be described in a single general account.

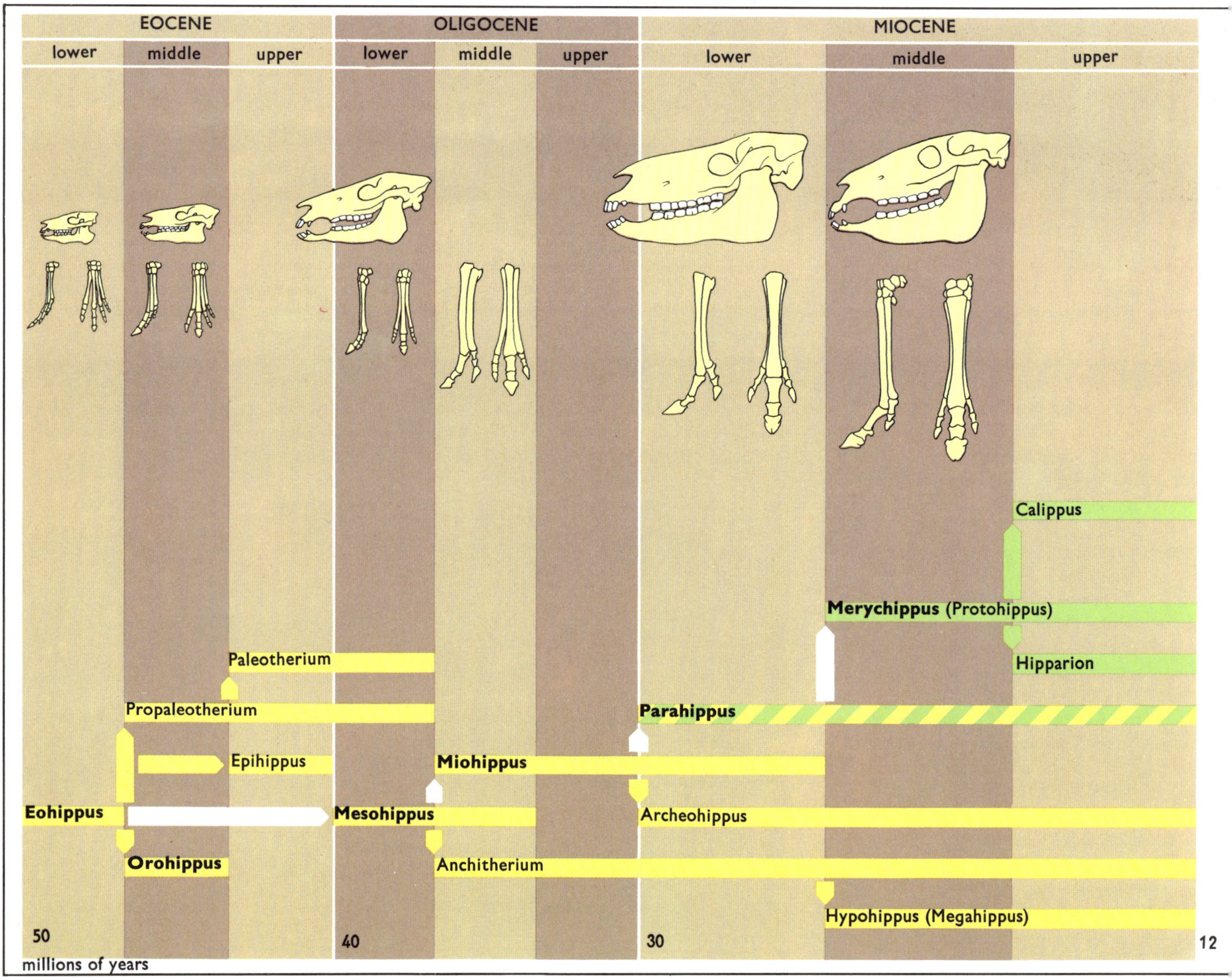

Fighting. Stallions fight for mares, and several types of fighting can be distinguished: circling, running, neck-wrestling, biting and kicking in stallions and biting and kicking in mares. Young animals, especially young stallions, play fighting games which consist of the same elements as serious fighting. The weapons of the equids, teeth and hoofs, are comparatively harmless and thus the chances of the partners injuring each other are minimal. Furthermore, the inferior one can always run off; he is, during flight, not vulnerable. Accordingly no gestures of submission are known in adult equids. If an animal gets killed in a fight, which happens occasionally in captivity, it is either by accident or because it could not escape.

Grooming. Equids engage in mutual grooming. Any two animals groom each other on their necks, shoulders and thorax, places which they themselves cannot reach with their mouth. They scratch each other with their teeth. In mutual grooming man can be a partner as well. Other parts of the body are scratched and cleaned when the animals rub themselves on trees, stones, termite hills and on the ground when lying down. Equids take sand baths and roll on the ground; Mountain zebras even in wet sand. In this species, the adult animals do not roll over on their backs.

Sexual behaviour. Equids are polyoestrous, i.e. their reproduction is not restricted to a certain season and mating can take place at any time of the year. A post-

Donkey stallion displaying flehmen, with the head held up and the upper lip curled back exposing the teeth.

partum (after birth) oestrus occurs a few days after foaling and usually mares conceive then. When a mare is not fully in oestrus she is not receptive and runs away from the stallion, kicking out at him. In full oestrus the mare stands more or less still and permits copulation. In the donkey a certain amount of running seems to be part of the precopulatory activity. However, their mating is far from being a 'rape' as had been assumed previously. This misinterpretation probably originates from observations of captive animals who were only allowed together for the purpose of mating. Mares in oestrus have a typical posture with their hind legs apart and their tails lifted. This stance attracts the stallions from far away, whereas the smell of the oestral secretions seems to be effective only over a short distance. The stallion mounts with his penis erect and then intromission takes place. Coition is of the frictional type and lasts for several minutes.

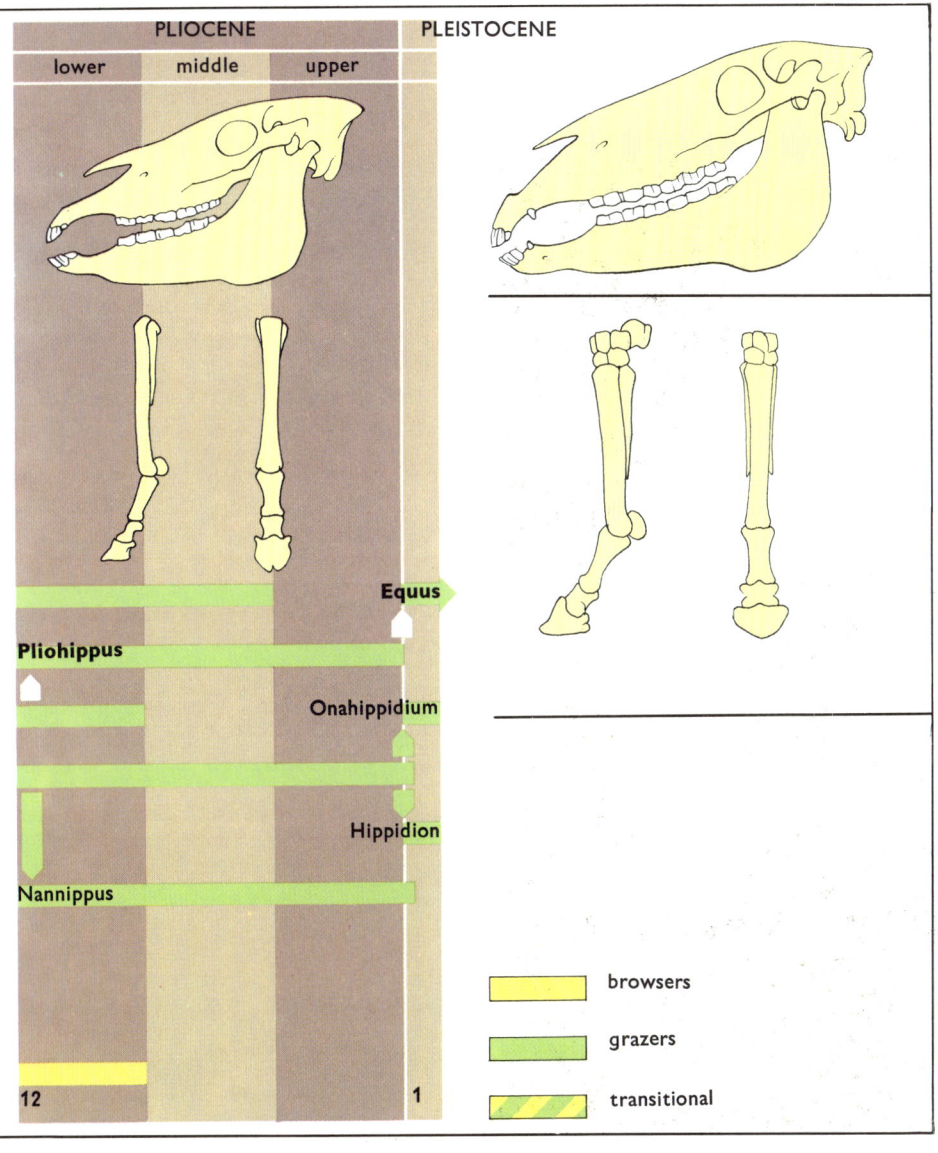

The horse has provided a very complete record of its origin and evolution. Only the intermediate stages between Eohippus and Mesohippus is uncertain. Living equids, including horses, asses and zebras, are very similar in appearance and in anatomy. The third digit is the only developed one of the original four and is covered with a hoof. They all belong to the genus *Equus*, the evolution of which is marked by white arrows in the diagram. Originally browsers, equids became grazers with a transitional form, Parahippus, in the Lower Miocene. The skull and skeleton of the left front foot are shown on the same scale. The development of the foot shows the disappearance of the first digit and a continuing decrease in size of the second and third. The change in feeding habits, from browsing to grazing, is expressed by the increasing elongation of the cheek teeth. This is not obvious in the chart because most of a cheek tooth is embedded in the jawbone, so their increasing length is better reflected in the depth of the lower jaw.

Equivalent species

New Forest pony foals licking each other's back in mutual grooming.

The only surviving species of wild horse *Equus przewalskii*, or Mongolian wild horse.

Facial expressions. Several facial expressions can be distinguished in the equids. Some of them serve intraspecific communication and are also understood by other animals, e.g. man. When greeting each other, the equids have their ears forwards and this indicates friendliness. When threatening the animals have their ears directed backwards, their necks stretched and their heads lowered. Mares in oestrus have a typical facial expression with their ears backwards and sidewards; they chew with open mouths and exposed teeth. This expression is absent in the adult horse mares. All individuals of equine species, old and young and male and female, display flehmen when they sniff at faeces, urine and other 'interestingly' smelling things: the head is held up, the upper lip is curled back and the teeth are exposed.

Marking. Faeces and urine are of special interest to equids. Stallions as well as mares and even foals defaecate and/or urinate after having sniffed at faeces and urine of conspecifics. This behaviour pattern has been called 'marking' as it is similar to that of some other mammals who mark their territories. Marking is, however, displayed even in the non-territorial equids, e.g. in the horse and in two of the three zebra species. ORDER: Perissodactyla, CLASS: Mammalia.   H.K.

EQUIVALENT SPECIES, animals living in similar, but geographically separated, habitats with equivalent roles or *niches*. The gregarious kangaroos of the Australian grasslands have their ecological equivalents in the antelopes of the plains in Africa, Asia and formerly the bison of North America. These animals all occupy the habitat and feeding niche of medium-sized, ground-living animals, grazing at ground and browsing at shrub level. One scavenger niche in the Arctic is filled by the Arctic foxes which feed on the remains of seals killed by Polar bears; the jackals in Africa are the ecological equivalents of the Arctic foxes in scavenging from lion kills. The agouti of South America fills the niche of rabbits in North America and elsewhere.

The existence of ecologically equivalent species suggests that there are limited numbers of niches available in any particular type of major habitat; the number potentially present is dependent upon the availability of food and the complexity of the plant and animal community. The evolutionary process by which these niches become occupied is known as *adaptive radiation and results from selective pressures favouring the most efficient utilization of food resources with the minimum of interspecific competition. The adaptive radiation of placental mammals from insectivore stock occurred during the Paleocene and Eocene. The causes of the widespread extinction of many reptile groups toward the end of the Mesozoic are not understood, but the vacation of the major habitats by the reptiles left niches that in due time were occupied by ecologically equivalent placental mammals. It is generally accepted that Australia separated from the Indo-Malayan continental mass during the Mesozoic, before the rise of the placental mammals, so that only monotremes and marsupials were present in the original Australian fauna. The marsupials independently underwent adaptive radiation and a variety of forms evolved, each filling a niche which has its placental mammal counterpart elsewhere. The marsupial and placental mammal stocks radiating in similar habitats on the land masses of the world have, in many cases, become adapted to the same environmental factor or combination of factors, so that equivalent species may show striking resemblances to one another. This is known as convergent evolution. The Tasmanian 'wolf' *Thylacinus cynocephalus* is a marsupial convergent with the canine carnivores; the marsupial 'tiger-cat' *Dasyurus maculatus* is equivalent to the feline carnivores, and the Banded anteater *Myrmecobius fasciatus* is a marsupial convergent with the South American anteaters. Perhaps one of the most striking examples of convergent equivalent species is the Marsupial mole *Notoryctes typhlops* and the Golden mole *Chrysochloridae* of South Africa. This convergence of shape and the adaptation of the forelimbs for burrowing in a subterranean habitat is also shown by the European mole *Talpa europaea,* the mole-rat *Spalax* of Asia, the Prairie mole *Scalopus* of North America, and even some insects, e.g. the Mole-crickets *Gryllotalpa*. Convergence in equivalent species is frequently the result of adaption to specialized foods. Those mammals that have become adjusted to a diet of ants and termites have cylindrical tongues and a reduction of teeth, for example the Spiny ant-eater (Monotremata), the Banded ant-eater (Marsupialia), the aardvark (Tubulidentata), pangolins (Pholidota), and New World anteaters (Xenarthra). All except the Banded anteater also have large claws for digging into the nests of ants and termites.

The Darwin finches colonized the Galapagos at a time when there were probably no endemic passerine birds on the Archipelago. In the absence of interspecific competition these finches have adaptively radiated to occupy the available niches on the islands and show convergence, in the structure of their beaks and feeding habits, to birds in similar niches elsewhere in the world. Six of the Darwin finches are ground finches feeding on seeds, or cactus in one case, and have powerful beaks resembling those of typical seed-eating finches. Six further species are tree finches inhabiting the humid forests. One of these occupies a niche equivalent to that of woodpeckers and resembles these birds in its ability to climb up and down vertical tree trunks, excavating holes in branches in search of insects. But whereas the woodpecker inserts its long tongue into holes to capture the insects, the finch picks up a twig or cactus spine which it pokes into the crack, subsequently dropping the twig to seize any insect which emerges. Of the other five species of tree finches four are insectivorous with small sharp beaks and one is vegetarian. Finally there is a Slender-billed warbler finch present on all the main islands which closely resembles true warblers in its form and habits.

Two species of animal with overlapping ranges cannot indefinitely occupy extremely similar niches without the extinction or niche divergence of one species. When two previously geographically isolated faunas meet in some area, intense competition will occur, particularly between equivalent species, and it is usually the animals from the larger and ecologically more varied region which are the victors. For example, a number of species of mammals from Europe and Asia have been introduced into Australia, where they are now abundant; this is true of dingoes (not an endemic species but probably introduced by Pleistocene man), foxes, rabbits, and also camels and horses which have run wild. At the present time many native Australian mammals, such as the Tasmanian 'wolf' are either extinct or on the verge of extinction. On the other hand, no Australian mammals have become abundant in Europe, although there are a few wallabies running wild near Whipsnade Zoo in England. This could be explained on the grounds that placental mammals have certain advantages in competition with their equivalent species of marsupials. It may also be that they have not had enough time to spread. A similar situation exists where some of the Darwin finches on the Galapagos Archipelago are displaced on certain islands where they are in competition with other birds of the order Passeriformes which have migrated from the American mainland in comparatively recent times. The possible explanation of these situations may be that the great land masses of Asia, Europe and America have provided a wider range of environmental conditions than have the isolated southern continents, or than the many smaller islands. These variable conditions have brought about the evolution of a greater variety of plants and animals on the larger land masses, and at the same time greater variety of species causes more intense competition for food resources. For example, antelopes must be able to escape from a variety of predators of the cat and dog families, and must compete with a variety of other herbivorous mammals, whereas kangaroos have no predators native to Australia and relatively few herbivorous competitors. Species which have evolved in these more stringent conditions have later proved successful in competition with equivalent species from regions with a less varied fauna. J.M.A.

ERMINE, strictly speaking the fur from the *stoat *Mustela erminea* in its white winter coat with the black tipped tail. The fur has long been associated with robes of royalty and nobility. In North America the name is applied to the living animals of several species of weasel which in the northern parts of their range similarly assume a white coat in winter.

ERUPTIONS, explosive migrations of animals outwards from a centre of very rapid population build-up. It has much the same meaning as *irruption but relates more especially to the centre of origin.

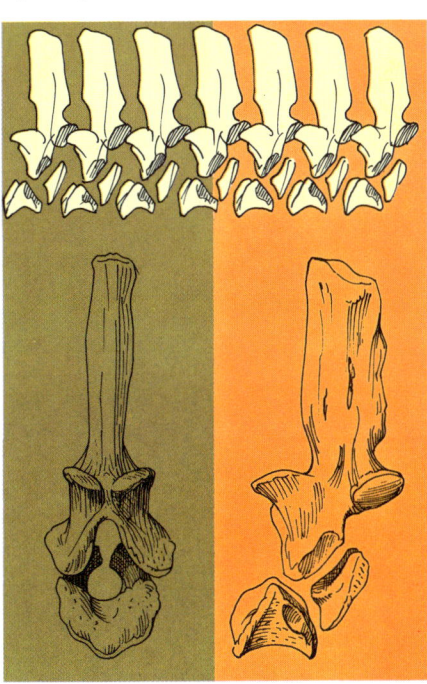

The vertebrae of *Eryops* are characteristic of the labyrinthodonts and consist each of four parts, the centrum being made up of three parts, only two of which are shown in the side view, bottom right.

ERYOPS, a representative of the extinct group of Amphibia known as the *Labyrinthodontia. It lived in the early part of the Permian period (about 260 million years ago) in Texas and the adjoining southwestern United States. It was about 6 ft (2 m) long with a massive skull about 18 in (46 cm) long. The skull in side view looks somewhat like that of an alligator, but is seen to be much broader in top view. There were 23 vertebrae forming the backbone of the trunk, a small number for a labyrinthodont. This, together with the massive legs, suggests that *Eryops* was more terrestrial than most labyrinthodonts. The shoulder girdle and hip girdle are like those of other large terrestrial, primitive amphibians and reptiles, and the limbs were held with the upper arm and the thigh parallel to the ground so that the animal must have had a slow, ponderous gait.

The structure of the vertebrae of *Eryops* is characteristic of the group of labyrinthodonts to which it belongs. The vertebrae, known as rhachitomous, each consist of four parts. Dorsally, as in all vertebrae, there is a neural arch bearing a neural spine and also processes to link it to the ones in front and behind. The arch surrounded and protected the nerve cord. Below this is the centrum accounting for the remaining three parts and corresponding to the single spool-shaped centrum of most terrestrial vertebrates. A crescentic wedge of bone, shaped like a slice of melon, known as the intercentrum is situated ventrally at the front. The other two structures are a pair of so-called pleurocentra, diamond-shaped in side view, situated behind and somewhat above the intercentrum. It has been suggested that this type of compound vertebra was to allow controlled torsion of the backbone, which could twist easily through a small angle, thus allowing the animal to lift its forefeet from the ground without having to raise the heavy head.

Eryops is one of the few fossil vertebrates in which large areas of skin have been preserved. These show a pattern of oval horny scales like those of reptiles, each about ½ in (12 mm) diameter. Unlike those of most reptiles, however, these were underlain and supported by bone in the form of tiny bony plates, with many plates supporting one scale. It is unlikely therefore that *Eryops* could breath through its skin as do living Amphibia.

Although a large terrestrial animal *Eryops* is likely to have lived near lakes or swamps and to have bred in water, perhaps having a tadpole stage. It was certainly a carnivore judging from its numerous large crocodile-like teeth, and perhaps fed on the large clumsy herbivorous reptiles which were its contemporaries. ORDER: Rhachitomi, SUPERORDER: Labyrinthodontia, CLASS: Amphibia. A.L.P.

ETHIOPIAN FAUNA, animals of one of the six major zoogeographical regions, which includes the continent of Africa with the exception of the northwestern fringe which is isolated by the Sahara Desert from the fauna of the rest of Africa and has been colonized mainly by European animals. The fauna of Madagascar is of African origin but now differs sufficiently from the present-day fauna of Africa to merit separate consideration.

Centred on the Equator and extending somewhat beyond both the tropics, the Ethiopian region is mainly tropical in its climate. The equatorial region of West and Central Africa is covered by rain-forest, which also occurs farther east as isolated patches on mountains. Much of the continent is covered by thorn-scrub or grass-land, with pronounced wet and dry seasons. These areas merge into the Sahara Desert to the north and into the deserts of Southwest Africa, which contain only a restricted fauna. It is easiest to understand the faunal composition of Africa today by first dealing with the dominant elements of its fauna, and then noting the few elements which may survive from earlier periods in its history.

The most eye-catching and famous animals of the present African fauna are the great herds of ungulates browsing over the grasslands of East Africa. These include the antelopes, hartebeest, gnu, giraffe, warthogs, zebra, rhinos and elephants. However, many of these mammals originally lived further north, in southern Europe and Asia. Their appearance, together with the hippos, in Africa in the Pliocene and Pleistocene was mainly the result of the gradual cooling of Eurasia and an associated increasing dryness

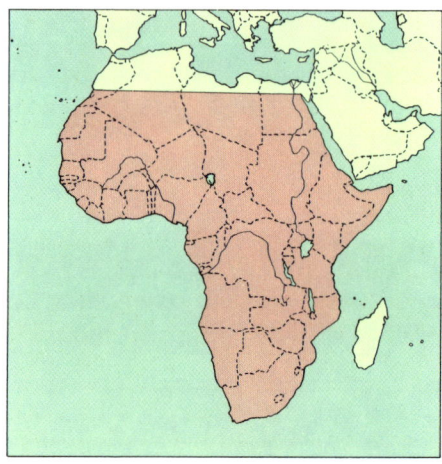

The Ethiopian region includes all Africa except the northwestern fringe, which is isolated from the fauna of the rest of Africa by the Sahara desert, and Madagascar.

in Africa. Previous to this, the dominant fauna of Africa had been a forest-fauna, including the lorises, the Old World monkeys, the apes, the pangolin *Manis,* the Old World porcupines, the chevrotains and the chameleons. This fauna originally extended from Africa through the Middle East to India and Southeast Asia (which together make up the Oriental zoogeographical region). The drier grasslands of East Africa and the deserts of North Africa and Arabia have since separated the African portion of this fauna from their closest relatives which still live in the Oriental region.

Even before the the Pleistocene migration into Africa, the land links between Africa and Eurasia had made it possible for widely ranging Eurasian animals to enter Africa. Among the mammals, such forms include the lions and hyaenas, the squirrels and the rabbits. The same is true of 53 out of the 67 families of African land and freshwater birds, and of most of the lizards, snakes and amphibians of Africa.

The Ethiopian region has never passed through a long period of isolation such as made possible the evolution of diversified major mammal groups in South America (the Neotropical region). Most of the animals found only in Africa today are therefore mainly either rather minor forms of restricted ecological importance which may have evolved there, or *relict forms. Such endemic animals include the otter-shrew *Potamogale,* the Cape golden mole *Chrysochloris,* the Elephant shrews, the aardvark *Orycteropus,* the African lungfish *Protopterus,* the bichir *Polypterus,* and the related reed-fish *Calamoichthyes.*

The larger Great Lakes of Africa, such as Lakes Victoria, Tanganyika and Malawi, are virtually inland seas. Most of the great variety of environments which these lakes provide have been colonized by the cichlid fishes. Adaptive radiations of these fishes have taken place in each lake, producing a great variety of species. As a result, the cichlids provide 60–70% of the total number of freshwater fish species of these lakes, and 97–98% of the cichlid species are each found only in one particular lake. C.B.C.

ETHOLOGY, meaning literally the 'study of behaviour', is applied particularly to the European school of behaviour workers. Their concern is the behaviour of the animal in the wild, paying especial attention to species-specific patterns of behaviour, or 'instinctive' behaviour. This contrasts with the interest of most American behaviourists whose work stems largely from comparative psychology and is concentrated on the study of the learning process, studies which are mainly if not entirely laboratory based.

The science of ethology was founded by zoologists so, like other branches of zoology, it is a comparative subject. That is, the evolutionary theory occupies a central position and the adaptive nature of behaviour patterns is considered and patterns of related species are compared. This can show the ways in which an animal's behaviour is related to its way of life. Thus the breeding behaviour of the kittiwake is basically similar to that of other gull species but it has variations which fit it for nesting on narrow cliff ledges.

Although at one time there was a serious division between ethologists and the American school, about the role of heredity and experience in the shaping of behaviour, there is nowadays a considerable measure of agreement. It is not surprising that the accent was on inborn behaviour since behaviour is viewed by ethologists in its adaptive role in the existence of species. The effectiveness of the behaviour patterns could be explained as the result of natural selection acting during the evolution of the species, a point of view which would not leave room for the variability of behaviour which would come about if it is individually acquired. In these early days there was, therefore, a considerable difference of opinion between ethologists and the American workers; both sides tended to take extreme positions but now the situation is changing.

The founders of ethology were Konrad Lorenz and Niko Tinbergen, whose ideas on *instinctive behaviour supplied the stimulus for renewed study of animals in the wild. The publication of Lorenz's paper entitled *Der Kumpan in der Umwelt des Vogels* in 1935 can perhaps be taken to mark the foundation of ethology, although Lorenz is the first to acknowledge the debt he owes to Oskar Heinroth whose studies on birds earlier in the century showed the beginnings of the new approach to behaviour as did Wallace Craig's work in America. Tinbergen's *An Objectivistic Study of the Innate Behaviour of Animals,* which appeared in 1942, can equally be taken as a manifesto on the methodology of ethology.

Ethology is the scientific study of behaviour and demands the usual rigorousness of a scientific enquiry. As far as possible description of behaviour patterns should proceed without introspection, thus enabling other workers to make the maximum use of the information in comparisons between groups in one place and another. It is a tenet of ethology that work should, whenever possible, not begin on a study of a part of an animal's behavioural repertoire until a general knowledge of the whole of the natural life of the animal has been obtained. J.D.C.

EUGLENA, the classic single-celled 'plant-animal'. It is the best-known genus of the euglenoid flagellates, a taxonomically isolated group with both pigmented and colourless forms. Most of the 50 species of *Euglena* are elongate, being fusiform, cylindrical or slightly flattened. The common laboratory organism *Euglena gracilis* is a cigar-shaped cell, 0·05 mm long and 0·01 mm wide. It has two flagella which arise within a deep depression in front but only one flagellum emerges as an organelle of locomotion, the second flagellum ending within the depression. The locomotory flagellum

Euglena viridis, one of the well-known plant animals, so called because they combine the qualities of plant and animal, and for a long time have been in dispute whether they should be relegated to the province of the botanist or the zoologist.

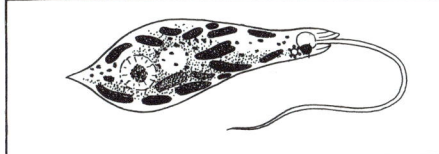

bears a unilateral array of submicroscopic hairs (a diagnostic feature of the euglenoids). *Euglena gracilis* has 6–12 shield-shaped chloroplasts per cell, containing chlorophylls *a* and *b*, which are the same photosynthetic pigments as in all higher plants. Each chloroplast has a central body, the pyrenoid, which is associated with polysaccharide formation. *Euglena* stores paramylon, a polysaccharide which has a different molecular structure from the starch stored by most plant cells (though it is also formed from linked glucose residues). There is an eyespot at the anterior end of the cell, unique among phytoflagellates in being independent of the chloroplasts. The eyespot lies opposite a photoreceptive swelling on the base of the locomotory flagellum, and eyespot and photoreceptor together control the swimming reactions of *Euglena* to light. The pellicle (outer or limiting layer of the cell) exhibits helical (screw) symmetry and consists of interlocking strips of an elastic protein. These allow extreme changes of shape when the cell stops swimming. Other structures visible under the light microscope include the contractile vacuole, which controls the water content of the cell and the large central nucleus. The nucleus divides by a unique form of mitosis. Euglena reproduces by longitudinal fission.

Nearly all species of *Euglena* occur in fresh water, often forming 'blooms' in polluted localities such as farmyards. Among the more bizarre habitats from which *Euglena* has been recorded are the mucous secretions of aquatic animals, the bark and leaves of trees, snow-fields, swimming pools, birdbaths and the public water supply of the city of New York.

Euglena is the preferred organism for much advanced research on photosynthesis, chloroplast structure, enzyme biosynthesis, carbon metabolism, lipid chemistry, phototaxis and flagellar movement. *Euglena gracilis* is especially studied for its nutritional versatility. It is called the classic 'plant-animal' because it behaves partly as a plant, partly as an animal. It feeds like a plant in the light but can also grow in the dark if provided with organic nutrients. It never ingests solid food, although the colourless euglenoid *Peranema* does so voraciously. *Euglena gracilis* cannot live without a supply of vitamin B_{12} and is therefore important in medicine as an assay organism for this substance, lack of which causes pernicious anaemia in man. Treatment of green cells of *Euglena gracilis* with heat, streptomycin or ultraviolet irradiation produces permanently colourless races. These strictly 'animal' cells can then be compared biochemically with their photosynthetic—and therefore plant-like—brothers. As far as is known there is no sexual reproduction in *Euglena*, the cells in one culture or in one wild population forming

an asexual clone of virtually identical individuals. See phytoflagellates. FAMILY: Euglenidae, ORDER: Euglenida, CLASS: Phytomastigophora, PHYLUM: Protozoa.
G.F.L.

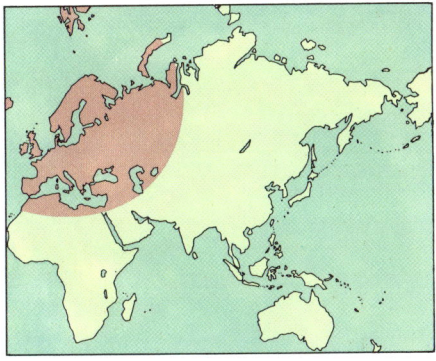

The fauna of Europe grades into that of central and northern Asia and is also very similar to that of the northwestern strip of Africa. Zoologically, therefore, Europe can only be demarcated on an arbitrary basis, as is done here.

EUROPEAN FAUNA, animal life of the westernmost part of the Palearctic zoogeographical region. The boundaries of Europe may be defined as the Ural Mountains to the east, and the Caspian, the Caucasus, the Black Sea and the Mediterranean to the south. It includes the continental shelf, British Isles and Iceland, while the northwestern part of Africa also has a fauna which is predominantly European rather than African.

Like the rest of the Palearctic region, the northern fringe of Europe is covered by arctic tundra. To the south of this lie, successively, belts of conifer forest to about 60°N, mixed forest to about 53°N and deciduous forest to about 40°N. However, because the warm Gulf Stream reaches the western seaboard of the British Isles, the climatic zones are here displaced northwards, deciduous forest reaching as far north as 58°N.

The climate and fauna of the northern parts of Europe differ from those of the southern parts for two main reasons. The climate of the southern part, since it borders the Mediterranean, is moister and warmer than that of Central Europe. This distinction between the two areas is sharpened by the presence between them of such mountainous regions as the Pyrenees and the Alps. These mountains also protected the southern regions from the effect of the Pleistocene Ice-Ages, which greatly affected the more northern areas. As a result, the lands around the Mediterranean are sometimes considered as a separate, minor zoogeographic unit.

Like that of the rest of the Palearctic region, the fauna of the northern part of Europe is a poor one, due primarily to the coldness of the winters. The fauna thins out progressively northwards, until within the

Euryapsida

Arctic Circle it is reduced to a few freshwater fishes, the frog *Rana,* two viviparous reptiles (the lizard *Lacerta vivipara* and the adder *Vipera berus*), a few land and rather more freshwater birds (mostly summer migrants), and a few mammals (as few as eight species in the far north of the continent).

Through the main part of central Europe there is a moderately diverse fauna of small mammals, including foxes, cats, many mustelid carnivores (such as the weasel, stoat, ferret, otter and badger), a variety of small rodents (such as the fieldmouse, lemming, hamster and squirrels) and rabbits. Through much of this region, the natural poverty of the fauna has been accentuated by the density of the human population, together with the consequent degree of change due to industrialization and agriculture. As a result, few of the larger mammals remain in western Europe, except in isolated mountainous or forested regions, and it is mainly in the east and north that one can still find bears, wolves, reindeer *Rangifer* and elk *Alces*. Others no longer extend into Europe, the wild horse *Equus przewalskii,* wild ass *Equus asinus* and the saiga-antelope *Saiga* now being confined to Asia. Yet others, such as the European bison *Bison bonasus* are only found in captivity, or are completely extinct, such as the aurochs *Bos primigenius,* which was the ancestor of modern domestic cattle. Many other larger mammals, such as hippos, rhinos, tapirs, hyaenas and monkeys once lived in Europe when its climate was far warmer than today. These were driven southwards by the Ice Ages of the Pleistocene Epoch, and are now found only in the tropics.

The fauna of the British Isles is even more restricted than that of the rest of northern Europe, since nearly all of its earlier fauna was destroyed by the Ice Ages. As a result, the present fauna is almost entirely composed of animals which were able to enter the British Isles in the 3,000 or so years between the end of the last glaciation and the breaking of the land connection to the continent about 6,000 years ago. Only about half of the European species managed to enter during that time.

In the southern, Mediterranean area, a number of animals are found which, normally more characteristic of the sub-tropics, do extend north into this warmer part of Europe. This is particularly true of the cold-blooded land vertebrates such as the reptiles, e.g. the tortoise *Testudo* and the skinks, agamids, geckos and chameleons among the lizards.   C.B.C.

EURYAPSIDA, an assemblage of extinct and varied reptiles adapted for terrestrial, amphibious, or completely aquatic life. Apart from the presence in euryapsids of a single perforation on each side of the skull roof for the passage of jaw muscles, the member groups have little in common. The Permian protorosaurs were at the most semi-aquatic in habit, the Triassic placodonts were marine with an armoured turtle-like body and teeth for crushing shellfish, and the plesiosaurs were marine reptiles of the Jurassic and Cretaceous adapted in every feature of their body for life in the open seas. No euryapsid survived the close of the Mesozoic.

EURYPTERIDA, an extinct order of aquatic arthropods whose nearest living relatives are the *Horseshoe crabs. The order contained the largest of all known arthropods. Large individuals of *Pterygotus* reached a length of at least 7 ft 9 in (236 cm) but most eurypterids were 4–8 in (10–20 cm) long.

The body, enclosed in a chitinous exoskeleton, was divided into a cephalothorax and abdomen. The cephalothorax was wide and flattened. On its upper surface were a pair of small, simple eyes close together near the mid line and a pair of large, compound eyes nearer the sides. Its lower surface bore the mouth and six pairs of jointed appendages. The first pair, the chelicerae, were small and ended in pincers, or chelae, used in feeding. The remainder were all walking legs although in some species the last pair were flattened to form swimming paddles.

Eurypterids first appear in the Ordovician and died out in the Permian. They are rare in marine deposits and probably lived in fresh and brackish water. Although they may only occasionally have entered the sea, they have sometimes been called Sea scorpions. Their gills were well protected and it is possible that they were able to spend short periods on land.

A few years ago it was reported that the exoskeletons of some specimens of eurypterids, although nearly 300 million years old, were found on examination to have altered little, physically or chemically. CLASS: Merostomata, PHYLUM: Arthropoda.   Jo.G.

EVERGLADES KITE, a species of kite that is confined, in the USA, to the Florida Everglades, but is more widespread and abundant in Central and South America. See Snail kite.

EVOLUTION, the name given to the changes undergone by living organisms since life originated on the earth. Most evolutionary changes have been progressive, but some have been regressive as in the degeneration into parasites with loss of structures and functions necessary for free-living existence.

History. Claims are sometimes made that the notion of evolution is to be found in the writings of the classical Greeks; but their speculations were so general and based on so little evidence, that it is not profitable to compare their views with those of modern times. The notion of evolution had a starting point at the end of the 17th century, when John Ray brought clarity in the concept of kinds of living organisms, or species, for everything that is alive belongs to one species or another. Ray defined species as groups of living beings which resembled one another more than they resembled other living beings, and which bred among themselves so that young of one species did not arise from parents of another species. Species were regarded as fixed and immutable, with the characters which they had at the original Creation.

Speculation that species might not be fixed, but could change into other species, were entertained by some French philosophers in the 18th century: Montesquieu, Maupertuis, Diderot, and also Buffon, until the censures of the theological faculty of the Sorbonne made him think it wiser to retract, because he had reached a point where he imagined that the ass was related to the horse, from which it could be argued that the ape was related to Man – unspeakable heresy. In England, Erasmus Darwin (grandfather of Charles) was led to believe in evolution because of the changes undergone by organisms during their embryonic development, changes brought about by cultivation and domestication and by crossing, resemblances in comparative anatomy, monstrous births, etc.

Some years later, in France, Jean-Baptiste de Lamarck, confronted with the duty of classifying the collections of the Paris Museum, found it so difficult to distinguish between species and varieties of species, that he concluded there was no difference, and

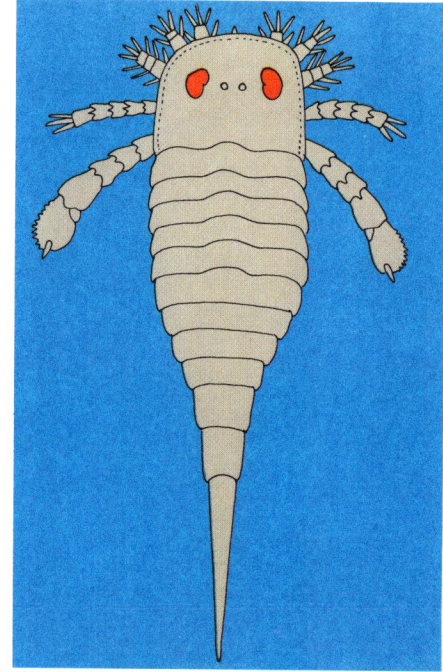

Eurypterus, a eurypterid or sea scorpion from the Silurian 400 million years ago and of which fossils have been found in abundance.

Evolution

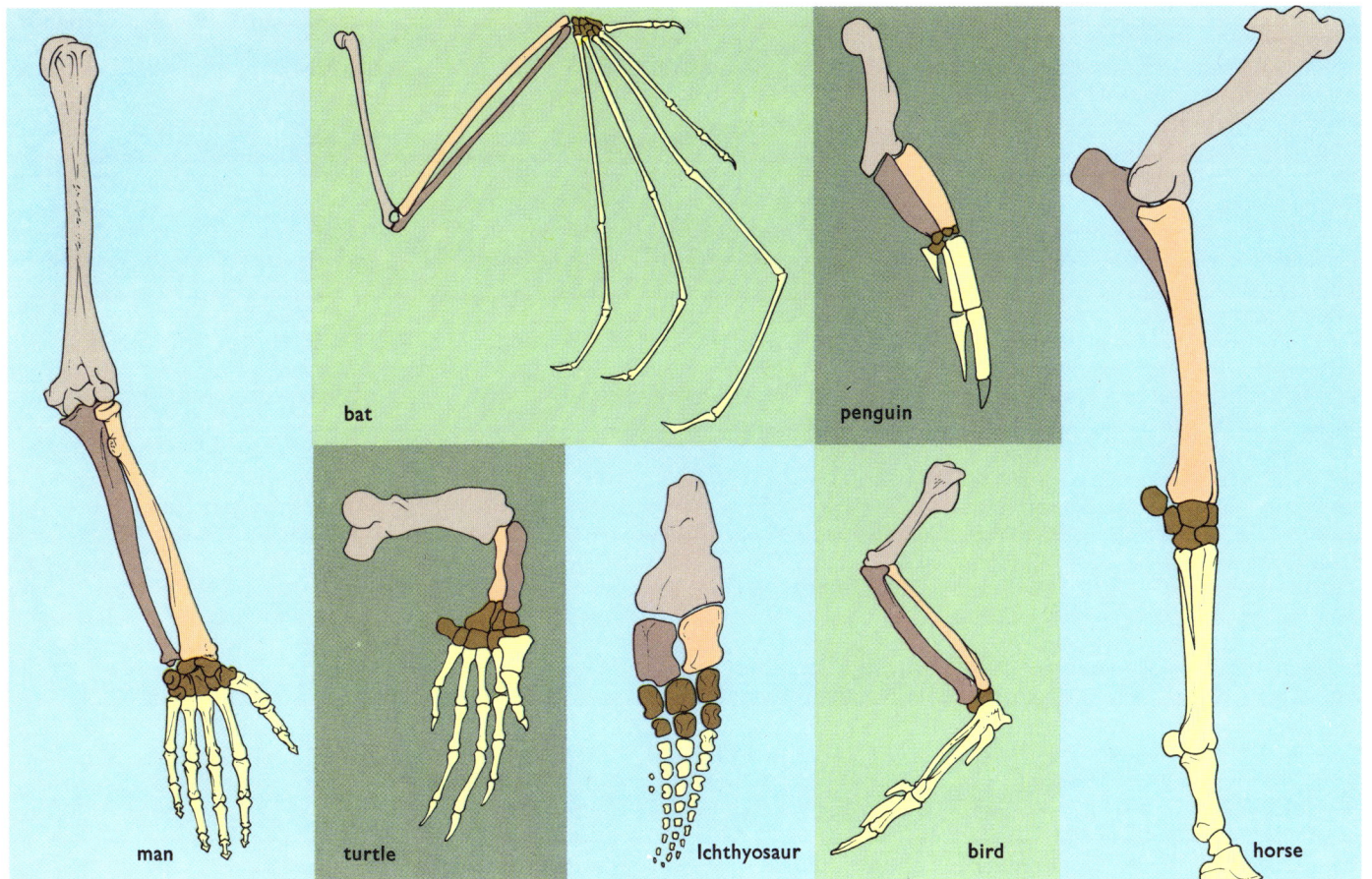

Outline drawings of the forelimb of some reptiles, a bird and several mammals, showing that in spite of wide differences in appearance their basic plans are almost identical, an important clue in the theory of evolution.

that species graded into one another. With this possibility of *transformisme* in mind, Lamarck, in 1809, constructed a system of evolution from microscopic animals called animalcules to Man. To explain evolution, Lamarck relied on two principles: first a tendency to increasing complexity and perfection (belied by the existence of degenerate animals) and a supposed *sentiment interieur*, or 'inner feeling', made responsible for introducing habits and causing movements that produced new organs which satisfied the animals' needs. A similar view had been put forward by Erasmus Darwin, as mentioned above, equally without evidence. Lamarck also believed that acquired characters and effects of use and disuse are inherited, and that the action of environmental factors cannot have permanent effects. This is now known as Lamarckism.

During his voyage in HMS *Beagle* (1831-6), Charles Darwin made some observations which he afterwards found that he could explain only if evolution had occurred. At the same time he saw it was useless to present a case for evolution if he could not at the same time explain its cause. He knew that artificial selection by man explained the evolution of cultivated plants and domestic animals and he worked out for himself the principle of natural selection for organisms in a state of nature; but he did not see how nature enforced its selection until he accidentally came across Malthus's fallacious argument that in man reproductive rate must potentially outstrip food-supply, so that the poor must suffer famine and death unless they practised population-control. Darwin saw that death is the sanction exacted by nature on those forms least well fitted to their conditions of life. Darwin kept his views to himself until, in 1858, Alfred Russel Wallace hit upon precisely the same mechanism to explain evolution. Their joint paper was read and published in 1858, and Darwin's *Origin of Species* was published in 1859. This was followed in 1871 by his *Descent of Man*.

The origin of life. When the Earth had reached a physical condition of temperature suitable for life to be possible, and oceans of liquid water existed in which it could arise, between 3,000–4,000 million years ago, the atmosphere contained no free oxygen, but consisted chiefly of hydrogen, water-vapour, methane (marsh-gas) and ammonia. Into an artificial 'atmosphere' of such composition, S.L. Miller in 1953 introduced energy in the form of electric discharges, at ordinary room temperatures, and obtained large numbers of different fatty acids, and amino acids which are the building blocks of proteins. All these were previously regarded as 'organic' compounds only produced by living organisms, but it became clear that they, and many others, can arise by chemical synthesis without life at all. The energy for the original formation of these substances is believed to have come from solar ultra-violet radiation.

Experimental synthesis has now made great progress. Compounds formed in this way can combine to produce more complex compounds, such as the constituents of chlorophyll in leaves of green plants, of haemoglobin in animal blood and the constituents of nucleic acids. The importance of these and other results can hardly be overestimated, because life is defined as the power to synthesize complex compounds similar to the synthesizer out of simpler components, and of reproducing similar systems. Proteins carry out the former function, and nucleic acids the latter, so that the criteria of living organisms are already met by these two kinds of chemical molecules. This is why it is not absurd to say that the principles of life existed before there were living organisms.

For the formation of living organisms, it was necessary that quantities of suitable molecules, hitherto existing free in the water, became surrounded and enclosed by mem-

Evolution

branes, converting them into cells. Possible ways in which this could happen have been shown by A.I. Oparin with coacervate drops (droplets containing inclusions and surrounded by membranes) and by S. W. Fox with microspheres formed from protein-like substances after heating and cooling of amino acids in water.

At first, these cells would have fed on the compounds in the soup in which they were bathed, by passage through their semipermeable membranes (as in amoebae today). But the supply of such food must have been limited, and from the condition of food-takers (primary heterotrophes), these first organisms must have developed mechanisms of synthesis by means of their proteins, enabling them to synthesize the complex compounds of their own substance from simple compounds in the surrounding water, using chemical energy as in some bacteria, or light energy as in other bacteria and in blue-green algae, thus converting them into food-makers (autotrophes). The most efficient system followed from the formation of chlorophyll, the green colouring matter of plants, which with its help, carbon dioxide in solution in water or in the air, energy provided by sunlight and simple salts in solution in the water or in the soil, are able to synthesize proteins, carbohydrates, and fats from inorganic compounds, and thereby to become the universal producers of the essential organic compounds necessary for all living organisms. Fossil unicellular algae have been found in geological formations nearly 2,000 million years old.

The origin of animals. As plants were the first established permanent factories of essential organic foodstuffs, fungi (which are not now considered to be plants) and animals evolved later, as a result of variation in directions which enabled them to make a cheap living without having to synthesize these organic foodstuffs themselves. As life involves not only synthesis but decomposition, some forms specialized in living on decomposition-products of former living organisms, and these became the fungi, and lost the power of synthesizing food from inorganic compounds with their loss of chlorophyll. Other organisms, again, varied in the direction of taking a short cut and simply devouring plants, or other organisms like themselves that live on plants: these are animals, which are wholly dependent, directly or indirectly, on the plants for their continued existence on earth.

The method of feeding evolved by animals had a profound effect on their structure and behaviour. At the unicellular level, an animal cell engulfed an unicellular plant. But at higher levels, a fundamental principle showed itself. Plants, and other animals that have eaten plants, have to be found before an animal can eat them, and so animals generally have evolved powers of movement, sense organs to locate the food and nervous centres to co-ordinate the movements.

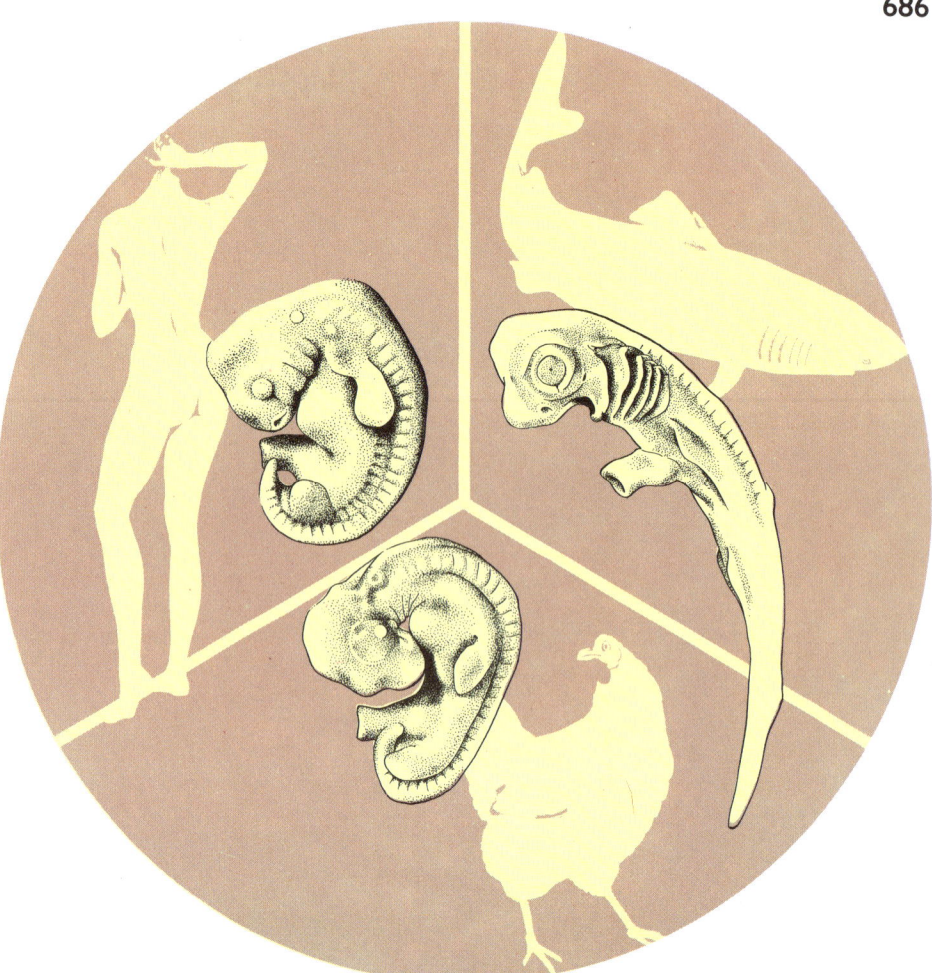

A human being, a live-bearing shark and a domestic fowl, each with its embryo, to show the similarity between the embryos contrasted with the dissimilarities of the adults.

The origin of multicellular organisms, obligatory death and embryonic development. The subdivision of the original unicellular body into the multicellular condition made it possible for organisms to reach larger sizes, and to become differentiated in their different parts, with consequent increase in efficiency of function. In animals, for instance, nerve cells serve for perception of sense-impressions and their co-ordination, muscles serve for locomotion, gut-cells for digestion, etc. But the advantage of the multicellular condition carries with it the necessity to respect the fact that sexual fusion, between gametes or germ-cells, virtually important for variation, can only take place between single cells, each with a single nucleus. In animals, as in all plants, a form of reproduction can take place simply by dividing the body into two or any other number. This is known as asexual reproduction, and its products are genetically identical with their scion, which means that no variation ensues. But there is another form of division, a splitting between single cells, eggs or sperm on the one hand, and all the rest of the body on the other. It is the eggs and sperm which then undergo fusion, or fertilization, to form a zygote, out of which an embryo and a new generation will arise. This is called sexual reproduction, and as it involves recombination of the genes in the germ-cells, it provides for heritable variation.

Unicellular organisms are potentially immortal, in the sense that as they reproduce by division, their products can in principle continue to do so indefinitely, until accident intervenes and they die. The same potential immortality applies to eggs and sperm, for the new generation which they produce can, in principle, continue to have descendants indefinitely. But the body of the multicellular organism, which produced the eggs and sperm, is itself inevitably condemned to die sooner or later. In the history of evolution, the appearance of multicellular organisms, and therefore of obligatory death of the body, cannot have been much later than 2,000 million years ago.

Evidence for the fact of evolution. Until the 1930s, the evidence that evolution was a fact was indirect; the logical form of the argument was that which Darwin himself presented: if evolution has occurred, then there is a simple, natural, and complete explanation of a vast number of problems which would otherwise remain inexplicable. Ten different branches of biology bear directly on the subject, and the indirect evidence for evolution which all of them provide is based on the significance of similarities found in different organisms.

(a) Comparative anatomy reveals similarities of plan of structure. Insects have bodies divided into head, trunk, and abdomen, three pairs of legs, and generally two pairs of wings, whether they be butterflies, bees, or bugs. Unless this basic similarity of structure is only arbitrary and meaningless, it must be due to inheritance of the plan from a common ancestor, for the similarities are far too great to be fortuitous. Similarly in vertebrates, the arm of a man, the foreleg of a dog or a horse, the wing of a bat, the flipper of a seal, are built on the same plan, and their bones can be recognized, bone for bone, however modified they are in detail conformably to their different habits of life.

(b) Embryology provides remarkable cases of resemblances in that very young stages of development of forms, as different as a mammal (including man), a bird and a reptile, are so similar as to be liable to cause confusion to anyone but an embryologist. This similarity can be explained if these different groups of vertebrates have inherited from a common ancestor a method of development which they repeat.

(c) Abortive organs are structures which no longer perform a function, like wings of ostriches which cannot fly, but the reduced wings of ostriches can be understood if ostriches were evolved from ancestors which did fly and subsequently lost the power of flight, in their case because they became too big and too heavy. The vermiform appendix in man is another abortive organ, no longer forming part of a large caecum or blind sac, in which herbivorous ancestors digested the plant food which they had eaten. Vestiges of the bones of the hindleg are found in snakes, and vestiges of teeth are found in the jaws of Whalebone whales. Marsupial mammals, which have been viviparous for at least 100 million years, may in their embryos still show a vestige of the papilla from which, in their egg-laying ancestors, there developed the egg-tooth by means of which the embryo cracked the shell of its egg and hatched.

(d) Transformed organs are those which correspond in position and basic anatomical relationship to other organs in different forms, where they perform different functions. Flies have only one pair of wings, but in place of the other pair, there are the little club-shaped halteres which vibrate and serve as gyroscopic organs which help in flight. The pineal eye on the top of the head in some fossil fish and reptiles, formed as an outgrowth from the brain, appears in mammals as an organ of internal secretion. Muscles when they contract always release an electric potential, and in some fish this property has been made use of to produce electric organs of such power that they deter predators and kill prey. All these transformations are easily explicable if the animals which show them were descended from ancestors in which the organs in question performed their original functions.

(e) Ethology or the study of behaviour reveals similarities between different forms, such as social instincts in ants, bees and wasps (termites are slightly different), nest-building habits among birds, and the nuptial ritual of courtship in different sticklebacks. In some cases it is possible to show how complex sequences of behaviour have been elaborated from simpler components, ritualized under different influences.

(f) Parasitology shows that every parasite is a living proof of its descent from an ancestral form which was free-living, whose descendants became adapted to live on, in, and at the expense of another living organism, which becomes its host.

(g) Taxonomy or systematics, the science concerned with the classification of living organs, reveals that all organisms belong to one species or another, and that each species is included in a larger group, or genus, this in a family, and, in ascending rank of category, in an order, a class and a phylum. The only explanation possible of this fact is that the hierarchical classification of animals is a direct reflection of the natural pattern of their descent from common ancestors.

(h) Biochemistry concerns the chemical structure and composition of all constituents of organisms. That they nearly all make use of adenosine triphosphate for the transfers of energy required in their metabolism argues in favour of descent from a common ancestor. Similarly, the presence of arginine phosphate in invertebrate animals, and of creatine phosphate in vertebrates, as molecules associ-

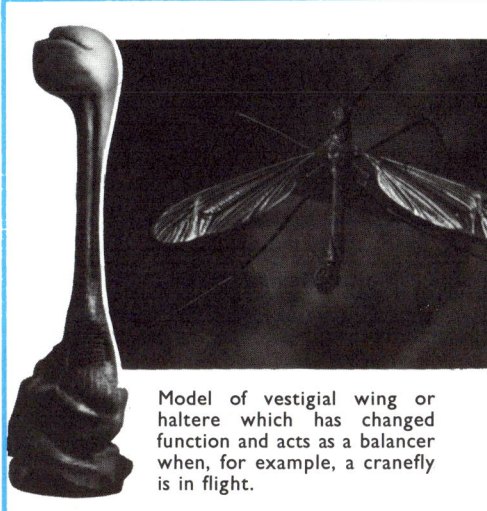

Model of vestigial wing or haltere which has changed function and acts as a balancer when, for example, a cranefly is in flight.

ated with muscular contraction, suggests not only that each group is descended from its own common ancestor, but that the difference between them is of long standing. The chemical nature of the pigment of the wings of butterflies shows differences which agree with their classification on other grounds. One of the most interesting cases is that of the composition of the pancreatic hormone insulin, found in different mammals. This enzyme is made up of 51 amino acids, arranged in a particular order which is, in general, respected. But where cattle insulin has serine, sheep insulin has glycine; and where both these have alanine and valine, horse and pig insulins have threonine and isoleucine. The general resemblances between these molecules of insulin in different species is explicable if they have inherited the general structure from a common ancestor, and modified it in detail in adaptation to their respective habits of life.

(i) Serology is a special case of biochemistry, concerned with the chemical composition of the blood, analyzed in connexion with the principles of immunology. Anti-human serum can be obtained by injection of human blood into an experimental animal, and its reactions when mixed with other samples of blood provide a measure of quantitative

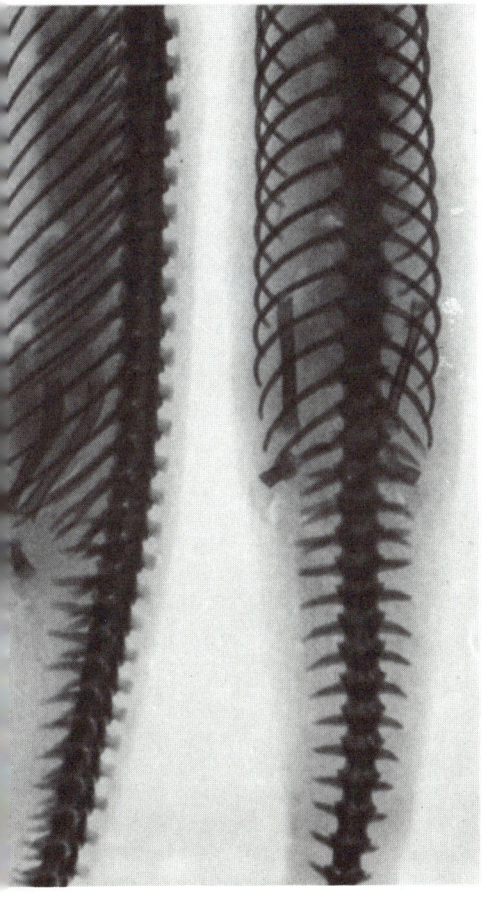

Some vestigial organs are so reduced that they can only be seen inside the body of animals, such as the main bones of the hindlimb skeleton in the python.

Evolution

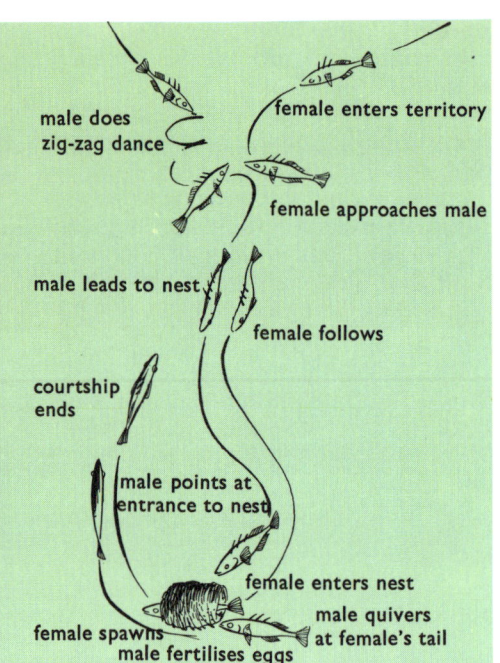

(Left) diagram showing sequence of movements in stickleback courtship. (Right) male stickleback constructing his nest, carrying nesting material in his mouth.

divergence between the species tested. Thus the amount of precipitation occurring when serum of one species is mixed with blood of another indicates the closeness of their relationship. Anti-human serum precipitates human blood 100%, gorilla blood 64%, orang-utan 42%, baboon 29%, ox 10%, deer 7%, horse 2% and kangaroo 0%. No sense can be made of these results if these various mammals have not evolved, with modification, from a common ancestor.

(j) Geographical distribution of animals presents many facts of significance. Why have Cape Verde Islands animals an African character, and Galapagos Islands animals a South American character? If they were each specially created, there is no explanation; but if each archipelago was populated from the nearby continent, the problem is easily solved. There are also remarkable cases of discontinuous geographical distribution. Tapirs today live in the East Indies and in South America. This is easily explicable if these animals originally evolved in a particular centre, migrated widely over the world, and became extinct everywhere else than where they are now found. This is proved by the discovery of extinct tapirs as fossils in Asia, Europe, and North America. [This case also shows that species originated once only, and in one area only.]

(k) Paleontology is the study of fossils which allow the course taken by evolution to be traced, often in minute detail. Moreover radio-active dating of rocks makes it possible to determine the absolute age of particular fossils, and also the speeds of evolution: they are slower in marine animals, faster in terrestrial animals. About 600 million years ago the Cambrian period began. Its rocks already show a very rich fauna of highly evolved animals: trilobites, echinoderms, graptolites, which must have had a long evolutionary history behind them. The oldest known fossil animal is a well-developed worm-like form, *Xenusion,* 800 million years old in the Pre-Cambrian period which was of enormous length, and from which only few

Charnia masoni a frond-like impression in a pre-Cambrian rock, one of the earliest fossils.

fossils have been recovered. The fact that the earliest rich fauna has been recovered from the Cambrian (and all subsequent) period has not yet been satisfactorily explained.

(l) Direct evidence of the fact of evolution has been obtained under human observation in the case of the change from grey to black in the Peppered moth in industrial regions of England, during less than 100 years. It will be referred to below under Industrial Melanism, because the mechanism involved reveals details of fundamental importance for the explanation of evolution itself.

The mechanism of evolution. The first thing to understand about how evolution is brought about is to realize that organisms do not live in voids, but in particular places in the environment, where chemical and physical factors, and the plants and animals which also inhabit them, constitute what is called an *ecological niche. Every species has its ecological niche, and it is because there are so many of the latter that there are nearly as many of the former. Next comes the fact that all the individuals of a species are not identical, in form, function, behaviour, or health, but show variation. Some deal more efficiently with the processes that are necessary to stay alive in a niche, to become adapted to it, than other individuals, which perish. It is this perishing, this mortality, which rams the more successful individuals into their niches, where they become the majority of the parents of the subsequent generations. Owing to the fact of heredity, these descendants will comprise individuals as well adapted as their parents, and others which, by the variations which they show, are even better adapted to their ecological niche. This is how heritable variation provides a spectrum for natural selection to choose from, in bringing about automatically the death of the less-well adapted, the survival of the better adapted, and providing a fool-proof mechanism for the continued improvement of adaptation to whatever ecological niche it may be. This is a simple statement of Darwin's principle of natural selection, by which he showed how evolution occurs.

H. C. Bumpus studied mortality of sparrows in North America during a particularly severe winter. The bodies picked up on the ice and snow all showed variation away from the mean of the species, and were either too small or too big, too light or too heavy, too old or too young, so it was the average sparrows in each respect which survived the bad weather. Natural selection acts not only through the physical and chemical factors of the environment, but also through predation by enemies, disease and imperfection of physiological function and behaviour.

It may be said straightaway that Darwin's principle of selection is accepted today as the chief cause of evolution; but there was one gap in Darwin's knowledge (and everybody else's at the time): the nature of variation, and how heritable variation arises. Although no contemporary realized it, the problem was in reality solved in 1865 when Gregor Mendel demonstrated his principle of genetics, based on irrefutable evidence from his breeding of peas. He showed that characters of an organism are controlled by discrete particles, now called genes, which exist in pairs in all organisms, one member of each pair coming from each parent. When the organism proceeds to form germ-cells, the two members of each pair separate (segregate) from one another so that not more than one member of each pair goes, at random, into any one germ-cell. Then, at fertilization, which is also random, pairs of genes are reconstituted. It may be noticed that this process of segregation of pairs of genes is exactly what happens at cell division when pairs of chromosomes separate from one another, and this is why the amount of DNA in a species does not become doubled at each generation. It is also why it was discovered that genes are carried in the chromosomes, and it is now known that genes are in fact, made of DNA. This unexpected convergence of evidence from genetics, cytology (behaviour of chromosomes) and chemistry (structure and function of DNA) is one of the greatest triumphs of science.

Mendel's discovery was ignored until it was rediscovered and confirmed in 1900, but its most important feature was misunderstood. It was known that genes occasionally

Typical, intermediate and melanic forms of the Peppered moth *Biston betularia* (right centre, top left, bottom left) furnish one of the best known examples of evolution taking place before our eyes.

Evolution

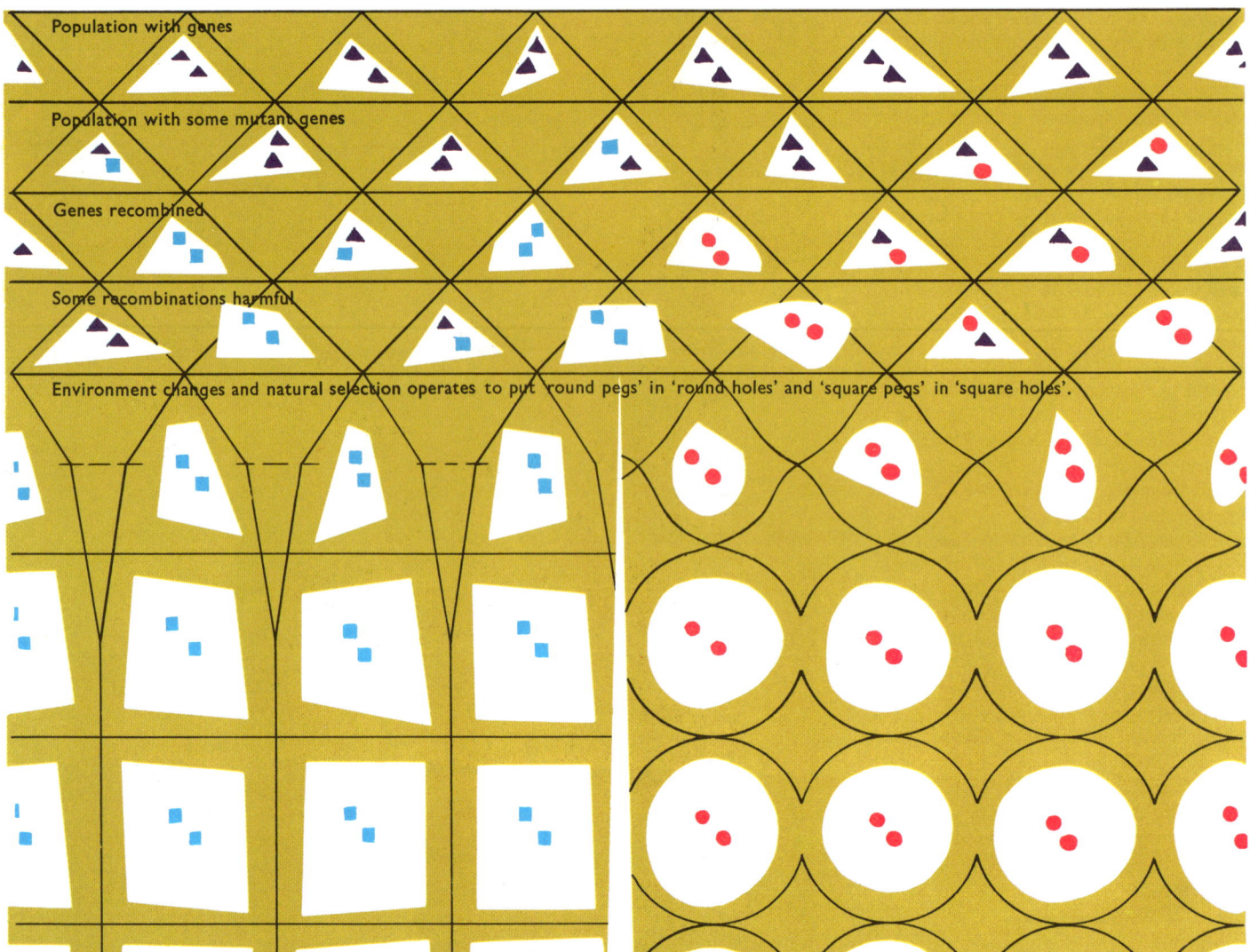

Diagrammatic representation of evolution as a result of variation due to mutation (shown as change from triangular to square and round 'genes'), followed by recombination (triangular with square, triangular with round, square with square, square with round, round with round), resulting in different genotypes, some disadvantageous and others advantageous when subjected to changed environmental conditions (shown by disappearance of triangular 'ecological niches' and appearance of square and round 'ecological niches'). Under the action of natural selection the different genotypes are forced into the 'ecological niches' to which they are best adapted, the population becomes divided into two isolated portions, each eventually giving rise to a different species.

undergo a change, so that the character which they control shows as a 'sport', now known as a mutation, and continues in that form until its gene mutates again. It has now been found that a mutation is an incomplete or imperfect replication of a short length of the DNA molecule. The result of a mutation is to make one of a pair of genes different from the other: they are then called alleles. Eventually one becomes stronger, or dominant, and shows in its character when inherited from only one parent. The other gene becomes weaker, or recessive and only shows in its character if it has been inherited from both parties, i.e. if both genes of a pair of alleles are recessive.

Since mutations were found to produce abrupt changes in characters, without any previous selection, geneticists took their stance on the fact that mutations are the only known way in which heritable variation can be produced (modifications induced by the environment are not inherited). They rejected selection entirely and proclaimed that mutation causes evolution. The Selectionists objected that mutation which bears no relation whatever to the ecological niches of the organisms, is quite incapable of explaining the origin and improvement of adaptation, and they threw into the geneticists' teeth the fact that the mutations (then known) were mostly pathological and many lethal.

The integration of these two opposing views was effected in 1930 by Ronald Fisher as a result of his experiments. He showed that a recessive gene is recessive because it is disadvantageous, and conversely that it is because a dominant gene is free from such a disadvantageous effect that it is dominant. He showed, further, that recessive genes have become recessive from a previous intermediate condition when neither gene of a pair of alleles dominates completely over the other, and similarly that dominant genes have become dominant. The remarkable point then emerged that it is all the other genes forming the gene-complex of an organism which are responsible for turning any given gene into a dominant or a recessive, and that it is natural selection which selects in favour of those gene-complexes which turn disadvantageous genes into recessives. In other words, there was experimental proof of the action of selection at the heart of genetics.

This was placed beyond doubt in 1940 by E. B. Ford, who in his experiments on the Currant moth, selected the same gene in different directions in two different lineages, and made it dominant in one lineage and recessive in the other.

Two more points call for attention. The first is that at the speed at which mutations occur (and they have been measured in bacteria, maize-plants, flies and man), mutation is utterly powerless to cause or direct evolution, which is why H. de Vries's 'Mutation Theory' is rejected. Mutation is also incapable of explaining adaptation. It is selection that determines the direction, speed, and intensity of evolution, provided that it has heritable variation in the population on which to work. In other words, the results of past mutations in providing differences between genes is essential if selection is to lead to any evolution at all. This is the reason why the sexual type of reproduction, allowing of recombination of hereditary material at each generation is of such fundamental importance; heritable variation is the result not only of such mutations as occur, but of the astronomically high number of possible permutations and recombinations of genes, which have segregated from their pair-mates at germ-cell-formation, and been recombined at random at fertilization of the egg by the sperm. It is why close inbreeding and incest soon lead to extinction, and why asexual reproduction (by budding, cutting or subdivision of the whole body) can never lead to any evolution at all. Selection is the key to evolution.

The second point is that, in fact, most mutations are turned into recessives. This is because, under the conditions when the mutations occurred, they were disadvantageous. This means that there is no such thing as a 'favourable breeze of mutations'; mutations occur blindly and most of them are unfavourable.

This also means that all attempts to explain evolution by imagining appropriate actions of environmental factors, inheritance of acquired characters, fulfilment of programmes, inner feelings or providential guidance (and what sort of guidance can it be that has led to appalling cruelties of predation and parasitism and to the extinction of 99% of all species that have ever existed?) are put out of court at the start: natural selection rejects nearly all novelties, and no principle other than natural selection can cover the facts, now known experimentally as well as from observation.

But a question then arises. If the majority of mutations are disadvantageous when they occurred, yet mutations are the only source of heritable variation, how do favourable new genes arise? The answer is that conditions of all organisms and all ecological niches change, owing to physical, climatological or biological factors, and a gene which is disadvantageous under present conditions, may be of service if conditions change. This is why wild organisms are found to be full of recessive genes, whose deleterious effects are masked and kept in check by their dominant alleles, but they are there, in cold storage, against the time when one or other of them might be of advantage. That this is no mere supposition but experimentally verified fact is seen in the case of Industrial melanism, direct evidence of evolution demonstrated in 1955 by H. B. D. Kettlewell.

Industrial Melanism. The Peppered moth *Biston betularia* was typically a grey mottled insect, admirably adapted to resemble the lichens on the bark of trees on which it rests to such an extent that it is often very hard to distinguish. About 100 years ago, a mutation occurred which turned the moth black. In this condition, on the grey lichen it was easily seen by its predators, birds, and devoured. The mutant forms were therefore soon extinguished, but, like most mutations, this black melanic mutation occurred again and again (more evidence of the blind non-adaptive nature of mutation), and was continually extinguished, until a curious thing happened. In the neighbourhood of big industrial centres, pollution of the air by soot and coal-dust killed the lichens on the trees and turned them black. Now it was the black mutant form which survived in such industrial environments, and the original grey form was penalized. The intensity with which selection acts in these cases, the selection-pressure, has actually been measured by H. B. D. Kettlewell, by counting and establishing the proportions in which the two forms black and grey survive in the two environments, natural and industrial.

Here, then, is a case in which a mutant gene, originally very disadvantageous and suppressed by selection, comes as a result of wholly unpredictable changes in the environment, to confer advantage on its possessors, by natural selection. This is a text-book example of how Fisher's synthetic theory of evolution accounts for all the facts. There are several other examples, including mimicry in butterflies and sickle-cell in Man.

Paleontological confirmation of the synthetic theory of evolution. The geological record of fossils is of prime importance in tracing the course of evolution, but unfortunately, many paleontologists, unequipped with any knowledge of genetics, have been led into thinking that they were in a position to explain its cause. This is why there have been so many errors flowing from paleontologists' pens, such as Cuvier's views of alternate creations and catastrophes to explain the sudden appearance of a fossil fauna at the bottom of the bed and its sudden complete disappearance at the top; the attempt by others to provide 'proof' of the theory of recapitulation by arranging ammonite shells in nice series, without regard to the fact that in so doing they reversed the geological order of the beds from which the fossils came; the attempt, by others again, impressed by the increases in size and complexity of the fossils which they found at successively high level, to conclude that there was a principle of orthogenesis, evolution in straight lines, a programme which organisms carried out. Such views have done nothing but harm to the principles of biological evolution.

George G. Simpson is a paleontologist who not only has an enormous amount of material to work on, but also is thoroughly conversant with the principles of genetics and population-genetics. His major work is concerned with the evolution of the horses, at the start of the Tertiary Era, about 60 million years ago, from a small animal the size of a fox-terrier dog, to end with the horse of the present day. This phylogeny has involved passage through about 30 stages, each of the taxonomic value of a species, from which it can be calculated that it has taken about 2 million years in the evolutionary history of horses to produce a new species. But most

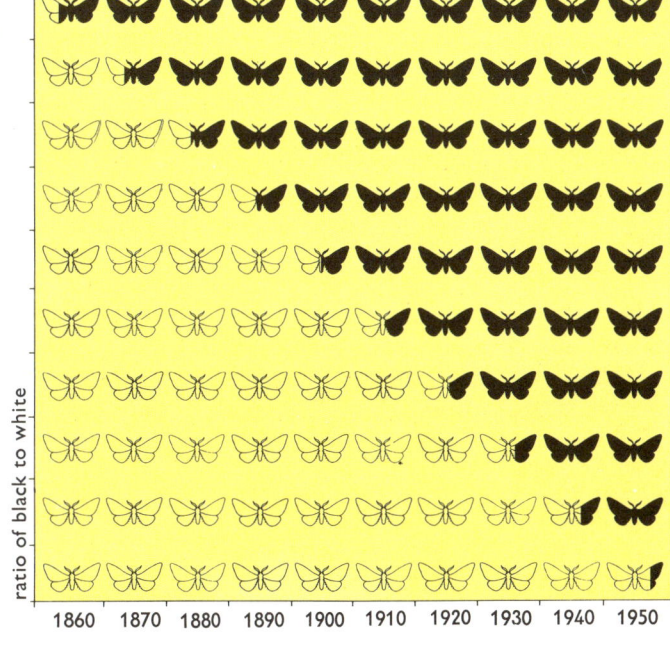

Chart showing how the melanic form of the Peppered moth increased in industrial areas from 1% to 99% of the population from 1848 to 1948.

Evolution

The lesser black-backed gull *Larus fuscus graelsii* in Britain has a dark mantle and yellow legs. It grades into the Scandinavian *L. fuscus fuscus*, which in turn grades into the Siberian Vega gull *L. argentatus vegae* with lighter grey mantle and dull flesh-coloured legs. This grades into the American herring-gull *L. argentatus smithsonianus* and this in turn into the British herring-gull *L. argentatus argentatus* with light grey mantle and pink legs. There is thus a continuous gene-pool of gulls round the North Pole in a range forming a ring overlapping in Britain where the lesser black-backed and herring-gull live sympatrically. Geographical variation has affected not only their colour but their habits. (Inset: island of Skokholm). The lesser black-backed gull breeds inland and is migratory in winter, the herring-gull nests on cliffs and is resident. They do not interbreed but behave like distinct species.

important has been the demonstration that there has been no question at all of any evolution in a straight line from the small ancestor of 60 million years to the large horse of today. It has been a series of zigzags the determination of which, at each stage, has been the environment and the adaptation of the animals to it. At the start, in the Eocene period, the land was swampy and the vegetation lush. The early horses had four toes to each foot and low-crowned teeth with which they browsed on the leaves of the vegetation. But the vegetation then became grass-like, and as grass contains silicon which wears down teeth, advantage accrued to many-toed forms with high-crowned teeth which grew by persistent pulps and made good the wear of grinding grass. Then the ground became harder, and advantage went to larger forms with feet ending in single toes with spring-joints, like those of the horse. At each stage, forms which continued along the lines of previous progress, no longer advantageous, went extinct. The evolution of the horses is not correlated with the coefficients of variability of the fossils, nor with their individual lengths of life. Nothing but natural selection to each environment, as it changes, accounts for the facts. Thus evolution is seen to be governed by a process, natural selection, which is rigorously determined by the ecological conditions of the time, but not predetermined in any way, and opportunistic and devoid of design.

The origin of species. Evolution is not synonymous with the origin of new species, and a certain amount of evolution can take place, as seen in industrial melanism, without transgressing the species-boundary. In addition to the definition already given of a species as a group of organisms which resemble each other and which arise from similar organisms, the most fruitful definition of a species is as a gene-pool, such that a mutation in a member of the pool anywhere in its range, can, in principle, be transmitted by sexual reproduction to any other individual, anywhere else in its range. New species arise when a barrier is introduced between one portion of a population and the remainder, and the barrier can be geographical, ecological, or genetic. An example is provided by the Herring gull and the Lesser-black-backed gull in Britain. The British Lesser-black-backed gull with its dark mantle and yellow legs grades into (and is fertile with) the Scandinavian Lesser-black-backed gull, which, in turn grades into the Siberian Vega gull with its lighter grey mantle and flesh-coloured legs. This grades into the American Herring gull, which in turn, grades into the British Herring gull with its light mantle and pink legs. In Britain, the Lesser-black-backed gull co-exists with the Herring gull, but does not co-habit with it, for the former breeds inland on moors and is migratory in winter, whereas the latter nests on cliffs and is resident. Geographical and ecological factors have erected a reproductive barrier between these two portions of populations, which overlap at the extreme limits of their circumpolar range, and they behave in Britain as distinct species. They will be completely different species whenever the ring-shaped range round the North Pole is interrupted.

The origin of new species, or speciation as it is called, is the result of selection of portions of a population in different directions, collecting different genes, in adaptation to their modes of life, until there is a genetic incompatibility between them as well as a behaviouristic aversion. In any case, speciation is nothing but a byproduct of the process of becoming better adapted on the part of portions of population, for it is portions of population which are the evolutionary units. From the point of view of wider evolution,

Excretion

GEOGRAPHICAL VARIATION AND SPECIES - FORMATION IN GULLS

THE ISLAND OF SKOKHOLM (Pembrokeshire) herring gull nests on cliffs is resident (see green strip)

The lesser black-backed gull (see red dots) breeds inland and is migratory in winter;

Siberian Vega gull · Scandinavian black-backed gull · American herring gull · British herring gull · Lesser black-backed gull

speciation is important because every new taxonomic unit begins by being a new species, before it proceeds (if it is sufficiently successful) to become a genus, family, order or higher category. But there is no 'magic' in the origin of species.

The evolution of Man. Natural selection played two important parts in the evolution of man: the increased development and power of function of his brain and the acquisition of a social habit. At the same time, a mode of evolution, namely pedomorphosis, also played an important part, as a result of which the human newborn is so delayed in development that at birth it is nothing but an 'extra-uterine foetus' which, only after a year, reaches the stage of development of an anthropoid ape at birth. Everything else is relatively delayed in the human: eruption of teeth, puberty, ossification of epiphyses of long bones and closure of the sutures of the skull. The utter helplessness of the human infant is compensated for by parental care, the parents forming a stable biological unit vital for the survival of the species. There is also the fact that the overlap between generations is made use of for the imparting from the parents to the infant of whatever they know as regards rules of conduct, and this, which Julian Huxley has called psychosocial evolution, is the basis of humanization and civilization. But as it is not inherited, it has to be started again, from scratch, at the beginning of every generation. The painter Auguste Renoir was right when he said that parents make children, but after they are born.
G. de B.

EXCRETION AND EXCRETORY ORGANS. Excretory organs are responsible in whole or part for the maintenance of the status quo of the body fluids. This includes: 1. regulation of the volume of the body fluids; 2. regulation of the concentration of the ions of the blood; 3. regulation of the acidity of the blood; 4. regulation of the osmotic concentration of the blood; and 5. removal of metabolic wastes and foreign molecules from the body.

With the exception of the coelenterates (Sea anemones, jellyfishes and hydroids), acoelomate turbellarians (flatworms), echinoderms (starfishes and Sea urchins) and tunicates (Sea squirts) all metazoans, that is many-celled animals, have specific excretory organs. These take many forms but functionally most of them can be included under one of the following headings: 1. pressure filtration systems (most vertebrates, molluscs, annelids and crustaceans); 2. secretory systems (some vertebrates, insects, arachnids and myriapods); 3. contractile vacuoles (Protozoa and freshwater sponges); and 4. flame cells and solenocytes (rotifers, cephalochordates, Platyhelminthes, some annelids and the larvae of molluscs and annelids).

Pressure filtration systems. Most filtration excretory organs are composed of one or more pairs of tubules which receive a fluid filtered from the blood and modify it as it passes to the exterior. The best known of such systems is the vertebrate kidney.

Vertebrate kidney structure. The kidneys of vertebrates are made up of large numbers of tubules called nephrons. The number depends on the size of the animal, about 1 million in man, 800,000 in the dog and 8 million in cattle. Each nephron is $\frac{3}{4}$–$1\frac{1}{2}$ in (2–4 cm) long. At the head end, in the cortex or outer layer of the kidney, there is a bulb-shaped structure, Bowman's capsule, which encloses a mass of capillary blood vessels, the glomerulus. Together these make the Malpighian corpuscle.

The vertebrate kidney probably evolved from a series of segmental tubules (coelomoducts) in the trunk region which led from the coelom to a common duct to the cloaca.

Excretion

Originally their function was probably primarily to convey genital products from the coelom to the outside. The anterior tubules retain connections with the genital coelom of the testes in many vertebrates but the opening to the coelom disappears in the nephron with a solely excretory function. Each of the latter develop a specialized region, Bowman's capsule, which partially encloses the glomerulus. In the fully formed nephron, the lumen of Bowman's capsule opens into a proximal convoluted tubule and this in turn passes via an intermediate region into a distal convoluted tubule. The distal convoluted tubule is prolonged into a collecting duct which, joining the collecting ducts from other tubules, eventually opens into the head of the ureter. In mammals the Malpighian corpuscle and the distal and proximal convoluted tubules lie in the kidney cortex whilst the intermediate section and collecting ducts are in the medulla.

Blood from the renal artery supplies the glomeruli via afferent arterioles. From the glomeruli the blood passes into efferent arterioles which are closely associated with the convoluted tubules and thence to the renal veins. In fishes, amphibians and reptiles a renal portal blood system also supplies the tubules.

Formation of urine. The hydrostatic pressure of blood passing through the glomerulus exceeds the sum of the colloid osmotic pressure of the blood proteins and the pressure in the lumen of Bowman's capsule. An ultrafiltrate of blood can therefore be forced across the leaky wall of the glomerulus into the lumen of the capsule. All the inorganic ions and small organic molecules such as glucose are present in the resulting ultrafiltrate in essentially the same concentration as in the blood, but substances with a molecular weight greater than about 60,000 cannot be filtered and remain in the blood. Blood proteins do not therefore form part of the primary urine.

The process of filtration permits the removal of waste or foreign molecule from the body even when no specific secretory mechanisms are available. Concentration of waste materials in the urine is achieved primarily by reabsorbing useful solutes and water as the primary filtrate passes along the tubule but certain substances such as creatinine, hippuric acid and diodrast can be actively secreted into the lumen by the tubular epithelium. In man, 30 times the blood volume is filtered through the glomeruli daily but as some 99·1% of this filtrate is reabsorbed farther down the tubule, only about 2·6 pints (1,500 cc) of urine is produced. Potentially waste materials filtered and retained in the tubule should be concentrated 110 times. In fact the concentration factor is usually somewhat less than this due to leakage of these substances back into the blood. Thus the nitrogenous waste product urea has a maximum concentration in human urine of about 70 times the concentration in the blood.

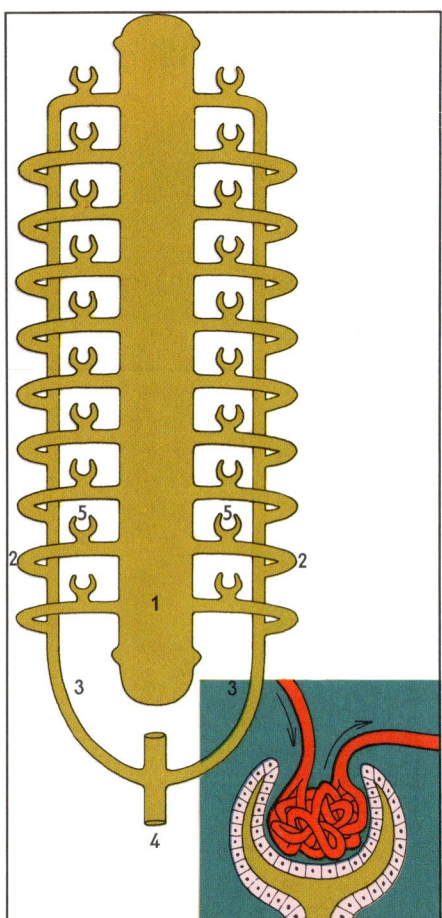

Hypothetical scheme for the ancestral urogenital system in which segmental coelomoducts open from the coelom: 1. coelom, 2. segmental urogenital tubules of trunk region, 3. archinephric duct carrying urine and genital products to cloaca, 4. cloaca, 5. Bowman's capsule; (inset) Bowman's capsule enlarged.

Much of the absorption both of useful materials and of water occurs in the proximal convoluted tubule. Glucose, phosphates, potassium, amino acids and vitamin C are reabsorbed in this region, together with about 80% of the water, sodium and chloride. If excessively high levels of the former group of substances are present the reabsorption mechanism may become overloaded and the substances escape in the final urine. Thus in the disease *diabetes mellitus,* glucose is present at such high levels in the blood that the reabsorptive capacity of the proximal tubule is exceeded and some glucose remains in the urine and is lost from the body.

Urine volume and concentration. The rate of filtration is more or less constant in man and variations in the volume of the final urine are achieved by adjusting the amount of water which is reabsorbed during its passage through the tubule.

The process by which water is reabsorbed makes ingenious use of the ability of the nephron to transport sodium chloride from the lumen outwards. Investigation of tissue slices of mammalian kidneys indicate that there is a rise in osmotic concentration affecting both cellular and extra-cellular fluids from the cortex to the medullary pyramids. Urine passing into the intermediate section (loop of Henlé) becomes progressively more concentrated by osmotic withdrawal of water as it moves down the descending limb, but is thought to be diluted once more in the ascending limb by the active transport of sodium and chloride from the lumen into the blood and interstitial spaces. When it reaches the distal tubule in the cortex the urine may again have approximately the same concentration as when it left the proximal convoluted tubule. Determination of the final concentration and volume of the urine occurs in the collecting ducts. When the body contains too much water, sodium and chloride are conserved by reabsorption and a large volume of dilute urine is produced. By contrast, if the body's requirement is the elimination of the maximum amount of salt and urea with a minimal water loss then reabsorption of water occurs in the collecting ducts. This latter effect is initiated by antidiuretic hormone (ADH) in the blood supply to the kidney. ADH, released from the pituitary gland, brings about an increase in the permeability of the cells forming the collecting duct and water is taken back into the body, decreasing the volume and increasing the concentration of the urine. The maximum concentration of the final urine is thus determined by the osmotic concentration built up in the medulla by the process of ion transport from the loop of Henlé.

As would be expected, therefore, the anatomy of the kidney often reflects the availability of water in the normal habitat of an animal. The relative size of the medulla of rodent species increases with increasing water lack in their environment. Therefore, beavers, which are aquatic, have only short loops of Henlé, and produce a dilute urine, whereas the desert Kangaroo rat *Dipodomys* which has long loops of Henlé can have a urine nearly ten times as concentrated.

Vertebrate groups, such as cyclostomes, teleosts, elasmobranchs, amphibians and reptiles, which lack the anatomical arrangement of the loop of Henlé and collecting ducts are unable to produce urine more concentrated than the blood. Birds have a poorly developed loop of Henlé–collecting duct countercurrent system and in general their maximum urine concentration is only some two to three times that of the blood.

The presence of the countercurrent system in mammals has also necessitated modification of the blood vessels through the medulla to ensure that the passage of blood does not dissipate the high concentration built up there. This is achieved by having the blood supply to the medulla also in the form of loops.

Urine pH. The final pH of the urine is determined in the distal convoluted tubule. The production of acidic urine involves the exchange of hydrogen and ammonium ions for sodium from the tubule together with the reabsorption of bicarbonate ions. Alkaline urine has a high fixed base and bicarbonate level.

Urine volume. Urine volume in man is regulated almost entirely by the antidiuretic hormone control of the amount of water reabsorbed in the collecting ducts, since only in the case of severe shock is the filtration rate reduced. The filtration rate of lower vertebrate groups is more variable. In the frog, for example, oxytocin, another hormone from the pituitary, brings about a decrease in filtration rate by causing the partial contraction of the afferent arterioles supplying the glomeruli. A reduced volume of urine in reptiles, fish and birds is also partly due to decreased filtration. Water reabsorption is proportionately much smaller in these groups than it is in mammals and so variations in the filtration rate provide a degree of flexibility in the total water output that would otherwise be lacking.

Several species which live in environments where they experience actual or physiological water shortage tend to have smaller and fewer glomeruli. In the desert lizard *Trachysaurus* the total volume of the glomeruli (number x average size) is only about $\frac{1}{7}$th that of a similarly sized mammal. Such reduction of glomeruli has been taken to its limit in several teleost fish which have no glomeruli. In these forms, of which the Angler fish *Lophius* is an example, urine formation is dependent upon a secretory process.

Endocrine functions. Mammalian kidneys in addition to their other functions also act as humoral organs producing a hormone, renin. This hormone is released if the oxygen supply to the kidney is inadequate as when blood pressure falls in the afferent arterioles, and also when plasma sodium levels are low. Renin reacts with the blood protein hypertensinogen to give rise to angiotensin. Angiotensin causes vaso-constriction and so produces a rise in blood pressure which tends to restore blood supply to the glomeruli. Angiotensin also increases the output of aldosterone from the adrenals and so contributes towards conservation of sodium by the body since this latter hormone promotes reabsorption of sodium by the nephron.

Invertebrate filtration reabsorption systems. Excretion in the majority of annelids, crustaceans and molluscs also involves filtration of blood into a coelomic space and then subsequent modification of the primary urine during its passage down the nephric tubules. The morphological details vary in the three groups.

Molluscs. Filtration from the heart into the pericardial coelom forms the basis of primary urine formation in molluscs, eg. clams and the snail *Viviparus*. From the pericardial coelom the urine passes into the paired (clams) or single *(Viviparus)* excretory organ via a reno-pericardial canal. The urine is modified in the excretory organ and freshwater forms such as *Viviparus* and *Anodonta* conserve ions by producing urine more dilute than the blood.

In terrestrial snails the pericardium does not appear to be involved in urine formation. Filtration in the snail *Achatina* takes place from the renal artery. The rate at which both this animal and the slug *Arion* filter urine appears to be about 5% of the body weight per hour, about half the human rate.

Ammonia is the main nitrogenous excretory product of aquatic molluscs. Terrestrial forms tend to excrete ammonia and urea when water is plentiful but produce and store uric acid when dehydrated.

The molluscan kidney was probably originally segmental. Six pairs are present in the most primitive living form, *Neopilina*. Some of these kidneys drain from the

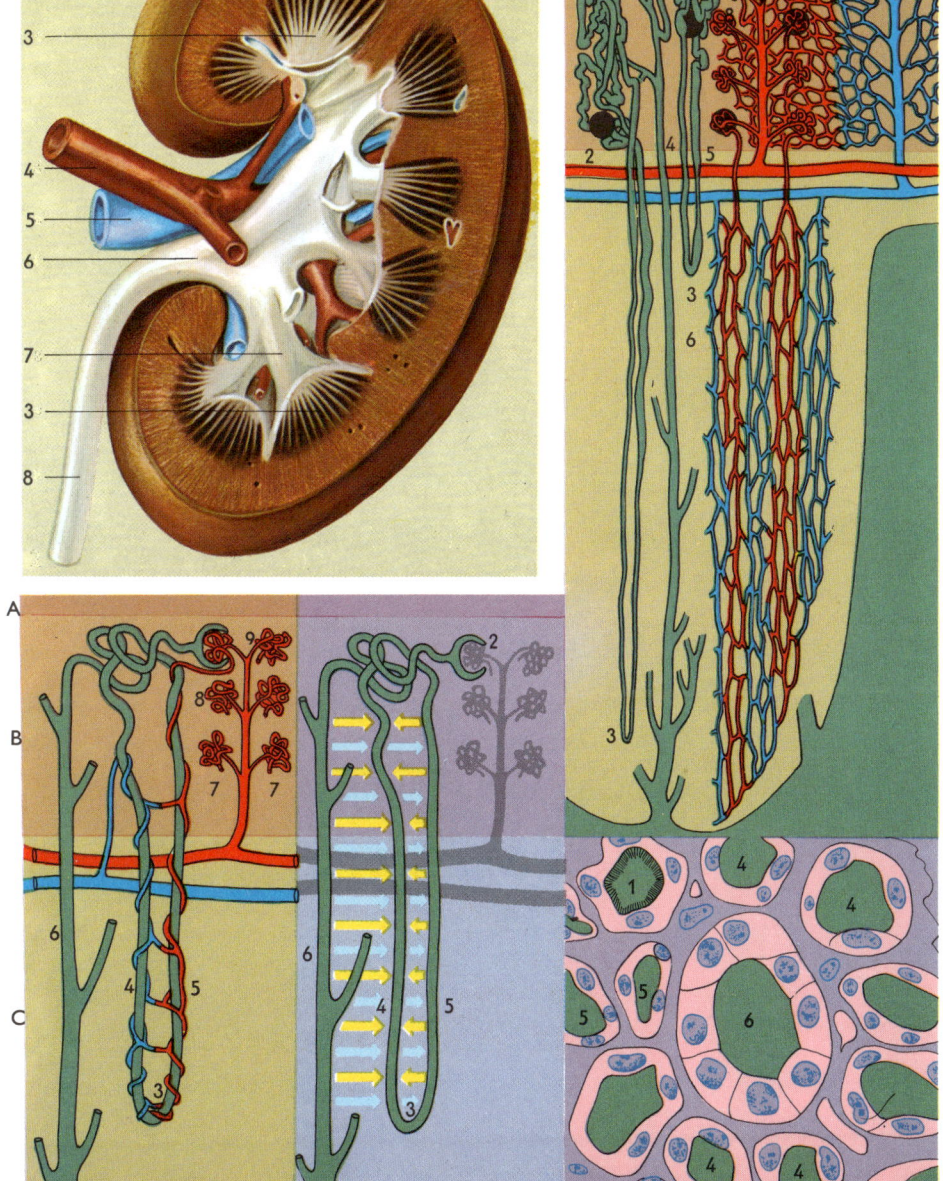

(Top left) Generalized section of a human kidney, three-quarters natural size: 1. capsule, 2. cortex, 3. pyramid, inner zone, 4. renal artery, 5. renal vein, 6. renal pelvis, 7. calyx, 8. ureter. (Top right) Diagram showing (on left) the arrangement of two nephrons with the continuation into the system of collecting tubules, and (on right) the arrangement of the blood vessels. A. capsule, B. cortex, C. medulla, 1. convoluted tubules, 2. Bowman's capsule, 3. Henle's loop, 4. and 5. ascending and descending limbs of Henle's loop, 6. collecting tubule, 7. glomerules, 8. efferent arteriole; 9. afferent arteriole. Arteries and arteries red; veins and venous capillaries, blue. (Bottom left) applies to the other diagrams: lettering also nephric tubule. Relationship of blood supply, salt movements (Bottom centre) Water, water, blue, from the nephric tubule resorption of a salt. (Bottom right) convoluted tubule; medullary ray fr capillaries in red. *rhesus*: a proxim note the brush

Excretion

coelomic cavities above and below the gut and others from the pericardial coelom.

Crustacea. Indications that the crustacean excretory organs may have been segmental are present in the cephalocaridian, *Hutchinsoniella*, but in other modern forms they are restricted to the antennal or maxillary segments of the head.

The two basic regions of the excretory organs are (1) an endsac which is a coelomic remnant and (2) a mesodermal excretory duct which may be variously modified to form a labyrinth and bladder.

In the decapod Crustacea (crabs, prawns, lobsters, etc.) primary urine is formed by filtration from the arterial supply to the endsac and labyrinth. Decapods (except freshwater crayfish) produce urine with the same concentration as the blood. Crayfish, together with some amphipods have hypotonic urine. No crustaceans can form urine appreciably more concentrated than blood.

The capacity to produce dilute urine is reflected in the structure of the excretory organs. Forms which can form hypotonic urine have longer excretory ducts than those which cannot. Final dilution of the urine in crayfish is effected by the reabsorption of ions in the bladder.

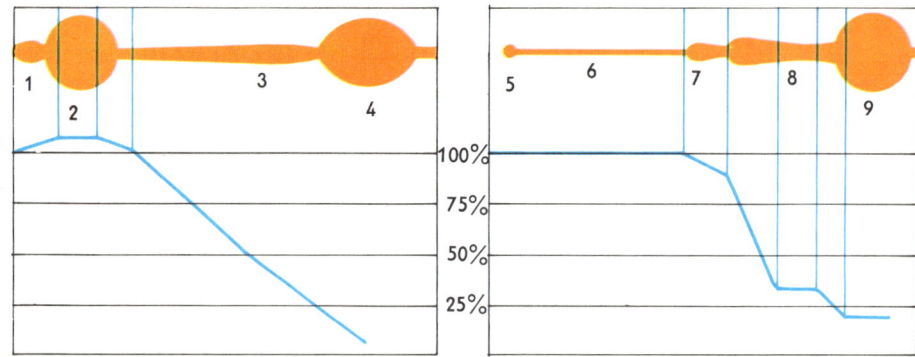

The production of urine by (left) a crayfish (after Peters) and (right) an earthworm (after Ramsay). The percentages indicate the urine concentration in the blood. 1. Coelomic end sac, 2. labyrinth, 3. tubule, 4. bladder, 5. nephrostome, 6. narrow tube, 7. middle tube, 8. wide tube, 9. muscular tube.

Useful materials present in the initial filtrate are reabsorbed in the tubule. Materials can also be introduced into the urine by secretory processes and by 'formed bodies'. The latter are subcellular vesicles which are budded off from the wall of the endsac and labyrinth and after passing down the tubule eventually rupture in the bladder. Their formation potentially permits the transfer of materials from the blood to the urine via the cells lining the tubule but their full function has yet to be elucidated.

Annelids. The excretory organs of annelids take a greater variety of forms than in other invertebrate groups. Typically there are a pair of excretory tubules (nephridia) in each body segment. The inner end lies in the coelomic body cavity and the other opens through the body surface. Certain primitive worms have nephridia whose inner ends are closed by solenocytes; in more advanced forms such as the earthworm *Lumbricus* there is a ciliated nephrostome providing an open connection between the coelom and the tubule lumen.

The true excretory ducts of annelids are of ectodermal origin, penetrating inwards from

Representative excretory organs in invertebrates: 1. crayfish green gland, 2. nephridium of earthworm, 3. excretory organ of a clam, 4. the digestive organs of an insect showing the Malpighian tubules, 5. contractile vacuole of a protozoan, 6. flame cell, 7. solenocyte.

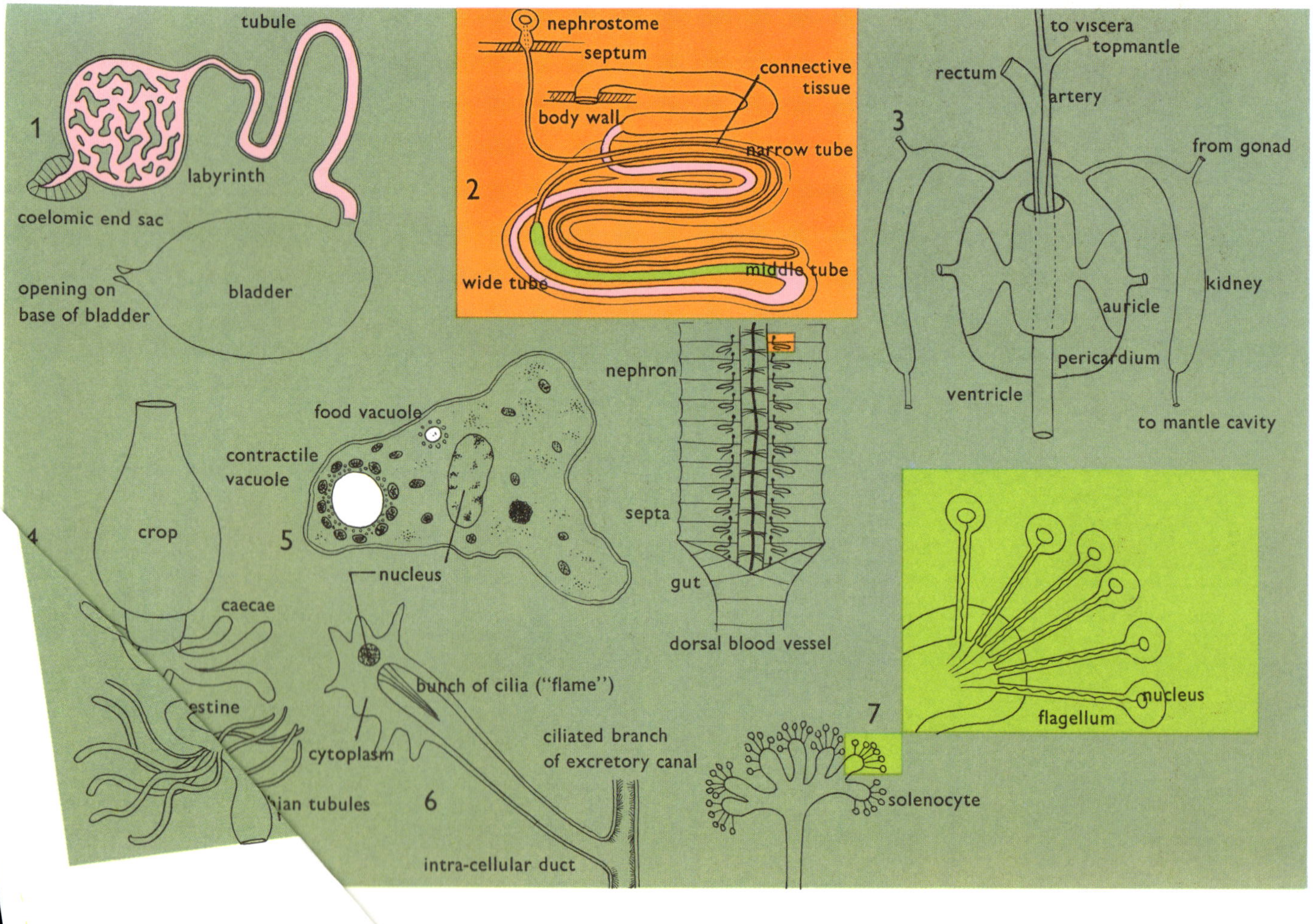

the body surface and are not homologous with the vertebrate, crustacean and mollusc tubules which are mesodermal, growing from the coelom outwards. However, many polychaete worms such as the lugworm *Arenicola* have tubules which are formed by the fusion of both coelomoducts and nephridia and which serve the dual function of excretory organs and genital ducts. Variations from the oligochaete condition as shown by the earthworm include (1) subdivision of the paired nephridia of each segment to form multiple micro-nephridia and (2) junction of the outer ends of the nephridia on each side of the body with a collecting duct which opens into the gut.

It is probable that primary urine is formed by filtration either from blood vessels into the coelom or from blood vessels into the tubule lumen. Marine worms are presumed to form urine isotonic with the coelomic fluid; the earthworm has hypotonic urine, dilution being effected in the middle and wide regions of the nephron.

Reabsorption of water by the gut wall may serve to limit urinary water loss in the case of those forms, such as the Indian earthworm *Pheretima* whose nephridia open into the gut.

Special functions for nephridia occur in a few species, Some of the anterior nephridia of *Pheretima* open into the pharynx and seem to produce digestive enzymes. An even more unusual role is performed by the anterior and posterior nephridia of terrestrial leeches. These serve to moisten the suckers and so increase their powers of adhesion to the host.

Malpighian tubules. These are secretory organs of excretion found in insects, arachnids and myriapods. They vary from two to 150 in different insect groups and are formed as outpushings from the gut in the region of the junction of the mid- and hindgut. The tubules receive no arterial blood supply and pressure filtration cannot therefore occur. Instead primary urine is formed by the active secretion of potassium and phosphate into the tubules with water and solutes of small molecular weight following passively. Most of the valuable ions, metabolites and water are reabsorbed as they pass through the rectum and the final urine may have an osmotic concentration considerably exceeding that of the blood. The Malpighian tubule–rectal system is, indeed, the only invertebrate excretory organ able to produce hypertonic urine.

The principal nitrogenous waste product of insects is uric acid. This is secreted into the upper part of the Malpighian tubules as urate in solution and is subsequently precipitated as the less soluble uric acid in the rectum where the pH is lower. Insects living in dry places reabsorb almost all the urinary water in the rectum releasing little more than necessary to produce a sludge of uric acid.

Contractile vacuoles. Contractile vacuoles are subcellular excretory organs responsible for eliminating excess water from freshwater sponges and Protozoa and marine ciliate Protozoa. Vacuoles rhythmically fill with liquid from the cell and then discharge this through the cell wall to the medium.

The process responsible for vacuolar filling remains uncertain. Any rise in water uptake by the cell is followed by an increased rate of vacuolar activity but the causative agent for filling is unlikely to be increased hydrostatic pressure inside the cell since in ciliates which possess two contractile vacuoles, these operate alternately. Remaining alternatives are the active secretion of water, solute linked secretion as in the Malpighian tubule or a

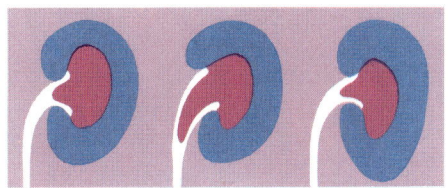

Kidneys of rodents from different environments showing relationship between size of medulla and availability of water in habitat: (left) general terrestrial habitat, (centre) arid regions, (right) semi-aquatic.

form of reversed pinocytosis. In favour of the second alternative is the fact that the sodium concentration of the vacuole contents in *Tetrahymena* is up to 8 times that of the cytoplasm. However the possibility that the vacuole is filled by a process analagous with pinocytosis in reverse is not ruled out since numerous tiny vessels surround the vacuolar membrane. The matter remains to be resolved but as numerous mitochondria surround the membrane it is clear that an active process of some type is present in this region.

Flame cells and solenocytes. Flame cells are found in certain invertebrates such as rotifers and platyhelminths. They are single large branched cells one of whose faces closes the end of an excretory duct. This face bears a bundle of cilia. Solenocytes are similar but have a single flagellum instead of the cilia.

The mode of urine formation by flame cells and solencytes is uncertain. One theory is that the beating of the cilia or flagellum creates a negative pressure in the excretory tubule large enough to cause filtration to occur through the cell from the surrounding interstitial fluid (or coelom). However, apart from the observation that the rate of flagellum beat increases when the rate of urine production rises, there is little actual support for this view. A.P.M.L.

EXCRETION BY NOSE. Some vertebrates carry out extra-renal salt secretion; that is, they lose salt by a process not involving the kidneys. All such animals live in the sea where they take in copious amounts of salt water. The kidneys are unable to deal with such large amounts of salt and the surplus is excreted through the tear glands. These glands usually secrete a salty fluid to lubricate the eyes but in these marine animals, the glands are enlarged and they secrete large quantities of fluid. Extra-renal salt secretion is found in seals, seabirds such as gulls and penguins, turtles and Sea snakes. In the seals the fluid flows from the eyes as tears which can be seen when they are on land. In seabirds the fluid flows down the nostrils and can sometimes be seen as a 'dew-drop' on the tip of the bill.

EXPERIENCE, the sum total of the events in an animal's environment which impinge upon it and its responses to them. Moreover, an animal's later responses may be affected by its previous experience. Thus an insect's reactions to humidities will be affected by whether it has been kept immediately previously in dry or moist conditions, similarly the sign of its reaction to light may be reversed after being in the dark. Experience in the form of practice is required for the perfection of some behavioural patterns but generalized motor experience may influence the development of patterns quite unspecifically (see heredity and environment).

EXTINCTION. Of recent years there has developed an increasing recognition that many species of animals are threatened with extinction. This has come too late for the once prolific Passenger pigeon of North America, migrating flocks of which formerly darkened the skies. They were slaughtered by the million till the last living specimen, Martha, finally expired in the Cincinatti Zoo in 1914. The last Great auk was killed in 1844. The dodo which has achieved immortality by entering our language as a common idiom was last seen alive in 1681. Flightless birds of oceanic islands were especially vulnerable to the attentions of pigs and goats which sailors would leave on the islands for future provisions. The pigs ate the eggs and young and the goats destroyed the habitat. Today oceanic flying birds are being systematically wiped out so that certain islands can be made safe for military aircraft. Other famous animals so threatened include the rhinoceros killed for the imagined aphrodisiac qualities of its powdered horn, and the leopard whose skins are much sought after for the glamorous adornment of the human female.

A somewhat more sinister aspect of extinctions at the present-day is graphically provided by the whaling industry. Already it appears that the Blue whale—the largest animal that has ever existed on the earth—was thought to be doomed to extinction. Current ideas, in 1971, are that it will

Extinction

probably survive, yet the history of this whale is worth examining. Of 100,000 inhabiting the oceans in 1935 only some 600 now survive. The whales are an important source of oils and proteins and are the basis of a large international industry. With modern explosive harpoons and factory ships they are easily hunted. The race for this product has resulted in the depletion of stocks to such a disastrous extent that the industry itself will shortly have completely destroyed the source of its wealth. The serious nature of this situation led to the setting up of the International Whaling Commission in 1946 and the establishment of quotas of Blue Whale Units (the standard measure of the industry) which can be cropped. Unfortunately not only are these quotas illegally exceeded by some of the major whaling nations but the scientists' views on what constitutes an acceptable quota (i.e. one which will allow the population to maintain its numerical strength) is rarely accepted. The net consequence of these policies is that the whale harvest has been diminishing at an accelerating rate over recent years.

The whaling industry is going into a decline from which it is unlikely to recover. A policy of thoughtlessly exploiting a natural commodity, with no thought for the long term maintenance of the industry, leads to marginally higher profits in one year followed by rapid decline. In 1963 it was recommended that the 1964-5 catch should not exceed 4,000 BWU. Japan, Norway and Russia in particular decided on a limit of 8,000 BWU—they only managed to catch under 7,000. In the 1965-6 season the scientists suggested 2,500 but under pressure this was raised to 4,500. The actual catch was only 4,000. By 1967 the fleets were trying to achieve a catch of 3,500 BWU—had the advice of the scientists been heeded they could have been taking between 7-8,000 BWU in the 1966-7 season. Arthur Bourne has commented 'posterity will rightly be scornful of the generation that, through greed and stupidity, destroyed the world's largest and most valuable creature'.

It is evident that extinction at the present time is a consequence of mankind's activities, albeit in some cases merely as a result of ignorance. Surprisingly this seems to have been also the case during the recent geological past. Paul S. Martin has demonstrated that the major extinctions of large mammals which took place during the latter part of the Quaternary Period did not coincide with climatic changes or indeed any other kind of physical environmental factors. In fact, in different areas of the world these extinctions occurred at different times. The one factor they had in common was the arrival of man the hunter. In Africa the development of the Acheulian hand-axe culture, a significant degree of advance in weapon technology, led to severe inroads into the game fauna. In North America the arrival of fluted-point hunters resulted in dramatic extinctions. Large animals are always the most vulnerable and sensitive to any ecological changes and seemingly the advent of man must have tipped the scales.

When the present-day fauna and flora are considered the impression is gained that man is the major factor responsible for extinctions. However, when we examine the forms of life that existed before man had evolved, it is strikingly obvious that extinction has been the normal fate of the majority of species.

Extinction by evolution. Extinction can be of two distinct types. Many forms of life no longer exist and hence by definition are extinct, they became so not by dying out but by gradually changing, by evolving into new forms. For example, certain lobefinned bony fish, the rhipidistians, became extinct because they evolved into the first land vertebrates, the amphibians. The mammal-like reptiles evolved into mammals, the ape-men evolved into true men. In a sense this is extinction. It may be significant that all the major evolutionary advances that have taken the development of living things forward seem to be in predatory carnivorous lines. Explosive evolution in which there is a sudden radiation of a group which subsequently peters out, seems to be characteristic of herbivores. As these always seem to be dead ends, they can have played little part in the long term picture of vertebrate evolution.

The lobefinned fish, the coelacanth, was thought to have died out 70 million years ago but was found alive in 1938. According to Professor Glenn Jepsen 'this kind of transient demise, confidently shown on our charts and based upon lack of proper data, might be called chartacide, and is the only kind of mass death from which instantaneous and complete recovery is possible and rather common'. There is quite a suite of animals that by all accounts should have become extinct but which perversely continue to hang on through countless millenia. The tuatara lizard of New Zealand survives from the Triassic period of 200 million years ago, but the most sensational living fossil is the limpet-like primitive mollusc *Neopilina* discovered in the 1950's which was supposed to have died out some 500 million years ago. These forms that survive always seem to be those that first appear, that originate major evolutionary radiations. The group as a whole becomes extinct with the exception of the very same primitive forms from which the advanced forms had been derived. This seems to be a constant pattern, the first and last members of a group seem to be the same. Great evolutionary advances, remarkable adaptions to the environment, highly successful specializations, always seem to lead to extinction. As Sir Gavin de Beer has stressed 'the paths of adaptive glory lead but to the grave of extinction'. This seems to be one of the great paradoxes of evolution: there is always a tendency for organisms which are better adapted to their environment to be selected and hence to be successful and flourish. This process seems to be a virtual guarantee of their ultimate demise.

Puzzle of the dinosaurs. The classic example of extinction as a consequence of overspecialization that is familiar to all was the sudden end of the *dinosaurs at the end of the Mesozoic Era, 70 million years ago. This dramatic event has exercised the minds of scientists for a considerable time and innumerable suggestions have been put forward to account for the disappearance of the dinosaurs. Professor Jepsen has provided one of the most comprehensive catalogues of the theories that have been offered:

'Authors with varying competence have suggested that the dinosaurs disappeared because the climate deteriorated (became suddenly or slowly too hot or cold or dry or wet), or that the diet did (with too much food or not enough of such substances as fern oil; from poisons in water or plants or ingested minerals; by bankruptcy of calcium or other necessary elements). Other writers have put the blame on disease, parasites, wars, anatomical or metabolic disorders (slipped vertebral discs, malfunction or imbalance of hormone or endocrine systems, dwindling brain and consequent stupidity, heat sterilization), racial old age, evolutionary drift into senescent over-specialization, changes in the pressure or composition of the atmosphere, poison gases, volcanic dust, excessive oxygen from plants, meteorites, comets, gene pool drainage by little mammalian egg-eaters, overkill capacity by predators, fluctuation of gravitational constants, development of psychotic suicidal factors, entropy, cosmic radiation, shift of Earth's rotational poles, floods, extraction of the moon from the Pacific Basin, drainage of swamp and lake environments, sunspots, God's will, mountain building, raids by little green hunters in flying saucers, and lack of even standing room in Noah's Ark'.

It is possible to choose any one or combination of the above theories according to one's individual taste. Unfortunately whatever opinion is held it is always possible for serious objections to be raised.

During the Cretaceous period the modern flowering plants became established and their siliceous nature must have profoundly affected herbivorous dinosaurs used to feeding on soft plant material. The commonest dinosaurs during the latter part of this period were the Duck-billed dinosaurs which had evolved a dentition designed to cope with tough fibrous plant material. These animals

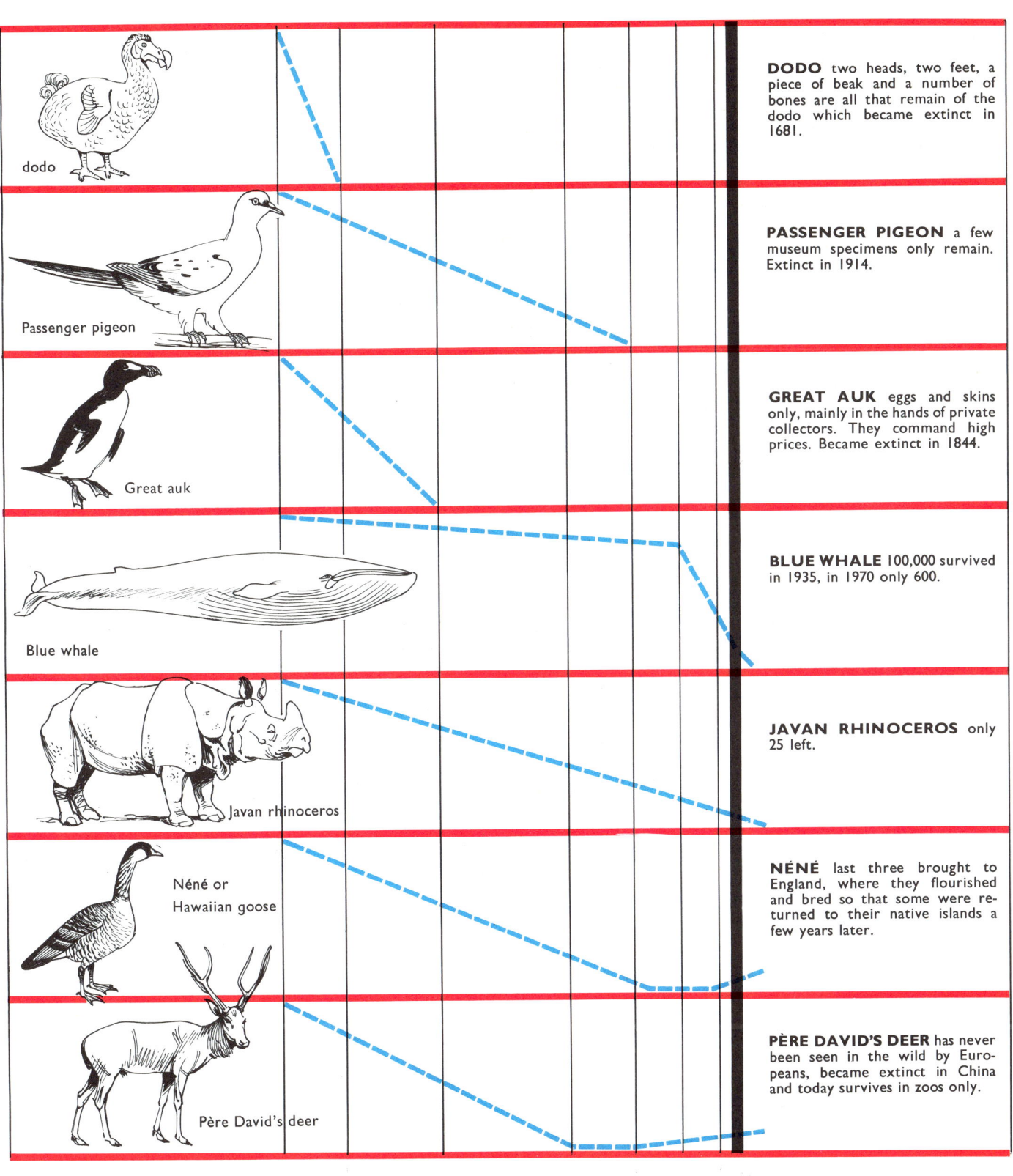

Extinction

appeared to be perfectly adapted to the new type of flora and hence it is impossible to account for their disappearance. The brains of the evolving mammals are occasionally postulated as contributing to the decline of the dinosaurs, but it seems most unlikely that the intelligence of nocturnal and crepuscular animals like hedgehogs and shrews could have had any significant effect on the situation.

Unfortunately even if a theory could be established to account for the extinction of the dinosaurs, for it to be viable it would also have to explain the simultaneous extinction of the marine reptiles and the flying reptiles (pterosaurs). Problems of upsetting ecological balances simultaneously in the oceans, on the land and in the air seem to be insurmountable. If in spite of these difficulties, a satisfactory explanation can be offered, then one is faced with the equally difficult problem of having to account for certain groups not dying out, as well as groups which had begun important radiations during the latter part of the Cretaceous and which continued them through into the succeeding Tertiary Era. The modern lizards and snakes, the main lines of the radiation of the birds, several modern orders of mammal including the Primates to which man belongs, as well as the modern bony fishes, were all established during the period of the dinosaurs. Their evolution was unaffected by the mass extinctions at the end of the Cretaceous. In spite of the fact that several reptilian groups were declining during the latter part of the Mesozoic Era, the actual final extinction seems to have been a sudden event. Much the same pattern has been recorded by Jake Hancock with reference to the marine invertebrates, although as with the vertebrates a number managed to linger on into the early part of the Tertiary.

No room for giants. It has been suggested that on the land, in the sea and in the air, the modern type faunas were evolving contemporary food-chain relationships and that in this context the giant animals became an irrelevance. The actual cause for their final failure still remains a complete mystery. It is significant that the two groups that heralded the age of reptiles, the crocodiles and tortoises, should have continued right through basically in the same primitive state they were in at the beginning. Their ultimate success is attested by the fact that they are still with us.

Perhaps one of the remarkable features of the great Cretaceous extinctions is that there was a considerable time lag before the birds and mammals filled many of the ecological niches left vacant by the disappearance of the dinosaurs and the other reptilian groups. The mammals did not venture back into the sea until the Eocene, this niche remained unoccupied during the whole of the Paleocene period as far as we know.

This same type of hiatus has been noted by Frank Rhodes in his discussion of the extinctions of marine invertebrates which marked the boundary between the Paleozoic and Mesozoic Eras. His main conclusion, however, is that these periods of extinction are 'routine, everyday' and are a common factor throughout the fossil record although we remain ignorant of their causes.

Occasionally it is possible to trace extinctions that are the result of the gradual ecological replacement of one group of organisms by another. This is clearly seen in the sequence of Triassic reptile faunas. At the beginning of the period, life on the land was dominated by the mammal-like reptiles which were evolving towards the mammalian condition. The ancestors of the dinosaurs were crocodile-like living in rivers and lakes. They occupied an ecological niche ignored by the fully terrestrial mammal-like reptiles and were thus able to evolve without any undue competition from the dominant land reptiles. As the semi-aquatic forms became better adapted for their amphibious way of life, they evolved strong hindlimbs and a powerful tail. These developments preadapted them for a bipedal gait when they ventured on to land. Not only were they then able to compete against the mammal-like reptiles but by the close of the Triassic period they had ousted them. By this time the stock of mammal-like reptiles was virtually non-existent—those that survived were rat-sized furry mammals which by virtue of their warm-bloodedness were able to flourish during the Mesozoic Era in occupancy of the new ecological niche of night—a niche denied the cold-blooded reptiles.

Such extinctions by invasion are only possible when one group is able to evolve in ecological isolation from the dominant one of the time. It may then achieve sufficient structural advance to be able to enter an already occupied niche and compete effectively with the original inhabitants.

Extinction in the future. Having considered the phenomenon of extinction with reference to both the present and the past, it only

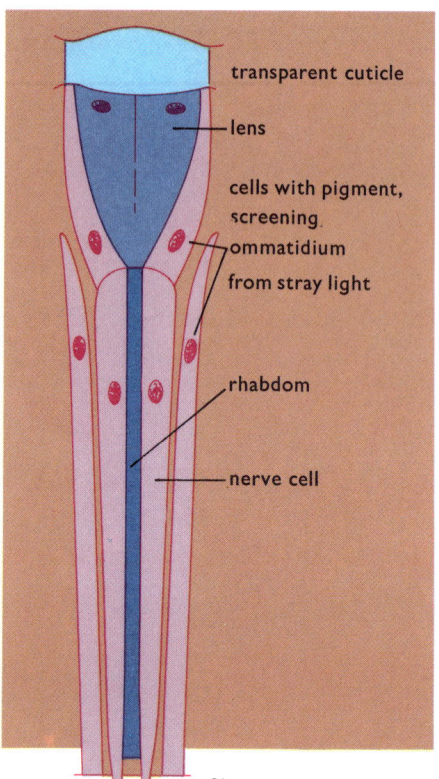

Detail of a single ommatidium, thousands of which form the compound eye.

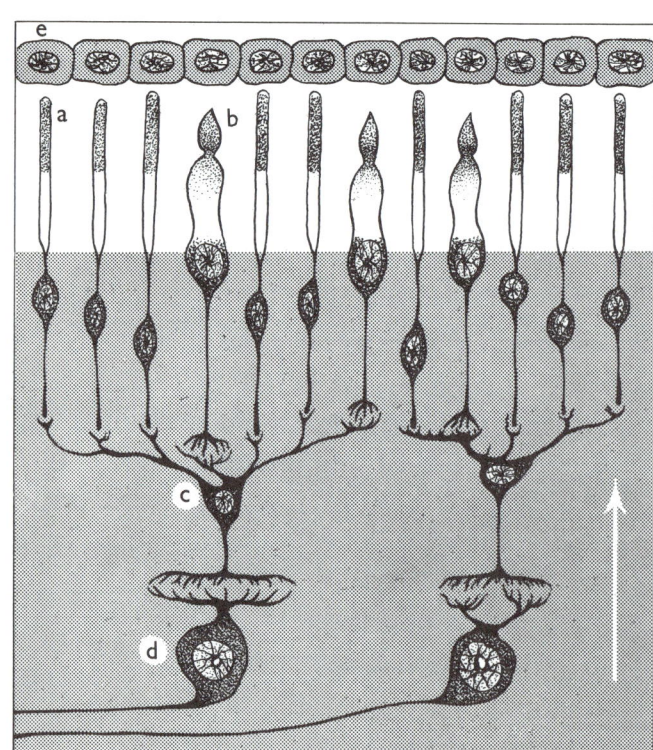

The human retina contains a large number of sensory cells which are sensitive to colours or shades of colour: a. rods, b. cones (colour perception), c. and d. sensory cells, e. layer of pigment cells.

 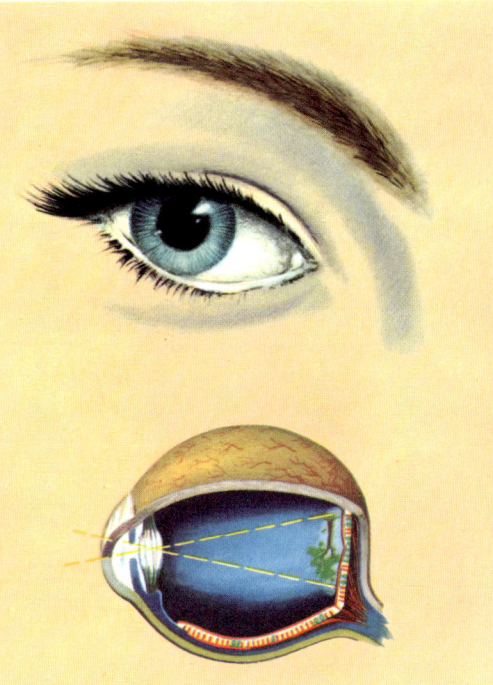 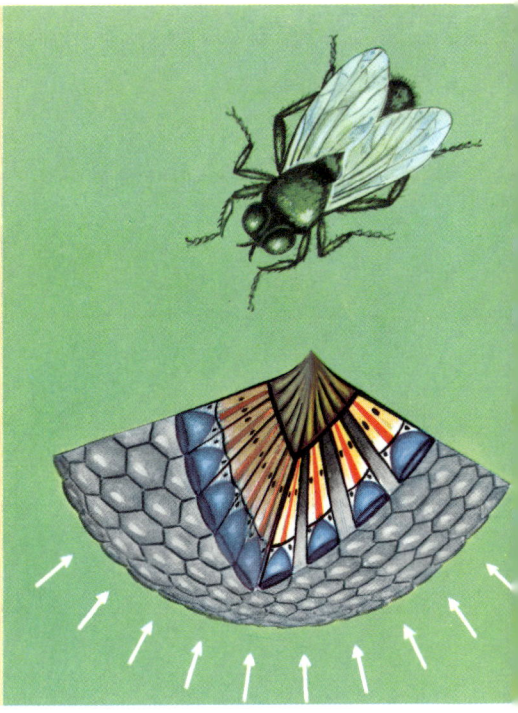

remains to discuss the future and in particular the possible fate of our own species. In many ways it is possible to draw parallels between the evolution of human societies and the evolution of major groups of animals. Such comparisons are particularly apposite when the development of highly specialized societies are contemplated. A rigid conformist society may appear to be successful, indeed an individual qualified for a particular task may similarly be highly successful, but should a new situation arise demanding different requirements then society is likely to collapse and the old specialist skills to become redundant. There is always a tendency in human societies for individuals to conform to the normal accepted patterns of behaviour, to become less than tolerant of the unorthodox. Unless a society can maintain variety and hence guarantee its future facility for change, its extinction will be assured. A truly strong society can be measured by the degree to which it can accommodate dissent from its stated social mores. To continue the parallel it can be expected that the advanced societies of today will be replaced by others of more vitality. In particular it may well be that the future will arise out of the present turmoil of Africa. On past showing there is no certainty that the advanced societies of today will lead on to the next stage of development—indeed on present showing it seems most unlikely.

The extinction of forms of society is not the same as the extinction of the species. This latter, however, is one of the few certainties of life on our planet. Ultimately man will no longer exist on earth, we will join other forms of life that have become extinct. It is merely a question of timing. Our aim should be to raise the quality of life in the interim which after all could last for hundreds of millions of years.
L.B.H.

EYE, the specialized organ in most animals that is sensitive to light. In echinoderms, some insects and lampreys, however, there is evidence for a general (dermal) light-sensitivity. All eyes contain light-sensitive cells in which there is a visual pigment the breakdown of which under the influence of light energy causes electrical changes in the

Left: The eyecup of nautilus has a small opening with no lens. Centre: The addition of a lens enables more lightrays to contribute towards forming images. Regular focusing is required for a clear image either by moving the lens as in fish, or by changing the thickness of the lens as in man. Right: In insects the eye consists of a large number of ommatidia which allow mainly vertical lightrays to penetrate to the sensitive area. Each ommatidium perceives only one point of the object; the more ommatidia there are, the clearer the image.

Enlarged dorsal view of head of a winged insect, the psocid *Graphopsocus cruciatus*, showing large compound eyes of many facets.

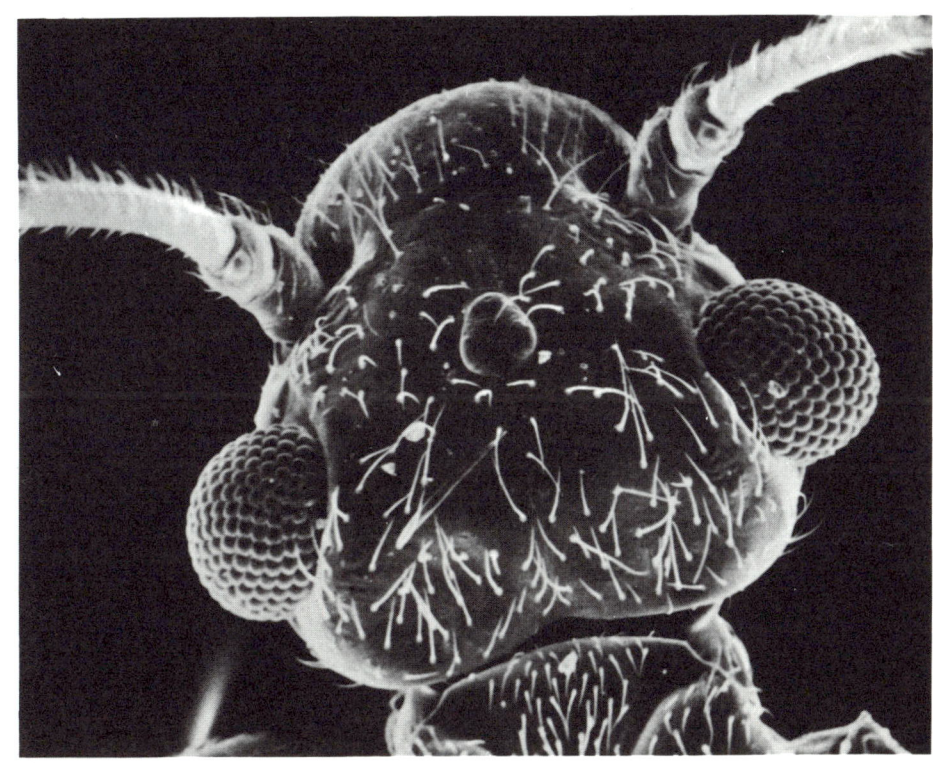

Eye

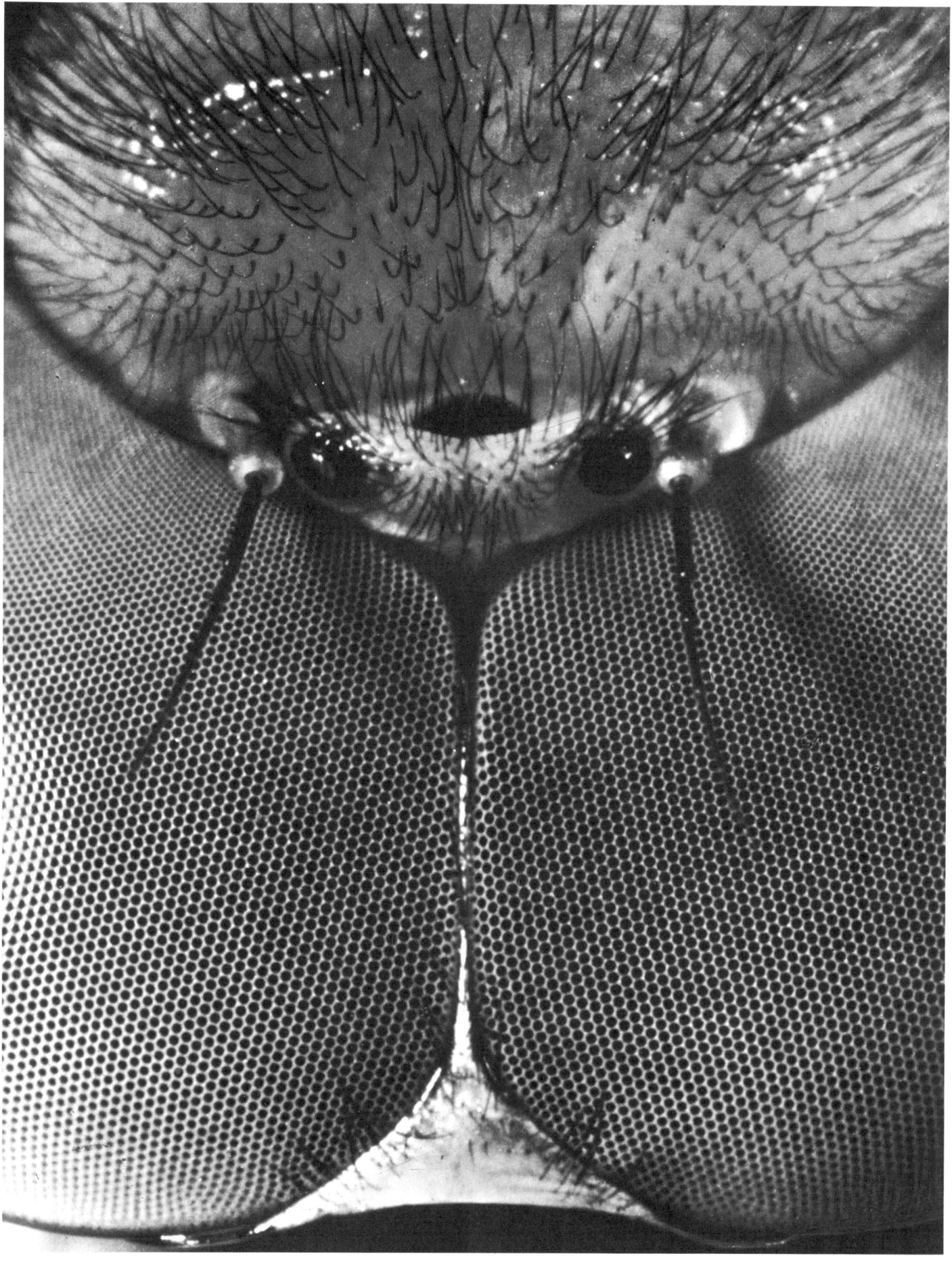

Eye, compound

cell initiating an impulse in the nerve leaving the cell. Such cells are primary receptors and may connect directly to the central nervous system, though they often lead to ganglionic layers. These layers have been proved to both integrate and select from the impulses caused by the images falling on the eye in octopus and in mammals.

The simplest eyes may consist of little more than light-sensitive retinal cells. They are, however, usually backed by a pigment layer; the arrangement in planarian worms is typical. By this means they are stimulated only by light coming from one direction and thus give information on the position of the light source, which is used in orientation. Eyes of this sort, which are unable to form an image on the retinal cells, are euthoscopic eyes. The addition of a lens increases the light gathering power of the eye by concentrating light onto the retinal cells. Eyes like this are found in polychaete worms, echinoderms, gastropod molluscs; the ocelli of insects are of the same pattern.

Eyes capable of forming images are termed eidoscopic. The reception of images is possible only when the lens system throws a sharp image onto the retina but the amount of detail in that image which can be perceived depends upon the number of retinal cells per unit area; the more there are, the better the animal will see. Thus, cone cells are crowded together in the fovea of a mammal's eye which is the area of the retina giving the most acute vision.

For a sharp image of near and distant objects, focussing is necessary. The lens either needs to be moved relative to the retina or its shape can be altered thus changing its focal length. The lens in the eye of the squid *Sepia* can be moved back and forth by muscular action. This eye in common with that of other cephalopods, mimics the vertebrate eye in general structure. A spherical eyeball is lined with retinal cells and wrapped in a pigment coat. Light enters through a pupil and is focussed by a lens onto a retina.

The method of accommodation (focussing) in a vertebrate is different for the shape of the lens is altered, being flattened by contraction of the ciliary muscles and becoming more nearly spherical under its own elasticity when the ciliary muscles relax. Special muscles in the eyes of some diving birds enable extreme distortion of the lens so that the eye functions both in air and beneath the surface of the water. J.D.C.

EYE, COMPOUND, instead of having only a single lens focussing on to a sensitive area as in the vertebrate eye, the compound eye is made up from a number of small units each of which has its own lens, hence the term compound. The basic unit of the compound eye is the ommatidium and there may be as many as 10,000 ommatidia in large eyes, such as those of dragonflies. Compound eyes are found in the arthropods, insects, crustaceans and Horseshoe crabs.

Like the rest of the arthropod body, the ommatidium is covered by a cuticle, but here it is transparent and lens-shaped. The main lens, however, is beneath the cuticle, shaped like a cone and beneath this again are the sense cells, usually seven or eight of them, arranged in a rosette round the long axis of the ommatidium. The sense cells are often very long and all down the edge facing the centre of the rosette the cell walls are produced into narrow projections pointing towards the centre. A pigment, called the visual pigment, is present in the projections. This is changed chemically by light falling on

One of the most remarkable sets of eyes in the animal kingdom, the jewel-like eyes of a scallop.

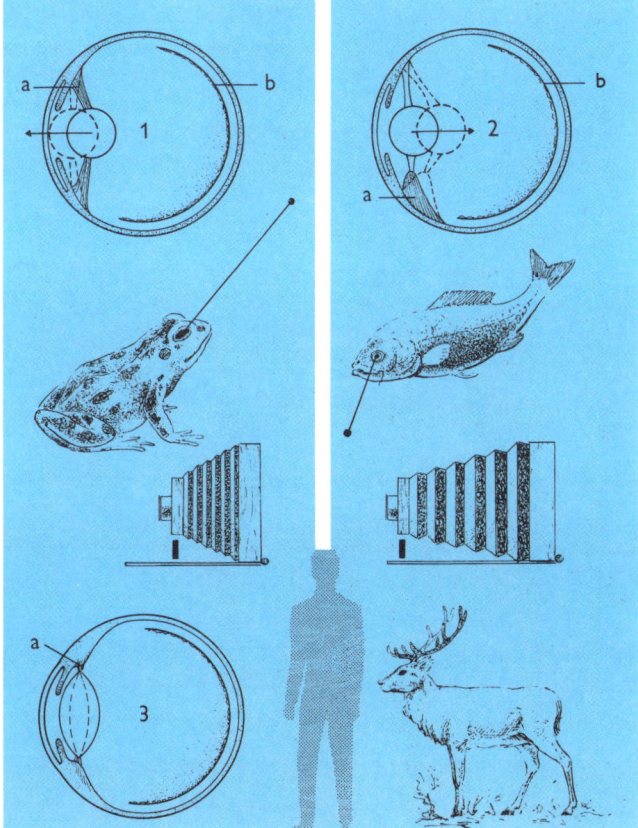

◀ The eyes of a dragonfly consist of many thousands of small units called ommatidia. This predatory insect, which pursues its prey in the air, has therefore acute vision for an insect.

Accommodation. Focusing in amphibians and fish occurs as in a camera. The lens is moved by accommodation muscles (a) relative to the retina (b). In frogs (1) the eye is at rest when the object is far away, in fish (2) when nearby. Mammals and man accommodate by changing the form of the lens (3); to see clearly objects which are near it is made more convex through accommodation muscles (a). In birds and reptiles this is achieved by changing the pressure in the eyeball.

it and forms the basis of vision, just as in other animals. The rows of projections from the seven or eight sense cells together are known as the rhabdom and their alignment may differ somewhat in different groups of arthropods.

When light falls on an ommatidium it is focussed on the rhabdom and produces an electrical impulse following the chemical alteration of the visual pigment. Different ommatidia, however, face in slightly different directions so that if an insect is looking at an object each ommatidium will receive light from a slightly different part of the object. Hence the amount of light focussed by each lens system on its rhabdom will be proportional to that reflected from the particular part of the object from which the ommatidium receives light and we can visualize the image formed by the whole eye as a series of spots of light of different intensities, forming a picture in the same way as a coarse newsprint picture. Each spot of light stimulates one rhabdom and produces an electrical impulse in proportion to its intensity and this information is conveyed to the brain of the insect.

Such a system will only produce a sharp picture if the light from one ommatidium is not scattered into adjacent ommatidia. Scattering is prevented by cells containing pigment which clothes each ommatidium; the pigment absorbs any scattered light before it gets to the next ommatidium. This is not the important visual pigment but a screening pigment and any light absorbed by the screening pigment is wasted as far as vision is concerned. This does not matter as long as there is plenty of light, but in poor light so much may be lost in this way that the animal is hardly able to see at all. Many insects and crustaceans are able to overcome this by withdrawing the screening pigments, when light is poor, into parts of the eye where they do not interfere with vision. Hence light is scattered through the eye and the best use is made of the light available, but the image formed is very blurred compared with that produced by ommatidia separated by screening pigments. The eyes of some moths and other arthropods are, however, modified to function efficiently in the dark.

The structure of compound eyes is such that they are particularly sensitive to movement because this causes an image to move from one ommatidium to another and thus produces a change in stimulation. It is probably true that animals with compound eyes do not perceive the detail of objects which our eyes can make out; the outline is more important to the insect than the detail.

Many of the arthropods having compound eyes are colour blind, but some insects at least are able to distinguish different colours, and this is especially true of flower-visiting species like bees and butterflies. The range of colours which insects can distinguish is, however, rather different from our own. In general they do not see well at the red end of the spectrum. The wavelengths which produce the sensation of red in our eye often do not stimulate the eye of an insect at all and the insect will only have the impression of blackness. But at the other end of the spectrum insects turn the tables completely, for they can see ultraviolet while we cannot. The male Brimstone butterfly, for instance, looks uniformly yellow to us, but an insect able to perceive ultraviolet light sees the wings as patterned because they reflect ultraviolet in some parts.

The compound eyes of some insects and crustaceans can appreciate the planes in which light waves vibrate, the planes of polarization of the light. Light reflected from the sky is often polarized to some extent and these animals can perceive this and, in some cases at least, direct their movements accordingly. Bees for instance use the polarization of light from the sky in their navigation.

Arthropod eyes are not movable in sockets as are ours so the insect or crustacean cannot follow movement by moving its eyes, but the same result is achieved in other ways. Many insects have large eyes which cover most of the head so that they can see virtually through 360° without moving their eyes at all. Sometimes, as in mantids, the head is very freely movable and these insects follow movements of their prey by turning their heads, rather as people in a crowd follow a race. Many crustaceans, like crabs and lobsters, go one better. Although their eyes are fixed they are mounted on short stalks which are movable and these animals can flick their eyes to and fro in a most amusing, but useful, manner.

Compound eyes are very efficient giving the animal a view of the world much like our own, but they achieve this in a rather different way and they can do some things which our eyes cannot. See vision. R.F.C.

EYED LIZARD *Lacerta lepida*, also known as the Spanish or Ocellated lizard. It lives in southern France and the Iberian Peninsula and grows to 2 ft (60 cm), of which 16 in (40 cm) is tail. It is brownish green to reddish with black spots which sometimes form rosettes with black centres. On the flanks are bluish oval markings, the so-called 'eyes' or 'ocelli'. FAMILY: Lacertidae, ORDER: Squamata, CLASS: Reptilia.

FABRE J. H., 1823-1915. A French teacher and entomologist, he was the author of the ten volumes of the *Souvenirs entomologiques* (1879-1907) which became justly famous and did much to spread interest in and understanding of insects and spiders. Most of Fabre's work was centred on direct observation of animals in their natural environment, but he also performed simple experiments, and was one of the first to carry out research in animal behaviour. After teaching in Carpentras, Ajaccio, and Avignon, he retired to Serignan in 1871 to devote himself to his studies. These studies—particularly on bees and wasps, beetles, grasshoppers, moths and spiders—added considerably to our knowledge of these groups and were frequently of a pioneering nature. He did not, however, agree with the theory of evolution, and considered certain aspects of insect behaviour to be intelligent rather than instinctive. But these shortcomings were far outweighed by his work as a discoverer and popularizer.

FAIRY-BLUEBIRDS, two species of thrushlike birds usually regarded as leafbirds (Irenidae) but possibly more closely related to the orioles. Males of the Blue-backed fairybluebird *Irena puella* have bright iridescent blue on crown and back, with velvety black plumage elsewhere, and dark red irides, while females are greenish-blue. This species occurs from India to Malaysia. *I. cyanogaster,* in which both sexes are similarly glossy blue and black, occurs in the Philippines. The bill is short and slightly curved and the legs short. These are arboreal birds of forest areas and usually occur in pairs but may gather in small flocks at fruiting trees. They feed on small fruits and may take some nectar. The nest is a shallow cup of twigs and moss in the lower layers of forest growth. The clutch is of two eggs, white with heavy brown markings. FAMILY: Irenidae, ORDER: Passeriformes, CLASS: Aves.

FAIRY SHRIMPS, crustaceans differing from other Branchiopoda in lacking a carapace and in bearing stalked eyes. The body is elongated and cylindrical. The anterior part, or thorax, usually consists of 11 segments bearing limbs, but in *Polyartemiella* there are 17 and in *Polyartemia* 19 such segments. Behind the thorax there are two genital segments, which in the female bear a brood pouch on the underside. The terminal part of the body, or abdomen, consists of five or six segments, together with the telson, which bears a pair of caudal rami.

The elegant, elongated body is propelled through the water by the thoracic limbs, which are flattened, with several lobes and a row of fine setae on the inner or medial edge. They do not beat in unison, but in a rhythm in which one limb is one sixth of a beat ahead of the limb in front. This means that the spaces between the limbs are alternately enlarged and reduced, pumping water in and out. The limbs are arranged so that water flows into the interlimb spaces from the mid-ventral line, and flows out at the outer edges. The flaps or exites on the outer edges prevent water from entering at the side, but allow it to escape and direct the current backwards. This current provides the propulsive thrust when the Fairy shrimp swims forwards. The normal swimming position for a Fairy shrimp is with the back downwards and some, such as *Chirocephalus,* can adjust their limb movements so that the animal appears to hover in the water.

The beating of the thoracic limbs also forms the basis of the feeding mechanism. Water flowing into the interlimb spaces is filtered by the fine setae on the median edges

Blue-backed fairy-bluebird, of India to Malaysia, one of two species of fairy-bluebird.

Falanouc

of the limbs. Small particles trapped on these setae are freed by another series of setae which project through the filter as the limbs move close together. The freed particles are moved forwards to the mouth by subsidiary currents flowing down the median line between the two rows of limbs. When they reach the mouth the particles are bound together by a sticky secretion, pressed into a compact mass by the mandibles and then swallowed.

The male Fairy shrimp has enlarged and often extremely complicated antennae, which serve as grasping organs when it transfers sperm to the brood pouch of the female. The male approaches the female from the side, seizes her in the region of the brood pouch and then bends his body round hers so that his own genital region comes into contact with the opening of the brood pouch. This is a complex structure with two lateral pouches, into which the eggs are first laid, and a median pouch. After a few days in the lateral pouches the eggs are passed into the median pouch from which they are eventually released.

Most Fairy shrimps lay a single type of egg, with a tough outer coat and a capacity for resisting both freezing and drying. This is an adaptation to the usual habitat of Fairy shrimps since most of them live in temporary ponds which either dry up or freeze solid according to their location. One species, *Branchinecta paludosa,* is widespread in arctic regions, where it lives in small pools that are frozen for six months or more of the year. This species also has two interesting relict populations, one in the High Tatra Mountains of Czechoslovakia and Poland and the other in the Rocky Mountains. In both these localities the arctic form is found in cool mountain lakes. Various other species occur in temporary fresh waters throughout the world. The only species capable of living in sea water and higher salinities is *Artemia salina* the Brine shrimp.

In Britain there is only one species of Fairy shrimp, *Chirocephalus diaphanus*. It occurs in temporary pools, mainly in the south of England, particularly in the New Forest area. The pools are often extremely shallow and there is even a record of *Chirocephalus* from a cart rut in Epping Forest. In North America there are about 27 species, including the remarkable *Branchinecta gigas,* which reaches a length of 4 in (10 cm) and has changed from being a filter feeder into a predator feeding on other smaller Fairy shrimps.

The colours of Fairy shrimps are very variable, even within a single species. The most common colours are orange and pink. The orange colours are caused by carotenoid

Falconer with goshawk *Accipiter gentilis*, West Pakistan.

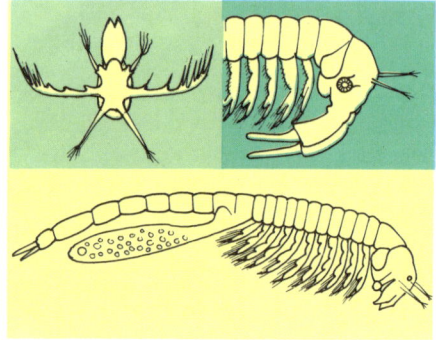

Branchinecta, a fairy shrimp from the United States, showing a female with brood pouch, the enlarged head of a male with its enlarged antennae used as 'claspers' when mating, and a nauplius larva.

pigments derived from plant foods, and some of the pink colours are derived from the same source. Many species have the tip of the abdomen and the caudal rami intensely pigmented with bright red carotenoid. A pink colour may also be caused by the respiratory pigment, haemoglobin, in the blood. Some species have a blue or green colouration. This is sometimes caused by a carotenoid linked to a protein and, like the blue colour of the lobster, it changes to red or orange on boiling. Green or blue colours may also be caused by bile pigments, as in *Chirocephalus* where the amount of bile pigment varies with the amount of haemoglobin in the blood. The amount of haemoglobin varies in turn with the oxygen content of the water in which *Chirocephalus* lives. When there is little oxygen in the water the blood becomes red with haemoglobin and a blue-green bile pigment is deposited around the gut and at the bases of the limbs. When oxygen is abundant the blood is pale and there is less blue-green pigment.

The eggs of Fairy shrimps give rise to nauplius larvae, which pass through a series of moults and gradually change into a form resembling the adult. The length of time from hatching to maturity varies with different species and is markedly influenced by temperature. At high temperatures some of the species that live in desert pools may become mature in a week. But *Branchinecta paludosa* in its cool arctic pools may take well over a month to reach maturity. FAMILY: Chirocephalidae, ORDER: Anostraca, CLASS: Crustacea, PHYLUM: Arthropoda. Ja.G.

FALANOUC, also called the Small-toothed mongoose, although more nearly related to *civets. There are two species, *Eupleres goudotii* and *E. major*, living in Madagascar, about 3 ft (1 m) long including a bushy tail 1 ft (30 cm) long. The general form is mongoose-like but the head is long and the snout is strikingly pointed. FAMILY: Viverridae, ORDER: Carnivora, CLASS: Mammalia.

FALCONRY, or hawking, the practice of catching wild animals with birds of prey. As a sport this has developed elaborate routines, techniques, equipment and technical terminology that rivals those of other long established sports. Falconry has been practised since 1,000 BC, developing in Asia and later spreading to Europe where it became the sport of the nobility in particular. Each social rank, from kings to common people, were allowed to own certain birds of prey; kings flew peregrines while yeomen were allowed sparrowhawks, and kestrels were used for instructing children. In Europe, falconry went into decline after the introduction of firearms and enclosure of the land. It still survives, however, in modern Europe and North America, and peregrines are sometimes used

Falcons

Peregrine falcon, famous bird now becoming scarce.

to clear airfields of flocks of birds. Falconry also survives in Arabia and elsewhere in Asia.

The birds used in falconry are divided into long-winged falcons, such as gyrfalcons, lanners, merlins and peregrines, which hunt in open country, and short-winged hawks, such as goshawks and sparrowhawks, which hunt in woodland. They are flown at a variety of prey, from herons and cranes, partridges and bustards to rabbits and rooks. Falcons and hawks are always taken from the nest and trained by exploiting their hunger. There is, however, a very strong bond between the bird and the falconer or austringer, as a hawk's owner is known.

FALCONS, medium-sized, diurnal predatory birds, mostly in the genus *Falco*. Falcons are some of the finest and most highly evolved birds of prey of the world. In flight they display a characteristic silhouette, arising from their large heads, broad shoulders, long pointed wings and longish tails. At rest the sharply pointed strongly curved bill, large eyes and powerful talons present a fierce appearance. They have close associations with man through falconry and as a competitor for game birds.

The classification of the predatory birds has proved difficult. As the primary adaptations of most raptorial birds are swift flight to overtake prey, the size and strength necessary to hold it and powerful talons to kill it, it is not surprising that they have evolved to a basically similar form. Apart, therefore, from a difference in size, related to prey size, predatory birds represent a remarkably uniform group, the sub-divisions of which still have not been satisfactorily worked out and still rely to a considerable extent on superficial similarities.

Many authorities now accept four main groups of the Falconiformes (see Birds of prey). The family, Falconidae, is split into four subfamilies: Polyborinae the caracaras, Herpetotherinae the Laughing and Forest falcons, Polihieracinae the Pigmy falcons and Falconinae the true falcons.

It is assumed that the evolutionary sequence of the falcons probably started with rather generalized carrion-feeders. The scavenging caracaras, which have sufficient similarities to the true falcons to be included with them in the Falconidae, may therefore provide an indication of the more primitive ancestral falcon stock. The caracaras possess weak bills which are only slightly hooked, weak legs and thin, almost straight, claws. Of the caracaras, the genus *Milvago* differs least from the true falcons and may illustrate a transitional stage to them. *Milvago* differs from the other caracaras in being more slightly built, in having fewer bare, that is unfeathered, areas on the head, and in possessing sharp, rather hooked, claws.

The Herpetotherinae include two genera: *Herpetotheres*, the Laughing falcon and *Micrastur*, the Forest falcons. The Laughing falcon *H. cachinnans* is a renowned snake-eating falcon of Mexico and Central America. It shows certain resemblances to the caracaras, which suggest that they are probably related, but is more closely allied to the Forest falcons. These birds constitute a distinct genus of about five species highly adapted to life in the tropical forests of the New World. Their short, rounded wings, long tail and thin legs are reminiscent of true hawks *Accipiter*. The falconets Polihieracinae comprise eight or nine species in four closely related genera: *Spiziateryx*, a kestrel-sized forest-dweller of northern Argentine; *Polihierax,* small shrike-like birds of East and South Africa; *Neohierax,* a bird of forest clearings from Burma to Indochina; and *Microhierax,* the Asiatic falconets, bird- and insect-feeding falcons of lowlands and hill country.

Within the order Falconiformes as a whole, the true falcons *Falco* and true hawks

Above: a falcon 'stooping'. Below: 1. gyrfalcon, 2. merlin, 3. American sparrowhawk, 4. hobby, 5. peregrine.

Falcons

Red-legged falconet *Microhierax caerulescens* or Rufous-thighed falconet.

Accipiter appear closely related and both are highly successful, each being the largest genus in their respective families. Similarities between the two include the external appearance of their eggs, the sequence of plumage from immature to adult, sexual dimorphism, the breeding behaviour with the female playing the major role, and many of their general habits. Nevertheless, there are a number of basic differences. These include anatomical differences (summarized by Friedmann 1950); a different sequence of moult of the wing quills; the eggs of hawks are green internally, those of falcons are not; and behavioural differences, for example hawks usually build nests, falcons do not.

The falcons also possess some similarities to the owls Strigiformes, for example their head musculature is much the same, both kill prey by biting and severing neck vertebrae, hold prey in one claw, neither has the nest-building instinct, the young hiss, and they have the same habit of head-bobbing. Despite these similarities, however, there are numerous basic anatomical grounds for separating the falcons and owls in addition to their different appearance and general habits.

There are about 35 species of true falcon, genus *Falco*. Doubt over the precise number arises from the difficulty in certain cases of distinguishing between true species and races of existing ones, for example the peregrine-like falcon in the North African deserts is paler above than the nominate race of the peregrine and lacks the heavily barred underparts. It is also slightly smaller and has a separate range, so the two rarely interbreed. Some authors consider it to be a race of the peregrine *Falco peregrinus pelegrinoides*, while others give it full specific rank as the Barbary falcon *Falco pelegrinoides*. The largest member of the genus is the Gyr falcon *F. rusticolus* which can go up to 24 in (60·9 cm) and weigh 2 lb (0·9 kg) and the smallest is the Seychelles kestrel *F. araea* of only 8 or 9 in (20·3–22·9 cm) length and weighing 6 oz (170 gm). The typical falcon is about 12 in (30·5 cm) in length, has a round, blunt head, short neck and dark moustachial stripes running from the edges of its mouth. The short, steeply curved bill is conspicuously 'toothed' in the upper mandible, with a corresponding notch in the lower one. The orbital region is often bare and brightly coloured like the legs. The nostrils are round and contain a tubercle in the middle. The body is slender and streamlined and covered with hard, compact feathers. The legs are usually short and almost entirely bare of feathers while the toes are powerful and, especially the middle one, often long, carrying sharp claws the undersurface of which is broadly grooved or concave. The wings are long and pointed and the tail feathers tapered at the tips. The colouration of the upper parts is often grey and that of the underparts rufous, flecked or barred black-brown; immature birds are usually darker and more heavily streaked. Colour phases are sometimes present, thus the arctic form of the Gyr falcon *F. rusticolus* can be almost white with only slight black flecking, while the subarctic form is usually dark grey or even brown and heavily marked below. In the larger species the females are considerably bigger than the males, but their colouration is similar. In the smaller species, for example the kestrels, the size difference is much less, but colour dimorphism is often pronounced. It has been suggested that these size and colour differences are alternative means of sexual distinction, of importance during the breeding season. In such large aggressive birds as the Gyr and Peregrine falcons, female dominance may even be an essential factor in establishing a pair-bond.

Gyr falcon, largest of the falcons, ranges through the Arctic of Europe and North America.

The true falcons can be considered in five groups. First the kestrels of which there are ten species, together with four others (the African and Madagascar kestrels *F. ardosiaceus*, *F. dickinsoni*, *F. zoniventris* and the Red-footed falcon *F. vespertinus*) regarded as aberrant kestrels. The kestrels have a characteristic mode of hunting by hovering and include a high proportion of small mammals, reptiles and ground-dwelling insects in their diet. They are found throughout the world and are mainly solitary and sedentary, nesting on ledges, in cavities or old nests of other species. The exceptions are the Lesser kestrel *F. naumanni* and the Red-footed falcon, which nest in colonies and migrate south in large numbers in winter to Africa.

The second group contains the two species of merlin, the Turumti or Red-headed falcon *F. chicquera* of India and Africa and the holarctic merlin *F. columbarius*. These are small dashing falcons, which take other small birds in full flight. The merlin nests on the ground on moors or in old nests of other species, as does the Turumti falcon. The merlin migrates south in winter.

Thirdly are the hobbies, some twelve species of typically very long-winged falcons renowned for their swift flight. Most of their prey is taken in full flight and includes a high proportion of large, flying insects as well as small birds. They occur throughout the world and, with the exception of the colonial Eleanora's falcon *F. eleanorae*, are solitary nesters using ledges, holes in trees or deserted nests of other species. Being highly insectivorous it is not surprising to find that half of the species are migratory.

Old World kestrel *Falco tinnunculus*.

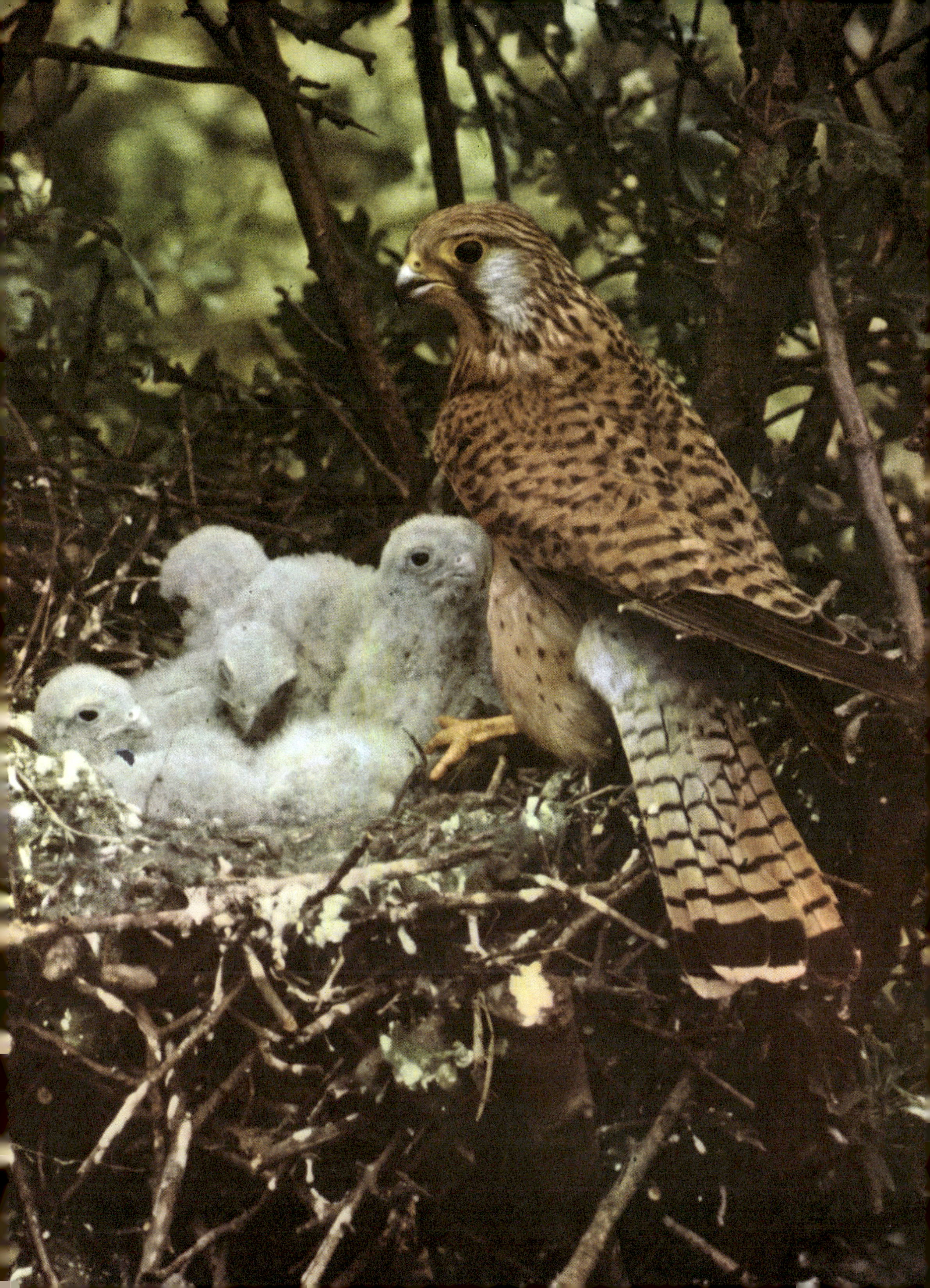

Fallow deer

The fourth group contains the great falcons: the lanner *F. biarmicus* of Africa, Italy, Greece, Yugoslavia and Asia Minor; the Prairie falcon *F. mexicanus* of North America; the saker *F. cherrug* of central Europe and Asia; the lagger *F. jugger*, which replaces the lanner and saker in India; and the Gyr falcon of arctic Europe, Asia, North America, Greenland and Iceland. These are the most impressive of the falcons by virtue of their size, all are over 17 in (43 cm) in length, and they dominate all other falcons. They are swift flying and will take large birds in flight, particularly game birds, but all include ground-dwelling small mammals, reptiles and insects in their diet. In this they contrast with the peregrines and this difference in hunting method is reflected in their relatively less powerful feet and shorter toes. They are solitary and mainly nest on cliff ledges. Only the saker is truly migratory.

The last group contains the peregrines. These are the finest of the falcons, highly specialized for preying on flying birds, which they grasp or knock to the ground at the end of a tremendous stoop. The males are about 13 in (33 cm) in length and the females 19 in (48 cm). The feet and toes are very large, the outer toe being longer than the inner. The peregrine *F. peregrinus* is one of the most widely distributed and successful birds in the world. 18 races are recognized from various parts of the world, varying slightly in size

The Laggar falcon *Falco jugger*, used by falconers in India.

and colouration from the nominate race. The northern races are migratory in winter to tropical or sub-tropical countries. The peregrine is territorial and solitary, typically nesting on cliff ledges in a traditional eyrie which may be used for many years in succession. Peregrines have, however, also nested on buildings and in Europe have occupied tree nests of other species and nested on the ground in bogs. They are replaced in tropical South America by the Orange-breasted falcon *F. deiroleucus* and in Africa by the Taita falcon *F. fasciinucha* and by Kleinschmidt's falcon *F. kreyenborgi* in southern South America.

Many members of the genus *Falco* have been trained for falconry and still are today in numerous parts of the world. Kestrels are poor hunters and only used as beginners' birds. Merlins were used in England for many years for lark-hawking and in mediaeval times were known as the ladies' falcon. The hobby, although faster than the merlin, has never proved as successful as the latter for falconry. The most highly prized falcons have probably always been the great falcons, but there can be little doubt that the perfect hunter and the most widely used bird of all times has been the peregrine. In all species the larger, more powerful female is preferred and most falconers endeavour to obtain *passage birds,* that is young birds on their first migration. Wild caught adults, *haggards,* are often difficult to handle and a young bird taken from the nest, an *eyas,* lacks experience of hunting. FAMILY: Falconidae, ORDER: Falconiformes, CLASS: Aves. I.P.

FALLOW DEER, medium-sized deer with palmate antlers. See deer.

FALSE KILLER WHALE *Pseudorca crassidens,* a small whale closely related to the Killer whale but with an all black body and a small dorsal fin. First known from a half-fossilized skull found in 1846, the False killer whale has been known mainly from stranded specimens until recent years when it has been kept in captivity. See Killer whale.

FALSE SCORPIONS, tiny arachnids, more nearly related to the spiders than the scorpions, but superficially resembling the latter except for the absence of both the post-anal abdomen and the tail sting. They rarely exceed $\frac{1}{3}$ in (7 or 8 mm) in length and normally their bodies are about $\frac{1}{8}$ in (2–3 mm) long as adults.

The body is divided into two regions: a cephalothorax and an abdomen. The cephalothorax is roofed by a large sclerite (horny plate) which may bear one or two lateral pairs of simple eyes. It is floored by the basal segments (coxae) of the last five of the six pairs of appendages.

View of underside and side view of a False scorpion.

The first pair of appendages, the chelicerae, are in front of the mouth and each has a movable and a fixed finger which may be toothed. The silk glands, present within the cephalothorax, open by ducts on the ends of the movable finger at the spinneret (galea). The silk produced is used to construct silken chambers for the purpose of moulting, hibernating and, in the case of females, for breeding. In addition the chelicerae are used for cleaning the other appendages and for grasping and tearing up prey.

The mouth opens on a tubular rostrum, or beak, which is compressed between the coxae of the second pair of appendages, the pedipalps. Only liquid food is ingested, being drawn through a complex straining and sieving apparatus in the rostrum by a pharyngeal pump. It then passes by a narrow oesophagus to the intestine. The intestine has two dorsal lobed sacs (caecae) and a simple ventral sac which merges with a thin tubular section before passing to the chitinized rectum and anus.

The pedipalps are both sensory and prehensile in function, serving to capture and kill prey and as a tactile organ. They are invariably six-segmented and the terminal podomere, the chela, has movable and fixed fingers bearing teeth. It also carries a definite number, usually 12, of long, thin tactile setae (bristles) as an adult. The venom apparatus, when present, consists of glands within the finger which open by a duct terminally on one or both fingers.

The remaining four pairs of appendages are the legs. The two anterior pairs are directed forwards and the two posterior pairs,

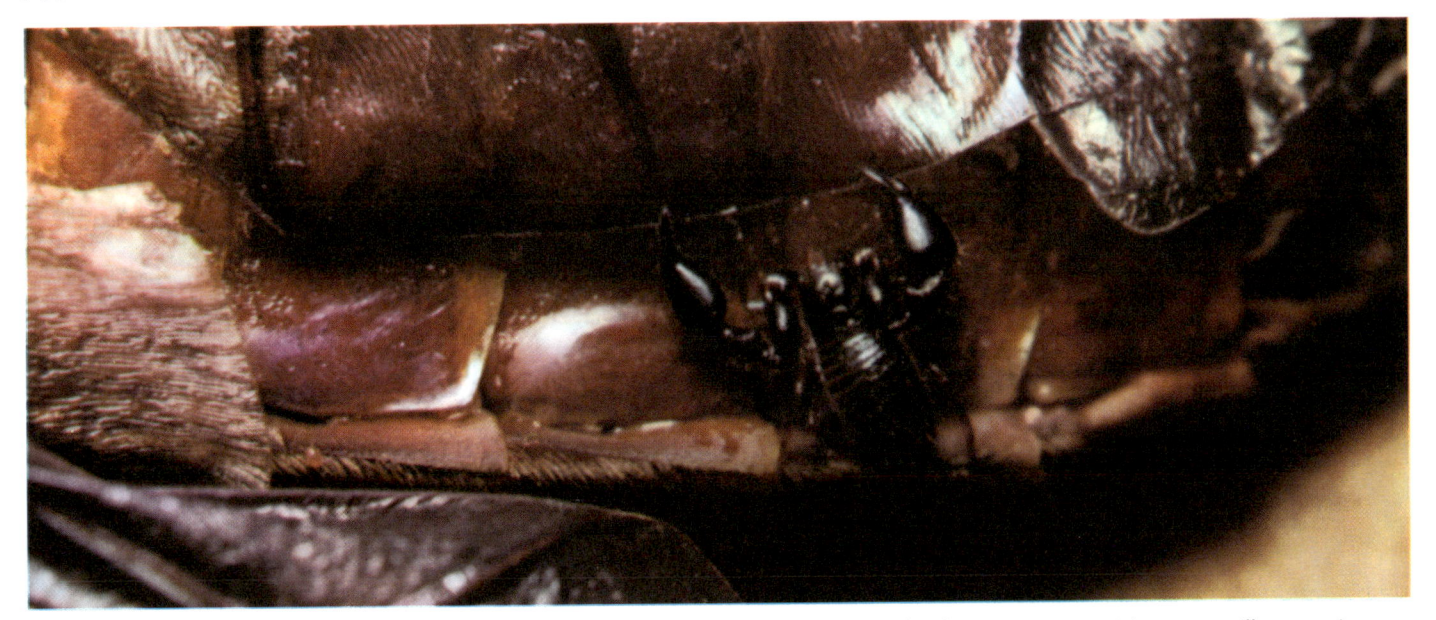

False scorpion *Cordylochernes*, one of 1,500 species of arachnids (spiders and relatives) which, but for their minute size, might pass as tailless scorpions.

more strongly developed, are directed backwards. False scorpions can run very much faster backwards than forwards.

The abdomen is broadly attached to the cephalothorax and consists of 12 segments, the last of which surrounds the anal opening. Dorsally each of the segments bears a tergal and ventrally a sternal plate and these are separated laterally by a pleural membrane. Both tergites and sternites may be divided longitudinally into two distinct and separate halves.

The sexes are separate, usually the same size and normally they can only be distinguished by their genitalia. The genital opening lies between the second and third sternites. The male genitalia are often extremely complex, well supplied by accessory glands, and serve as a mould for the production of spermatophores. The female genitalia are simpler but may include structures in which to store sperm (spermathecae).

Respiration is effected by means of tracheae which open to the exterior by two pairs of spiracles located laterally on the posterior margins of sternites three and four.

The order contains at least 1,500 species. They inhabit all except the polar regions but most are tropical or subtropical in their distribution. Nearly 100 species are recorded from Europe and just over 200 from the USA.

False scorpions live hidden in soil, leaf litter, in moss or decaying vegetation, under stones or under the bark of dead or dying trees and in caves. Some live in rock crevices on the sea shore, others are associated with stored products. Locally they may be extremely prolific; nearly 900 per sq yd (sq m) being recorded from beech litter.

Male False scorpions deposit spermatophores from which females take up sperm. In some genera (*Chthonius, Neobisium*) the spermatophores are produced in the absence of females, in others (*Cheiridium*) they are only produced in their presence. The females, attracted chemotactically, step over the spermatophore on raised legs and release a drop of fluid which triggers a swelling mechanism. This forces sperm out of the spermatophore into her genital opening. In these cases the spermatophores are upright and long-stalked and possess either a sperm-drop partially covered by a membranous coat and protected by a collar or a sperm-mass completely enclosed in a globular package.

In other genera pairing occurs. In *Chernes* the male grasps one or both chelae of the female and a courtship dance ensues in which both partners move backwards and forwards several times. The male deposits the spermatophore by lowering and then raising his abdomen and the female is pulled over it. In *Dactylochelifer* males court females by showing the extended ram's horn organs (extensible genital sacs) and vibrating movements of the body. Both partners move backwards and forwards but there is no bodily contact until the spermatophore is deposited. Then the male grasps the female's pedipalps and assists the female in taking up the sperm by pressing the sperm package with its modified first pair of legs. In both genera the spermatophore is complex. The stalk is inclined and the sperm package either has two blind tubes opening to a common duct or wing-like appendages. Both bear a drop of fluid beneath the package which releases a swelling mechanism forcing the sperm into the spermatheca. In *Chernes* the package is transferred to the female and the duct inserted into her genital opening.

Females lay eggs shortly after sperm transfer in *Chthonius* and *Neobisium*, but delay may occur in *Chernes* and *Dactylochelifer* which store sperm. Some species may lay as many as 40 or 50 eggs, others only two or three. Most females build a silken chamber in which the next stage of the reproductive cycle occurs.

Eggs, rich in fatty yolk but deficient in protein yolk, are normally laid and develop in a brood sac. This sac is secreted by and attached to the female genitalia prior to oviposition. Ovarian cells secrete a nutritive fluid, rich in protein, into the brood sac where it is ingested by the developing embryos. It is absorbed at first through the embryonic membrane but later a specialized pumping organ is developed which sucks up this fluid.

There are two embryonic stages. The first is concerned with the formation of the pumping organ, the cephalothorax and the rudimentary appendages. After a moult, which ruptures the egg membrane, the second embryonic stage sees the elaboration of the pumping organ, the development of the abdomen and the formation of the definitive appendages. A saw-like hatching organ cuts the cuticle of the second embryonic stage and ruptures the wall of the brood sac. Just prior to this moult the pumping organ is transformed into the rostral apparatus. The resulting nymph is a miniature copy of its parent. In most cases the nymph leaves the female's silken chamber and becomes free-living.

The nymph is transformed into an adult by undergoing three further moults. Each nymph is free-living prior to the construction of a silken chamber for the purpose of moulting. Post-adult moults have not been recorded.

Eggs are usually produced during the summer and each nymphal stage occupies about one month. The second two nymphs overwinter in temperate regions to mature the following spring. The cycle from egg to egg, therefore, occupies about one year. Adults live perhaps two to five years and breed at least once each year.

False scorpions are without exception

Fanworms

predatory arachnids. The prey is normally immobilized by the chelal venom and then transferred to the chelicerae which pierce and macerate the victim. Digestive enzymes are pumped into the prey and the ensuing 'soup' is sucked through the rostrum. They live on other arthropods such as Collembola, mites, beetles and fly larvae and some inhabit the nests of, and feed on, ants.

The silken chambers are often spherical in structure. The coalesced silk has the texture of thin paper and it may contain extraneous particles such as soil, bark or leaf fragments. Once the external framework is complete construction is carried out from within so that the False scorpion gradually imprisons itself. The silk is drawn out from the galea and brushed onto the substrate either by lateral movements of the chelicerae or by swinging body movements with the chelicerae immobile and held aloft.

The term *'phoresy' is applied to the phenomenon of utilizing another animal for transport. False scorpions are found attached to the legs of flies, bees, bugs and even grasshoppers. As most of the records of phoretic behaviour involve females of species which normally live in litter, it is believed that this represents a dispersal mechanism to enable False scorpions to colonize new habitats. ORDER: Pseudoscorpiones, CLASS: Arachnida, PHYLUM: Arthropoda. P.D.G.

FANWORMS, together with the 'Feather duster worms', are surely the most elegant of all the marine polychaete annelids. Pinnate or branched filaments radiate from the head to form an almost complete crown of orange, purple green or combination of colours. The crown is developed from the prostomium, the anterior unsegmented region in front of the mouth, by a process of elaboration and subdivision. It forms a feeding organ and, incidentally, a gill. The remainder of the body is more or less cylindrical.

All fanworms secrete close-fitting tubes in which they live. Typically, these consist of fragments of shell, sand or small stones or other debris cemented together with mucus secreted from a specialized 'building organ' located just below the mouth at the base of the crown on the ventral side. *Myxicola* secretes an entirely gelatinous tube consisting of a mucus which takes up water to form a thick protective jelly in which the worm lies and into which it can retract its crown. *Myxicola* is occasionally found in muddy sand near low water mark, but it more commonly occurs just below low tide level. Its tube is completely concealed within the mud, so that when the worm retracts it disappears completely. It does this so rapidly that a predator might well be puzzled. Other worms have more prominent tubes projecting like narrow chimneys from the mud or sand, or from pier-pilings or rock crevices or from among algal holdfasts.

The worms gain protection from their tubes, and although their often gaily-coloured crowns must tempt predatory fish, they can all contract with startling rapidity. These startle-responses are made possible by relatively enormous 'giant' nerve fibres which run from one end of the body to the other within the main nerve cord. In *Myxicola* this giant fibre occupies almost the whole of the nerve cord and is almost 1 mm across. It is one of the largest nerve fibres known and enables the worm to retract with great rapidity. All fanworms have these giant nerve fibres associated with particularly well-developed longitudinal muscles which enable the worm to retract promptly when danger threatens. Other movements are relatively slow.

Fanworms do not move about. They can, however, orientate themselves to a certain extent with respect to current direction and this is important in bringing them the food on which they depend. They can, of course, move about within their tubes, but these they never leave.

Reproduction is by eggs and sperm being shed into the water where a swimming larva develops. It settles later elsewhere to assume the adult mode of life.

The food of fanworms consists entirely of the small particles in the water which are strained out by the crown. The process is inefficient as compared with *Chaetopterus* or with other filter-feeders, like mussels, but the fanworms are generally found to prosper in regions where the water is rich in suspended matter and micro-organisms and, while much escapes through the crown, the animals manifestly obtain sufficient for often rapid growth and building of the tube. Some live for a long time; a few individuals in aquaria have survived for ten or more years. A feeding current is maintained by long cilia placed on the sides of the filaments. These cilia beat so as to cause a current to pass between the

Fanworms *Sabella pavonina* live in a leathery tube, which they secrete. They catch micro-organisms with the branched filaments of the crown.

Opposite top: Fanworm *Spirographis spallanzani* from the seas of northern Spain.

Opposite bottom left: *Sabella pavonina* tubes exposed at low tide, on a mud bank.

Below: *Bispira volutacornis*, twin fanworm with twin spiral fans exposed at mouth of tube.

Father lasher

spread parts of the crown into the centre. On the inner faces of the filaments much shorter cilia beat towards the mouth, the food particles trapped by mucus secreted by other cells on the crown travelling along the ciliary tracts to the mouth. Particles caught by the crown filaments are roughly sorted according to their size. Only the smallest particles which thus contain flagellates, diatoms and other unicellular organisms, pass into the mouth. Particles of moderate size may be selected for addition to the tube, but the largest particles are generally rejected, either by simply falling off the lips at the base of the crown or by being removed along special filaments known as the 'palps' on which the cilia beat towards the tip. The rejection current passes up the centre of the crown and into this stream faeces or waste is discharged. Faeces from the anus travel up the outside of the body along a specialized tract of cilia which emerges behind the head, where they are caught by the rejection stream. The nephridia also discharge by a single excretory pore just behind the crown.

The tube is usually open at the hind end so that by peristalsis of the body wall, water is circulated through it. Much respiratory exchange takes place through the crown which has a good vascular supply, but much also takes place across the body wall. *Myxicola* has a tube closed at the end. Here, virtually all the respiratory exchange occurs across the crown. If the crown is amputated the worm dies, In *Sabella* and most other sabellids, a new crown can be regenerated when this happens—the worm is able to remain alive by irrigating its tube and reconstituting its crown from its reserves. FAMILY: Sabellidae, CLASS: Polychaeta, PHYLUM: Annelida.   R.P.D.

FATHER LASHER *Cottus scorpius,* a shore fish of the eastern Atlantic belonging to the family of sculpins which includes the Miller's thumb. The common name is of dubious origin but is supposed to refer to the fish's habit of lashing its tail to drive away intruders. It is also known as the bullhead. It occurs over a wide range, from Greenland to the Bay of Biscay, and is commonly found in rock pools and shallow water round British

Wounds from a Father lasher's spines often turn septic.

coasts. It is sometimes taken in shrimpnets and is said to grunt when removed from the water. The head is broad and flattened and bears a number of spines. There are two dorsal fins and the pectoral fins are large and fan-shaped. The general colour is green-brown with darker markings. Large specimens may be up to 3 ft (90 cm) in length.
FAMILY: Cottidae, ORDER: Scorpaeniformes, CLASS: Pisces.

FEAR, a term which describes the emotional response of an animal in a situation which is dangerous or potentially dangerous. It is an adaptive response to danger and usually takes the form of flight or immobility; however, if either of these is impracticable, the animal may behave defensively or even attack its enemy. Certain physiological changes may accompany fear; in mammals, the hormone adrenalin is secreted which raises the blood pressure, increases the rate of heartbeat and the supply of blood to the muscles, thus preparing the animal for action. Flight, perhaps, is the fear response most frequently seen, but many animals rely on immobility to protect them.

Scientists are divided how far it is permissible to speak of fear in animals. We recognize in them symptoms akin to our own when we are experiencing the emotion we call fear, and to the casual view animals often appear terrified. On the other hand, there are examples of behaviour which indicate otherwise, as when a hunted stag having outdistanced the hounds will stop running and start to feed as though nothing untoward had happened. Furthermore, there are well-known instances of animal behaviour which carry the appearance of fear symptoms and yet seem to belong to a different category. A well-known example is the Virginian opossum *Didelphis virginiana* which lies absolutely still in moments of danger and will continue to sham dead even when picked up. This is the well-known 'playing possum', which relies for its efficacy on the fact that most mammalian predators only attack and bite moving prey. A parallel example, in the hyaena, puts a different complexion on this, because the hyaena will sham dead and continue to do so as long as the dogs molesting it continue to nose it, but the moment the dogs have relaxed because they have lost interest in an apparent carcase, the hyaena jumps to its feet and runs away.

Whilst the majority of animals which show immobility or a freezing response, as it is sometimes termed, take to flight if a predator approaches too closely, their young may not do so for they may be incapable of rapid movement. Niko Tinbergen describes how on one occasion he was concealed in a hide in a Herring gull colony. A parent gull perceived a movement which Tinbergen made and gave an alarm cry; its young ran at once for the nearest cover and froze motionless. The cover which they selected was, however, Tinbergen's hide and the gull chicks remained at his feet all the time their parent continued to call.

Chicks of the Greater black-backed gull *Larus marinus* hide themselves amongst the vegetation with their heads buried out of sight. The chicks may be picked up and will still remain motionless as if they were still hiding in areas of thick vegetation. Chicks in nests among rocks, however, take to flight. In intermediate areas where there is little cover, the birds may bury their heads in it but if picked up, they struggle and attempt to escape. Thus the response varies adaptively according to the situation in which the bird finds itself.

Some social animals have a distress call which they emit when in danger. It is now known that wounded or frightened whales have a distress cry which attracts their fellows. Brown and Caldwells describe how two whales of different species were kept in captivity together, one a False killer whale *Pseudorca crassidens* and the other a Common dolphin *Delphinus delphis*. When the latter was ill an attempt was made to remove it for treatment but it emitted a distress cry and at once the False killer whale pushed it out of the arms of its captor. The dolphin was caught a second time and held more firmly but the False killer whale seized the man's leg and pressed it gently with its mouth until he released the dolphin.

The difficulty of defining fear in animals, if in fact it exists as such, is increased by the way its symptoms vary according to circumstances. Thus, wild animals fear some species of animals and not others. Generally they ignore domesticated sheep and cattle, but fear man and predatory species. Not all wild animals fear man, however, and Darwin noticed that birds on oceanic islands are frequently so tame they can be caught by hand or killed with a stick. He concluded that 'the wildness of birds with regard to man is a particular instinct directed against *him* and not dependent on any general degree of caution arising from other sources of danger; secondly, that it is not acquired by birds in a short time even when much persecuted, but that, in the course of successive generations it becomes hereditary'.

When wild animals are very young they seldom show any fear of man. Many develop this fear soon after their eyes open. An interesting comparison can sometimes be made between wild animals and their domesticated counterparts. The European wild polecat *Mustela putorius* develops a fear of man soon after its eyes open when it is approximately six weeks old, whereas the domesticated ferret *M. furo* shows no fear of man. Darwin's assumption that fear of man is hereditary is borne out by the fact that young *M. putorius* × *M. furo* hybrids also show fear of man even though they have been reared by a mother who is herself a ferret. This fear can best be overcome by hand-rearing the young from the age at which their eyes open. Therefore although the fear of man is hereditary it can be overcome by creating special, abnormal environmental conditions.

Animals may, besides fearing predators, also fear members of their own species. In social animals, such as baboons *Papio ursinus,* the intimidated individual does not flee from the group but appeases its opponent with a specially evolved appeasement gesture.

Most wild animals show some 'fear' of unfamiliar objects; for example, wild Brown rats *Rattus norvegicus* avoid traps and food placed in their habitat. This neophobia, as it has been called, has survival value for a wild animal which only investigates an unfamiliar object when it has been present for some time without showing any harmful properties. Domesticated animals have generally lost the response of neophobia. See also flight response.
T.B.P.

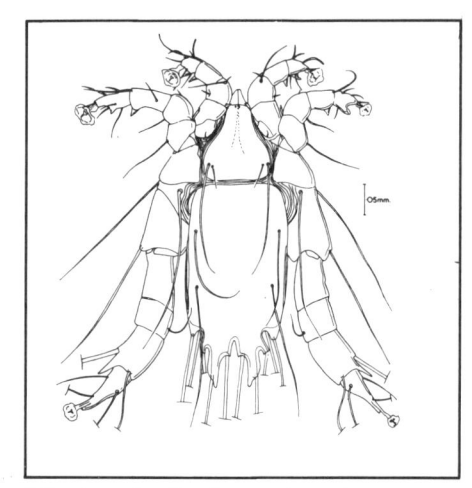

A Feather mite *Mesalges similis*, male.

FEATHER MITES, several families of mites which are epizoic (that is, living on rather than parasitic) on birds and are found sitting in rows along the barbs of quill feathers or on the harder parts of contour feathers. An example is *Pterophagus strictus*. They are acarid mites and are paralleled by forms living in a similar fashion on mammals. Some families are restricted to particular groups of birds, the Falculiferidae are restricted to the pigeons (Columbidae), for example. Moreover, there is restriction of particular species to particular parts of the body, some being found only on the flight feathers, for example, *Pterolichus obtusus*; others are only on the contour feathers of the head and neck, and so on. The mites feed on the sebaceous material produced by the preen gland and on the scales which they detach from the surface of the feathers. They do no apparent harm to the host and, unlike most true parasitic mites, do not leave a cooling corpse.

Feather mites have, in general, flattened bodies and the legs have a bell-shaped pre-tarsus at their ends, which is used to fix the mite onto the feather. The males may show an often extraordinary enlargement of the third pair of legs, used, it is said, to hold the female. Males without such enlarged legs also occur, and others may have an enlarged leg on one side only. Some mites invade quills of feathers and feed on the soft interior. They probably gain access through the superior umbilicus. Such mites, and those which live actually on the skin, may cause loss of feathers either directly or by the bird pecking because of the irritation. Beneath the skin of chickens non-feeding nymphs of nest-dwelling mites or cysts containing all stages of *Laminosoptes cysticola* can sometimes be found. FAMILY: Analgesidae, ORDER: Astigmata, CLASS: Arachnida, PHYLUM: Arthropoda. T.E.H.

FEATHERS, the structures which form the outer covering and flight surfaces, that is the plumage, of birds. Feathers distinguish birds from all other animals, past or present. They are so efficient in performing the functions for which they have been evolved that they must be regarded as a primary contributor to the success of the birds.

The most important function of feathers is probably temperature control, for without this birds would not be able to compete successfully with mammals. When heat loss is necessary the outer feathers are displaced; when the bird needs to conserve heat it fluffs the plumage in order to trap more air next to the warm skin. In this and other ways birds maintain their body temperature at about 106°F (41°C).

The surface continuity of the feather covering is important in waterproofing also, and preening maintains this continuity as well as cleaning the plumage.

Another function of the feather covering is camouflage. Most birds are countershaded, being lighter beneath in order to counteract the effect of their shadow. The plumage of many species also blends with the background pattern of their normal environment, particularly in the case of hen birds which are thereby rendered inconspicuous when sitting on the nest. The camouflage effect is thus enhanced by the animal's behaviour. This is even more striking in the case of the bittern which, when surprised, stretches up with the bill pointing skywards to maximize the camouflage effect of its longitudinal markings in its reedbed habitat.

Plumage-patterns and behaviour also go together in distraction display, in which the bird appears to lead a predator away from the nest or young. The flashing of special wing or tail patches seems to help hold the predator's attention.

Feather-patterns are also important in species recognition. Reproductive isolation is probably a major function of the plumes, crests and feather patches which are shown during breeding displays and are responded to only by the 'right' female.

Perhaps the most obvious function of feathers is the provision of surfaces adapted for flight. The flight feathers of the wing (the remiges) and of the tail (the rectrices) can be spread to provide a large strong and lightweight surface. The arrangement of this surface can be varied to give an efficiency of flight second to none in the animal kingdom.

There are two principal types of feather: the pennae, which are the outer feathers of a bird, divided into contour feathers and flight feathers; and the plumulae, or down feathers. Other types of feather are either intermediate between pennae and plumulae, or are derived from them.

The pennae are shaped like the traditional quill pen, having a flattened vane composed of many interlocking units growing out in one plane from a supporting central mid-rib or rachis. The latter is a continuation of the

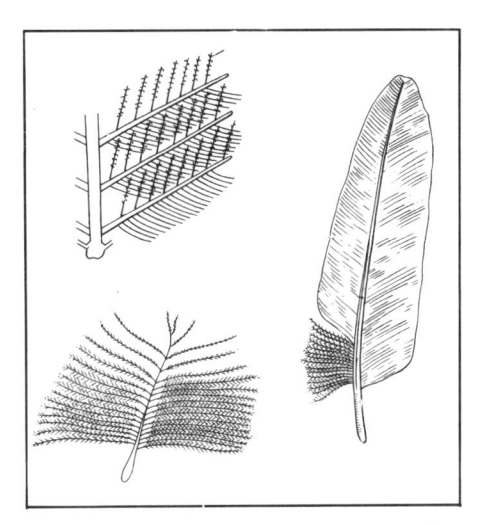

Typical bird feathers with (top left) their fine structure. From the central mid-rib project hundreds of barbs, each with many barbules, hooked, and unhooked.

basal calamus which is hollow allowing passage of nutrient materials from the skin in which it is embedded.

The structure of the feather vane is very complex. Along each side of the rachis project several hundred parallel filaments, or barbs, each of which has along its length several hundred pairs of barbules. The barbules along the side of the barb nearest the feather tip are hooked, and catch in the unhooked row of barbules on the near side of the next outer barb. Thus all the barbs can be hooked together like a complex zip fastener; and this hooking up is what the bird is doing when preening.

On a primary feather (flight feather of the 'hand') from a crane, Professor Alfred Newton counted 650 barbs on the inner web of the vane, each of which bore about 600 pairs of barbules, making about $\frac{3}{4}$ million barbules on the inner web alone. As cranes have several thousand feathers, which are replaced every other year, plumage renewal can be seen to be a somewhat complex matter.

In most birds the feathers grow in special tracts, or pterylae, with featherless areas, or apteria, in between; an arrangement which may be clearly seen in a plucked chicken. The feathers grow from special papillae, 'goose pimples', which produce one, two, or even three sets of feathers per year in most species.

The down feathers or plumulae are simpler and less varied than the pennae. They are widely distributed over the bird and are not confined to pterylae. The rachis is very short, and the barbs are not attached to each other so there is no vane. This results in the fluffiness of down feathers, which are primarily used in insulation. They are particularly well-developed in water birds.

Feathers known as semi-plumes, dispersed among the contour feathers in most birds, are probably loose-vaned pennae. They have a rachis but no hooks on the barbules and therefore have a floppy vane. Semi-plumes apparently aid in insulation and in packing out the other feathers.

The bristles found in a few birds also seem to be specialized pennae. They are found around the bill in aerial plankton feeders, for increasing the effective area of the gape, and in some birds, such as the cuckoo and ostrich, they form eye lashes.

The hair-like structures which remain after a bird has been plucked are known as filoplumes. They are found in most birds, but their function is obscure, except in the few cases where they have been elaborated to form display plumes.

The number of feathers on a bird varies according to the species and the time of year. The colder the climate the more feathers a bird has in the winter. And the bigger the bird, the greater the number of feathers in the plumage. For example, a Ruby-throated hummingbird in June has a total of 940 feathers, while a Whistling swan in November has 25,216. Few feather counts have been made, but perching birds seem to have between 1,500 and 3,000 feathers.

The total weight of a bird's plumage may be more than twice that of its skeleton. A Bald eagle weighing 4,082 gm, with a skeleton weighing 272 gm, carried 7,182 pennae weighing 586 gm, and 91 gm of down. P.M.D.

FEATHER STARS, a group of echinoderms related to the Sea lilies. In contrast to the Sea lilies, which are attached to the substratum by a stalk, the Feather stars are free-living, stalkless and can swim with the

Feather-winged beetles

aid of their long arms, although they are sedentary forms and most often are encountered sitting inactively on the sea bottom. The common genus *Antedon* is an example of this group. See also Sea lilies. ORDER: Articulata, CLASS: Crinoidea, PHYLUM: Echinodermata.

FEATHER-WINGED BEETLES, minute beetles, often no more than a millimetre in length, with a compact body, ovoid in appearance, with shield-shaped wing covers, sometimes reduced and varying in colour from black or grey to reddish brown. The flying wings are sometimes absent, but when present they are characteristically long and narrow, fringed with long hairs. Feather-winged beetles are often present in the moist leaf litter in beech woods, although they may escape detection owing to their small size and dark colouration. FAMILY: Ptiliidae, ORDER: Coleoptera, CLASS: Insecta, PHYLUM: Arthropoda.

FEEDBACK, a concept developed in the study of control engineering which has been seized upon by biologists as they see that there are many examples of this manner of control in living systems. Essentially feedback means that the product of a process controls the rate at which the process is going on, i.e. it 'feeds back' upon the process, and the process is self-regulating. Thus, as a steam engine speeds up, the governor comes into action and reduces the steam supply and slows down the engine: then as the speed decreases the governor ceases to act and speed can build up once again, and the engine maintains an even speed. This is called negative feedback because the governor reduces the speed, but if it were so arranged that the steam supply was increased as the engine speeded up, the engine would run faster and this would be called positive feedback. Almost all biological systems show negative feedback.

The maintenance of steady internal conditions (homeostasis) is a characteristic of living things and feedback plays a considerable role in this. Consider, for example, the control of the ventilation rate of the lungs in a mammal. The respiratory centre in the brain-stem shows rhythmic activity which operates the diaphragm and the intercostal muscles of the rib cage and fills and empties the lungs. However, there are stretch-receptors in the walls of the lungs which fire off nerve impulses when the lung is expanded over a certain point. These impulses pass through the vagus nerve back to the respiratory centre and modify its activity to produce the normal rhythm. In addition, other information modifies the breathing rhythm: the pH level (acidity) of the blood, which rises if ventilation is insufficient to get rid of carbon dioxide, is monitored by the carotid bodies while the aortic body monitors both carbon dioxide and oxygen levels. The carotid body is an organ in the carotid artery which is sensitive to oxygen and carbon dioxide tension in the blood. The aortic body plays a similar role in the aorta. Both these monitoring systems influence the rate and depth of ventilation by acting on the respiratory centre, stimulating it if carbon dioxide level rises or oxygen level drops or depressing it if the reverse happens, so the ventilation rate is self-regulatory.

There are many examples of feedback among the activities of the hormones. The production of the hormone thyroxine from the thyroid gland is under the influence of the thyroid stimulating hormone (TSH) produced by the pituitary. An increase in the amount of thyroxine in the blood stream reaching the pituitary slows the production of TSH, whereas a decrease in thyroxine concentration stimulates TSH production, which in turn stimulates the thyroid to produce more thyroxine. Injections of TSH cause a great increase in the production of the thyroid hormone, which decreases natural TSH production.

The control of sodium excretion by the kidney in urine production also illustrates the concept of feedback. When the concentration of sodium in the blood falls, renin is produced which in turn causes angiotensin to be formed in the blood. This substance stimulates the production of aldosterone (from the adrenals) which causes more reabsorption of sodium from the kidney tubule. Thus the level of sodium in the blood builds up and renin production is then reduced.

Control by feedback tends to produce fluctuations about a median level, for instance TSH secretion speeds up thyroxine production producing an excess. There is then a delay before this excess stimulates TSH which reduces thyroxine production and causes a deficiency. The better the sensitivity of the control, the smaller the fluctuations. In engineering terms, the fluctuations on either side of the median level are described as 'hunting'.
J.D.C.

FEEDING, the active uptake by the animal of foreign organic materials which are subsequently broken down within the digestive system, absorbed and used in the synthetic or energy-releasing processes of the body. In the vast majority of cases this uptake consists of ingestion of solid or liquid substances through the mouth or an equivalent structure, but in some instances, notably in endoparasitic and saprozoic species, liquid nutrients are absorbed directly through the skin. Virtually every organic product of the living world is utilized as food by some member of the animal kingdom, so that the foods used by animals include plants and plant products of every kind, living animals, parts of living animals such as blood and other tissues which are abstracted by parasitic species without immediately killing the donor, dead or decaying plants and animals, fungi and bacteria.

These general groupings of food materials contain an almost infinite variety of types, and animals have evolved equally diverse methods of making use of them.

It is impossible to systematize animal feeding processes within a framework of the standard taxonomic classification of animals into phyla, classes and orders, since the method of feeding is influenced as much by the nature of the food and its particle size relative to the particular animal as it is by the latter's level of organization. Animals of very different types, but sharing a common habitat, may utilize the same type of food by feeding mechanisms which, although not homologous anatomically, all work on the

Sawfly larvae stripping a sallow bush for feeding.

The larva of a glow-worm *Lampyris noctiluca* feeding on a snail.

same general principle. The inhabitants of a rock pool on the sea shore, for example, might include animals of different grades of organization, such as sponges, tubiculous annelids, bivalve molluscs, crustaceans and tunicates. All of these may be species which feed by filtering out from the sea water microscopic plants and animals, bacteria and general organic detritus, using filtration systems developed from modifications of the body wall, tentacles, respiratory organs, limbs or the anterior part of the gut itself.

Conversely, the same rock pool could also contain various members of a single taxon each one of which utilizes a different type of food by an appropriate feeding mechanism. The gastropod molluscs afford a convenient illustration here, in that some are herbivores and graze on seaweeds, others are carnivorous and prey on other molluscs or sessile crustaceans, such as barnacles, and still others are filter-feeders utilizing suspended particulate foods.

Thus any review of feeding and feeding mechanisms cannot be based on taxonomy. One possible method of grouping animals with regard to feeding is, of course, on the basis of the plant or animal nature of the diet and here two main classes, herbivores and carnivores, are to be recognized. These terms are so all-embracing, however, as to be of little practical value unless the species being distinguished in this way fall within a single taxon, as with the gastropod molluscs already cited.

Various classifications of animal feeding

King snake coils around mouse to suffocate it.

Mantisfly *Mantispa interrupta* seizing a fly in its spiked front legs.

Feeding

mechanisms based on other criteria have been suggested and perhaps the most useful and comprehensive of these is that proposed by C. M. Yonge. This is based on the particle size of the food taken and although constructed originally for invertebrates it can be extended to include chordates also. Yonge's classification, slightly modified, can be summarized as follows:

Mechanisms for dealing with small (microscopic) food particles

1. pseudopodial
2. flagellate
3. ciliary
4. tentacular
5. mucoid
6. setous

Mechanisms for dealing with large particles

1. for swallowing inactive food
2. for scraping and boring
3. for seizing the prey
   (a) for seizing and swallowing only
   (b) for seizing and masticating before swallowing
   (c) for seizing and effecting external digestion before swallowing.

Mechanisms for ingesting fluids or soft tissues

1. for piercing and sucking
2. for sucking only
3. for absorbing through the general body surface.

This classification will be used here as a basis for a brief survey of the major methods of feeding found in invertebrates and chordates.

Mechanisms for dealing with small particles. Feeding mechanisms of this type are restricted to aquatic animals and examples occur in every invertebrate phylum. Chordate examples, in contrast, are rare and are confined to the protochordates and a few higher representatives such as the Basking sharks and filter-feeding whales. The last two types are active free-swimming animals and differ, therefore, from most other filter-feeders which tend to be sedentary, slow moving or drifting species.

Pseudopodial feeding is characteristic of the rhizopod Protozoa where either a large lobed pseudopodium (protrusion) is used to engulf a food particle, as in *Amoeba* and *Difflugia,* or else the pseudopodia are filamentous and act as a drift net which entangles particles, as in *Globigerina.*

Flagellate feeding mechanisms occur in flagellate Protozoa and in the sponges (Porifera). The beating of a flagellum directs particles to a region of the animal specialized for ingestion, generally at the base of the flagellum. Examples in the Protozoa are *Peranema* and *Mastigina* and in the Porifera *Spongilla* and *Halichondria.*

Ciliary feeding is very common in the invertebrates and virtually every phylum, except the Arthropoda, has representatives which feed in this way at some stage of their life-cycle. Protochordates too (e.g. *Amphioxus*) make use of ciliary feeding. Basically, ciliary mechanisms depend on cilia to create currents which bring suspended particles to the mouth or special ciliated feeding organ. Mucus is used to trap the particles and then both mucus and food are ingested. The process is usually continuous and little or no selection of particles occurs except on the basis of size and density.

Examples of animals feeding in this way are the ciliate Protozoa, tube-dwelling polychaete annelids, bivalve molluscs (where ciliary feeding mechanisms reach their greatest degree of elaboration), some gastropod molluscs, ectoprocts, entoprocts and brachiopods, some echinoderms and, in the Chordata, urochordates, cephalochordates and most hemichordates.

Tentacular feeding involves the use of tentacles as filtration systems which collect small particles, usually with the aid of mucus. The tentacles are then placed in the mouth and the mucus, plus adherent particles, are sucked off. This type of feeding is seen in the Echinodermata in the holothurians (Sea cucumbers).

Mucoid feeding depends on the use of mucus alone to gather food particles. Sessile gastropods such as *Vermetus* retain the pedal gland, which in other species produces mucus used in locomotion, and the mucus produced by it is discharged as a veil into the surrounding water. The veil plus entangled particles is then drawn back to the mouth and swallowed.

The final type of feeding mechanism for dealing with small particles, the setous, is commonly found in the Crustacea. Here chitinous setae (latin 'seta'—bristle) form a fringe to body appendages and filter out particles as the appendages move. The particles are then transferred to the mouth and swallowed. Examples in the Crustacea are *Daphnia, Chirocephalus* and *Balanus,* amongst many more.

Very often in invertebrates the devices used for small particle collection are also used in locomotion, pseudopodia, flagella, cilia and setae often being integral parts of locomotory, as well as feeding, mechanisms.

Fish feeding on small particles include the herring *Clupea,* where gill-rakers filter food organisms from the respiratory current. In the birds, the flamingo filters out blue-green algae from the water by using the jaws and tongue, and in the mammals the mouth of the filter-feeding whales contains the baleen, rows of transverse keratinous plates, which filter out planktonic organisms.

Mechanisms for dealing with large particles. Feeding by swallowing large quantities of mud or earth is generally unselective and the animal gains its nourishment by digesting any organic materials present. No special feeding organs are involved and species feeding in this way are generally sluggish and slow moving. Examples are the various burrowing polychaetes and oligochaete annelids (worms), and some holothurian echinoderms.

Scraping and boring into large food

The anhinga *Anhinga anhinga*, a darter bird from America, spears a fish for feeding.

The main methods of feeding used by animals.

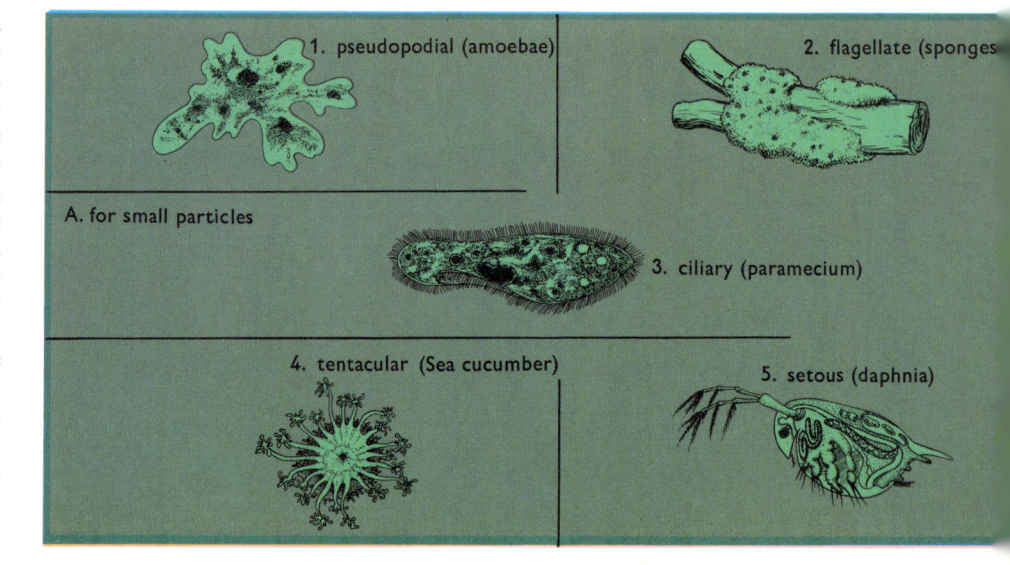

A. for small particles
1. pseudopodial (amoebae)
2. flagellate (sponges)
3. ciliary (paramecium)
4. tentacular (Sea cucumber)
5. setous (daphnia)

for large particles

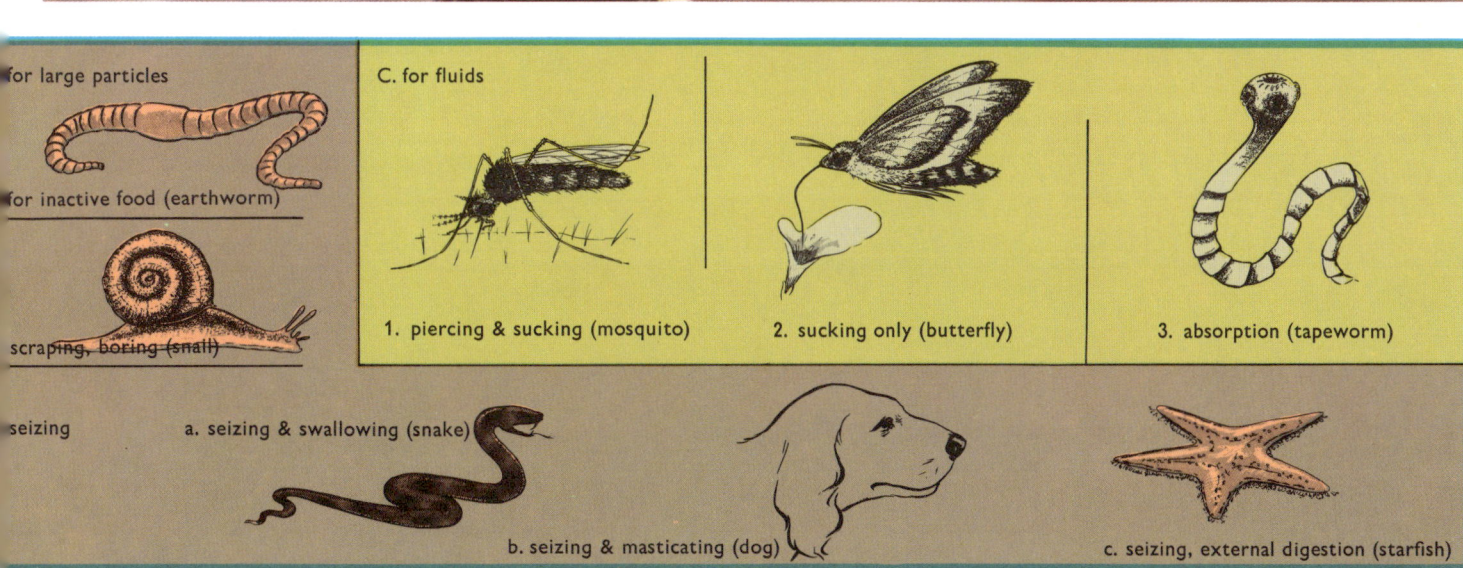

for inactive food (earthworm)

scraping, boring (snail)

seizing

C. for fluids

1. piercing & sucking (mosquito)

2. sucking only (butterfly)

3. absorption (tapeworm)

a. seizing & swallowing (snake)

b. seizing & masticating (dog)

c. seizing, external digestion (starfish)

masses, in contrast, has involved the development of specialized organs such as radulae, jaws, teeth and heavy mandibles. Gastropod molluscs feeding in this way (e.g. the snail *Helix* on land and the periwinkle *Littorina* on the sea shore) use the radula to rasp off plant food, whilst others (e.g. the whelk *Buccinum*) use it to attack other molluscs. The shipworm, *Teredo*, uses the shell valves to bore into timbers and feeds on the resultant particles of wood. Scraping and boring feeding mechanisms are common among insects, where jaws and mandibles form the basic apparatus for removing fragments of plant materials, and in the Echinodermata the Sea urchins use calcareous teeth to rasp off pieces of seaweed and encrusting algae.

The third major group of feeding devices for dealing with large food particles is that including mechanisms for seizing and swallowing, for seizing and masticating and for seizing and achieving external digestion.

Seizing and swallowing is a common method of feeding in all the major phyla. It is characteristic more of carnivores than of herbivores and the prey may be swallowed alive, or first paralyzed or killed by toxic secretions produced in the receiving portion of the digestive system. In the chordates teeth secure the grip on the prey and mucous secretions facilitate its passage onwards into the digestive system. Snakes possess a modified jaw suspension which allows a very wide gape to receive large prey and in the birds the bill shows tremendous adaptive radiation so that the different species utilize a vast range of food.

Feeding by seizing and masticating the food involves specialized organs which reduce the particle size of the food before it is swallowed. Invertebrates feeding in this way include cephalopod and a few gastropod molluscs and many arthropods, and in the chordates the mammals show specialization of the teeth, in terms of size, shape and numbers, for mastication.

External digestion before swallowing is effected by secreting or regurgitating digestive juices over the food, as in polyclad Turbellaria (certain worms), starfishes and some molluscs, or by injecting juices into the prey by modified mouthparts, as in the arachnids (scorpions and spiders).

Mechanisms for taking in fluids and soft tissues. Feeding mechanisms of this type are found mainly in invertebrates, and many fluid or soft tissue feeders are ecto- or endoparasites abstracting nourishment from higher plants and animals. Generally special mouthparts have been evolved for piercing and sucking and numerous examples occur in insects. Some are plant feeders, with mouthparts which penetrate plant tissues, but the majority are animal parasites feeding on blood. Examples of these are mosquitoes, Tsetse flies, lice, fleas and bugs. In these the salivary glands are normally modified to produce anti-coagulants, which facilitate a free flow of blood and prevent blockage of the mouthparts.

Feeding by sucking only is characteristic of many parasitic worms (trematodes and nematodes) and of the butterflies and moths (Lepidoptera). Specialized mouth parts are the basis of the feeding mechanism in the latter, but in the former the only adaptation is the development of a strongly muscular suctorial pharynx or oesophagus.

Absorption of nutrients through the general body surface is found in endoparasitic Protozoa, cestodes (tapeworms) and in a few endoparasitic molluscs and crustaceans. Generally the substances absorbed are already pre-digested and available immediately for use by the parasite. Species living in the gut of their host absorb the products of the host's digestive processes, and those in the blood stream or elsewhere in the body utilize food substances in transit or about to be used by the host. J.B.J.

FERAL, from the Latin *fera* meaning a wild beast, a term applied to animals or plants that have run wild. It refers more particularly to domesticated animals, or others such as mink that have been kept in captivity for commercial purposes, that have escaped to the wild and continue to breed.

FER-DE-LANCE *Bothrops atrox*, a common, widely distributed venomous snake found in Mexico, Central and South America and nearby islands, especially Trinidad. It is sometimes called the tommygoff, a word derived from the Spanish and meaning simply 'snake'. This name was first applied specifically to the fer-de-lance during the construction of the Panama Canal, where it was an ever-present danger to the workmen. Depending on the area involved, the species is also known as 'Barba amarilla' (Yellow beard), 'fer-de-lance' (Iron lance), Terciopelo (Velvet snake), Jararaca, 'Cantil' and 'Labaria'. See Pit vipers, FAMILY: Crotalidae, ORDER: Squamata, CLASS: Reptilia.

FERRET *Mustela eversmanni furo,* a domesticated form of the Asian polecat, a species usually smaller and lighter in colour than the European polecat *Mustela putorius* but having similar behavioural and ecological traits. The ferret has now been spread throughout Europe, interbreeding with the endemic wild polecat populations until the one can hardly be distinguished from the other. Because of a larger cranial capacity, the true polecats have rounder heads and 'pop-eyes' which the cross-bred polecat-ferrets do not have. FAMILY: Mustelidae, ORDER: Carnivora, CLASS: Mammalia.

FERTILIZATION, the union of two *gametes or male and female sex-cells to form the fertilized ovum or zygote from which the offspring develops. The female gamete is said to be fertilized by the male gamete. Both gametes are haploid, that is the number of chromosones have been halved by *meiosis

Great tit *Parus major* feeding on cheese keeps a watchful eye on two Blue tits *P. caeruleus*.

Purple emperor *Apatura iris* with tubular proboscis for sucking up liquids.

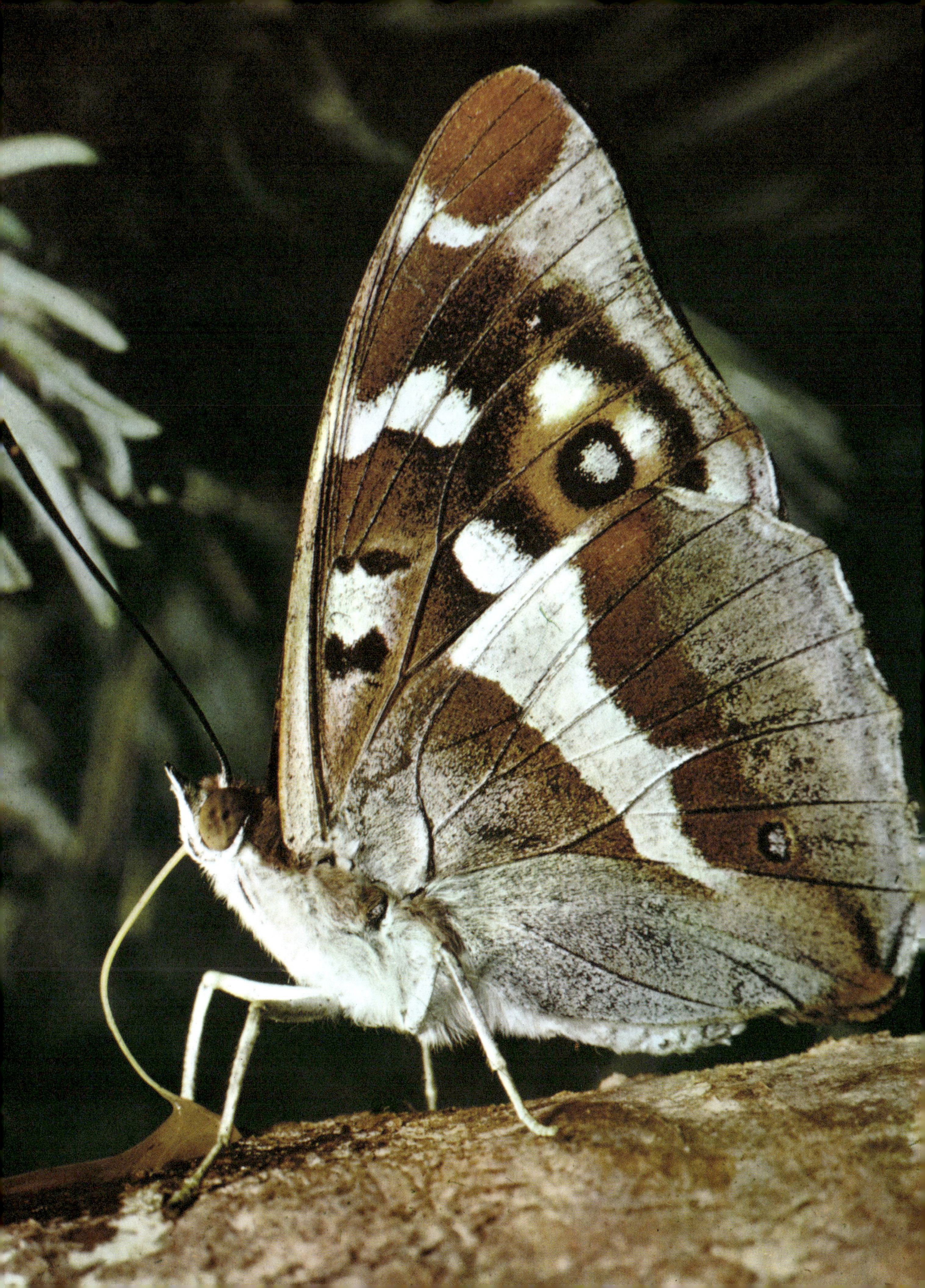

Fiddler crabs

and on fertilization the chromosones from each gamete combine to restore the diploid or paired condition in the zygote. The male gametes, spermatozoa or sperm, are generally smaller than the female gametes or ova. They are motile, being propelled by flagella, whereas the female gametes are sedentary and usually contain food stores.

The mechanism by which the sperm are attracted to the ova is not fully known but meeting is facilitated by both gametes being liberated at the same place and same time when fertilization takes place outside the body, or by copulation if fertilization is internal. Neither is the process by which the sperm penetrates the ovum understood. After the sperm has entered the ovum the membranes around the two nuclei disappear and the two sets of chromosones intermingle. After fertilization some change takes place in the membrane surrounding the ovum and the entry of other sperm is prevented.

FIDDLER CRABS. The male Fiddler crab *Uca* has one of its pincers very much larger than the other. The general form of the body is rectangular, and the eyes are borne on stalks that can be folded sideways to lie flat against the front of the head. The small pincer is used in feeding. Sand is picked up and passed to the mouthparts, which are beset with spoon-shaped spines. These spoons are of various shapes, and often bear small teeth. They are used to scour small particles of organic material from the surfaces of the sand grains. After a number (usually 6–16) of small pincersful of sand have been passed through the mouthparts a ball of sand is formed behind the mouth. This is then removed by the small pincer and placed carefully on the sand surface. This results in the sand surface around a feeding crab being dotted with small balls of sand. In some species they become arranged in a fairly regular pattern.

Fiddler crabs make burrows in intertidal sand and mud. Some species have been observed to occupy the same burrow for several weeks at a time. When the tide comes in the burrows are usually, but not always, plugged up. Sometimes the plug takes the form of a small dome. Some species also build sand shelters over the entrance to the burrow. These shelters are not designed for protection against the tide, but are built only by actively displaying males. Yet they are not essential, and do not seem to play any part in courtship. In *Uca stenodactyla* the females build walls around the entrances to their burrows. Each wall may be up to $\frac{2}{3}$ in (1·8 cm) in height, and is generally built at low tide. No reason has yet been found for this behaviour.

Male Fiddler crab, showing the enormous right claw used in courtship and in signalling occupation of a territory.

The large pincer of the male is used in combination with various leg movements to produce a display that is characteristic for each species. In general the movement of the pincer looks like a beckoning wave, and is generally considered to be a signal to any passing female that the male is desirous of mating. The males often have contrasting colouration, and this may change and become intensified during display. The detailed differences in display between species are related to differences in colouration, and the display is adapted to reveal any contrasting colours. The display is also used to warn other males to keep away from the burrow and display ground. If an approaching male is not deterred by the display a fight may ensue. The contestants wave at each other and then lock their large pincers together. The fight is basically a pushing contest lasting only a few seconds, after which the weaker male usually breaks away and escapes down his own burrow.

There are about 70 species of the genus *Uca*. They occur throughout the tropical regions of the world, and are often abundant in mangrove swamps. Some species extend into the temperate regions of North America, and may be abundant in salt marshes. In the tropics it is sometimes possible to find up to 15 different species in an area of about 600 sq ft (55 sq m). In such a region the total number of individuals would be over 100,000. This is a reflection of the immense productivity of tropical mud in producing enough food to support such numbers. SUBORDER: Brachyura, ORDER: Decapoda, CLASS: Crustacea, PHYLUM: Arthropoda. Ja.G.

FIDDLER'S TUNES. The waving of the giant pincer by Fiddler crabs is quite familiar but it is not so well known that Fiddler crabs also make sounds. There appear to be two types of sound, one produced by rapping the ground with the large pincer, the other by vibrating the walking legs. The function of the sounds seems to be the same as that of the pincer-waving and it is likely that the females detect them as vibrations through the ground rather than as airborne sounds. Study has shown that Fiddler crabs produce these sounds after sunset or when a crab is in its burrow; that is, when the visual stimuli of pincer-waving would be less effective.

FIERASFERS, an alternative name for cucumberfishes or pearlfishes.

FIGHTING FISHES, species of fishes belonging to the genus *Betta* and members of a family of labyrinthfishes. The Siamese fighting fish *Betta splendens* is chiefly found in Thailand but occurs also throughout the Malayan Peninsula. Because of the pugnacity of the male, these fishes have been 'domesticated' for a considerable time in Thailand and used for sport, wagers being laid on the outcome of a fight between two contestants. In the wild, the dorsal and anal fins are short and the colour of the body is variable but dull. As in the case of the goldfish and many other fishes kept in captivity, however, special varieties have been bred that have long fins and vivid colours. The males are always more spectacular than the females.

During a fight between two males, the fins are spread as far as possible and the mouth and gill covers are opened wide. This fighting is in fact a travesty of the male's normal courting behaviour except that the male does not bite the female unless the latter fails to respond.

A single male fish can be kept fairly well in a community tank. When full grown, these fishes are only 3 in (7·5 cm) in length and are usually peaceable but may occasionally nip another fish. To make a male display, a mirror can be placed against the side of the tank.

There are several other species of Fighting fish, such as the Slim fighting fish *B. bellica* and the Striped fighting fish *B. fasciata,* but these are rather rarely imported. The Fighting fishes construct *bubble nests. FAMILY: Anabantidae, ORDER: Perciformes, CLASS: Pisces.

FILARIA WORMS, roundworms parasitic in the blood and lymphatic systems of vertebrates and particularly common in tropical regions. Medically important parasites of humans include *Wuchereria bancrofti*, which blocks lymphatic ducts and causes elephantiasis, the 'Eye worm' *Loa loa* and *Onchocerca volvulus*. All of these nematodes are transmitted from host to host by blood-sucking flies, especially mosquitoes, and the discovery of the life-cycle of *Wuchereria bancrofti* was the first record of the transmission of a human blood parasite by an insect. See elephantiasis and Eye worm. ORDER: Filarioidea, CLASS: Nematoda, PHYLUM: Aschelminthes.

FILEFISHES, a term rather loosely applied to certain members of the triggerfish family, Balistidae, marine shore fishes of tropical and temperate seas. The filefishes were formerly placed in a separate family, the Monacanthidae (meaning 'one-spine'), a reference to the large spine of the first dorsal fin which lies immediately above the eye. They are mostly small fishes of less than 12 in (30 cm), but *Aleutera scripta* grows to a little over 3 ft (90 cm). Pelvic fins are missing

Two male Siamese fighting fish.

The filefish *Alutera scripta*, of tropical seas.

The Gouldian finch *Chloebia gouldiae*, of northern Australia.

and the highly compressed body is covered with rough scales. See also triggerfishes. FAMILY: Balistidae, ORDER: Tetraodontiformes, CLASS: Pisces.

FILTER FEEDING, used by some aquatic animals that filter, through a sieve-like feeding apparatus, small plankton or fine particles in suspension. See suspension feeding.

FINCH, a word used to describe small songbirds (order Passeriformes), which have heavy conical bills for breaking open seeds. At one time or another, the word has been applied to ten different subfamilies of varying degrees of affinity: the Fringillinae (chaffinches), Carduelinae (goldfinch-like birds), Emberizinae (buntings), Geospizinae (Darwin's finches), Pyrrhuloxiinae (cardinal-grosbeaks), Thraupinae (tanagers), Estrildinae (grass-finches), Viduinae (whydahs), Ploceinae (weaver-birds) and Passerinae (sparrows). All these birds have strong skulls, large jaw muscles and conical bills. They differ, however, in details of skull-structure and behaviour, particularly in the way they open seeds, and it is now generally agreed that some are of independent origin. They thus provide an example of 'convergent evolution', of unrelated animals growing to look like one another because they have the same way of life. Most modern taxonomists now agree that the word 'finch' should be restricted to members of the family Fringillidae and that this should comprise the two subfamilies, Fringillinae and Carduelinae.

Finches may thus be defined as mainly arboreal, seed-eating, songbirds, with nine large primary feathers in the wing and twelve tail feathers, in which the female builds an open cup-shaped nest and is responsible for incubation. Usually, both the incubation and fledging periods last 11–14 days. Most species have sweet melodious songs. The outermost of ten primary feathers is vestigial and hidden, except in the little-known Przewalski's rose finch *Urocynchramus pylzowi* of Asia, in which it is well developed and functional.

Members of the subfamily Fringillinae feed their young on insects and hold large

Two greenfinches in an aggressive display.

territories while breeding. There are three species, the chaffinch *Fringilla coelebs,* brambling *F. montifringilla* and Blue chaffinch *F. teydea,* all of which are about 6 in (16 cm) long and weigh around 1 oz (20–30 gm). In the chaffinch the male has a bluish head, pink breast, chestnut back and green rump, with white on the wings and tail, while the female is mainly a pale greenish-brown, also with white on the wings and tail. The chaffinch extends over most of Europe and is spreading east into Siberia. It breeds anywhere where there are trees, including deciduous and coniferous woods, parks, hedges and gardens. The compact nest is made of moss and lichens and lined with hair; and the eggs, which number three or four, are blue-grey with purple-brown spots. In summer the bird feeds largely on caterpillars from trees, and in winter on seeds from farmland, including spilled grain and weed seeds. Over most of its range, it is migratory, but the females tend to move further than the males. The Latin name *coelebs* (bachelor), which Linnaeus gave to the chaffinch was inspired by the fact that on the whole males remained to winter in his homeland (Sweden).

In the birch woods of northern Europe, the chaffinch is replaced as a breeding bird by the brambling, which, however, extends right across Europe and Asia, migrating south in winter. The male is a striking bird, in orange, buff, black and white, but the female is duller and paler. In breeding habits, it resembles the chaffinch, but lays six or seven eggs. It is probably the most highly migratory of all the finches, and in winter tends to concentrate wherever the beech crop is good, often in different countries in different

Goldfinch *Carduelis carduelis*.

Hen chaffinch at the nest.

years. In the winter of 1947/48, an estimated 11 million bramblings fed on the abundant beechmast near Porrentruy in Switzerland, and assembled each night in one small valley to roost.

The Blue chaffinch is restricted to the mountain pine forests of the Canary Islands. The males have bright slate-blue upperparts, pale blue underparts, fading to white on the belly and a bright blue bill; while the females are olive-brown above and ash-grey below. The bird breeds in June and lays only two eggs. It is regarded as the earliest form of the chaffinch to have reached the Canary Islands, and to have been driven to its present mountain-habitat by chaffinches of more recent influxes from the main range. The descendants of these more recent arrivals now occupy the more equable lowland deciduous-habitats.

The Carduelinae form the largest branch of the finch family, with about 122 species. They are more specialized seed-eaters than the Fringillinae and feed their young mainly on seeds, sometimes supplemented with insects. They nest either solitarily or in loose colonies and feed away from their nests in flocks. Many feed directly from plants and are adept at clinging to stems or hanging from twigs. They show considerable variation in bill-shape, an adaptation for extracting the seeds from different types of seed-heads. The largest are the *Mycerobas* grosbeaks of the Himalayas, which reach about 8 in (20 cm) in length and $3\frac{1}{2}$ oz (100 gm) in weight. The smallest is probably Lawrence's goldfinch *Spinus lawrencei* of eastern North America, which is about 4 in (10 cm) in length and about $\frac{1}{3}$ oz (8–11 gm) in weight.

The carduelines vary greatly in colour, but greens, reds, yellows and browns are prevalent, and the female is usually duller than the male. The eggs are usually whitish with pale brown spots and streaks.

Most species are found in temperate regions, with a few in the Arctic, deserts, tropics and subtropics. The Palearctic holds about 68 species in 21 genera; Africa about 36 species in nine genera; and the New World about 25 species in eight genera. But six of the New World species are also found in the Old World. The only regions where these finches do not occur are Madagascar, Antarctica and the south Pacific Islands; they have been introduced into Australia and New Zealand.

Carpodacus is one of the largest genera, with 20 species of heavily-streaked sparrow-like birds, the male being washed to varying degrees with red or purplish-red, and in some species having silvery feathers about the head and throat. Most live in scrub at great altitudes on mountain-sides. One Asian species, *C. puniceus,* is found up to 18,000 ft (5,500 m), probably higher than any other songbird. Only one species extends into Europe, the Scarlet rosefinch *C. erythrinus,* a lowland species which nests in thickets of alder and willow, and is currently spreading west.

Another large genus is *Carduelis* (= *Spinus*). It contains mostly brightly-coloured birds, which inhabit the edges of forests, open woodlands and parks. The most common European representative is the green-finch *C. chloris* in which the male is olive-green with yellow on the wings and tail, and the female is duller and brownish-green. This species is found over most of Europe, nests in thick bushes in parks, large gardens and cultivated land, and feeds largely on the seeds of weeds and spilled grain. Another familiar species is the goldfinch, which is recognized by its red face, chestnut-brown back and sides and prominent yellow wing-bars. This species breeds over the southern two-thirds of Europe, in villages, parks and gardens, and forages on waste land. It specializes on seeds of the plant family Compositae, especially dandelions, thistles, groundsels and burdocks. It is adept at clinging to the seed-heads and breaks into them with its long sharp bill. The delicate compact nest is placed high in a tree, four or five eggs form the usual clutch, and up to three broods are reared each year between May and September. The third European representative is the siskin *C. spinus,* a small green and yellow bird, the female being duller and more streaked than the male. In summer it occurs in conifer forests, where it feeds on seeds, shoots and insects from the foliage. In autumn it feeds on birch seeds and in winter on alder seeds. Its New World equivalent is the Pine siskin *Spinus pinus,* in which both sexes are streaked like the female of the Old World form. Three other goldfinch-like birds occur in North America. The best known is the American goldfinch *S. tristis,* in which the male is brilliant yellow with a black cap and the female is greenish. The bird breeds late, July-September, to coincide with the fruiting of the thistles on which the young are reared.

Another large genus is *Serinus,* containing about 15 species. These are small finches, usually greenish, brownish or yellowish in

Finfoots

Snow finch *Montifringilla nivalis*.

colour, often streaked on the back, with short swollen bills and slightly forked tails. Their stronghold is in Africa, and they are usually found in bushy country or cultivated land with groves of trees and orchards. It is from the wild drab green serin *Serinus canarius* of the Canary Islands that the various types of yellow domestic canary have been derived by selective breeding. Another race of this species is also found in Europe, and was formerly restricted to the Mediterranean region, but since the last century has been spreading north in cultivated land. It has now reached the Baltic Provinces and southern Sweden and first bred in Britain in 1967. The second European species, the Citril finch *S. citrinella*, on the other hand, is confined to conifer forests on certain high mountains in central and southern Europe.

Brambling finch of Europe and Asia.

The remaining cardueline species are grouped among 31 other genera, some containing only a single species. They include the bullfinches *Pyrrhula*, the Desert bullfinches *Rhodopechys*, the linnets and redpolls *Acanthis*, the crossbills *Loxia*, the grosbeaks *Coccothraustes*, *Eophona*, *Mycerobas*, and *Hesperiphona*, the Rosy finches *Leucosticte*, the Pine grosbeak *Pinicola enucleator* and others. FAMILY: Fringillidae, ORDER: Passeriformes, CLASS: Aves. I.N.

FINFOOTS, odd, grebe-like birds related to the rails. The family is made up of three species, one in South America, another in Africa and a third in Southern Asia, this widespread relict distribution suggesting an early origin. The rather long, but stout, bill suggests a rail, the long neck and short legs placed well back on the body with flattened lobes bordering the toes are grebe-like, while the long thin neck, low swimming position and longish graduated tail with stiff rectrices also suggest a cormorant or darter. The legs, placed well back for propulsion, give a horizontal body posture on land, but finfoots can run well and take to land when pursued. They swim with head-bobbing movements, presumably synchronized with simultaneous kicks of both legs. Although apparently modified for diving and hunting under water, or for swimming against fast currents, they show little inclination for either. They appear to dive infrequently and the food recorded is aquatic insects, frogs, crustaceans and shellfish, together with a little seed and vegetable matter.

They show a preference for still or slow-moving water at the edges of rivers, estuaries, or occasionally lakes, where thick vegetation comes to the water's edge or overhangs it. They can, however, cope with swift-moving water if necessary. They mostly keep to the cover of overhanging vegetation, and are adept at scrambling over low branches as well as swimming. When alarmed they hurry into cover, at times fluttering along the surface with the help of the wings. The wings, although well-developed, do not appear to be used for prolonged flights.

The three species are dissimilar. The African finfoot *Podica senegalensis* is over 2 ft (60 cm) long, the Asiatic finfoot *Heliopais personata* is a little smaller, and the South American finfoot *Heliornis fulica* is dabchick-sized, only 1 ft (30 cm) long with the slender neck extended. Foot-colour differs strikingly, *Podica* having bright red legs and feet, *Heliopais* having bright green feet with yellow lobes, and *Heliornis* having an exceptional pattern of transverse barring in black and yellow. The plumage is dull olive or rufous with some green or blue gloss dorsally. *Heliopais* has black on crown, face and throat, the last outlined with white, and white-centred on the female. *Heliornis* is similar but with black and white striped head and neck and orange cheeks on females. *Podica* is heavily spotted, with a white line along the side of head and neck, while breeding males lose most of the spots and have glossy blue-black above and grey below on head and neck.

The nest is a shallow structure of sticks and reed-stems on a horizontal low branch or fallen tree over water, often built on the higher lodged flood-debris. The clutch is of up to seven very rounded eggs, cream-coloured and spotted or blotched with reddish-brown and purple. Both sexes incubate. The young are downy, and may leave the nest soon after hatching, although this has not been definitely established. FAMILY: Heliornithidae, ORDER: Gruiformes, CLASS: Aves.

FINGERFISHES, a group of fishes dealt with under the name Malayan angels.

FINS, characteristic projections from the bodies of fishes, usually composed of hard or soft finrays with a thin membrane between the rays, basically for swimming movements but secondarily adapted for a wide variety of functions (defence, digging, display in courtship, gliding, flying, etc.).

In the earliest fishes it is assumed that a continuous ridge or fold of skin passed down the back and along the belly. If certain areas of this primitive fin-fold were of greater mechanical use than others, then it can be supposed that these would become larger, leaving gaps between, leading to the formation of discrete fins. There is no way of confirming this hypothesis but it is significant that in one experiment using a wax model shaped like the body of a fish, the passage of a fast current of warm water over the body produced a very similar pattern of ridges or fin folds. A continuous fin-fold is also found in the early larval stages of most fishes. In the earliest fossil fishes, however, the fins are already well developed but much can be deduced about the habits of these fishes from a study of the function of each fin and the part that it must have played in swimming.

During swimming, the body of a fish is thrown into a series of sinuous curves which become more pronounced towards the tail or caudal fin. If the tail is cut off, the fish can still swim forward but the tail end of the body vibrates very rapidly from side to side. Clearly, the expanded tail of the fish slows down these oscillations and makes the swimming smoother and more efficient. A large tail with a rounded margin, as in a pike, gives fast acceleration but its large surface area creates friction or drag so that prolonged swimming is tiring. So a pike habitually lurks among waterplants and darts out swiftly at passing prey. In oceanic fishes such as tuna the tail is crescentic and bound stiffly to the base of the vertebral column so these fishes can be constantly on the move. In long-bodied eel-like fishes the tail is either lost or is often joined to the long dorsal and anal fins. In such fishes, which are not fast swimmers, the body is thrown into a large number of sinuous waves and this is sufficient to propel the fish forwards.

The early bony fishes, as well as the sharks and sturgeons, possessed no organ of buoyancy (swimbladder) so that the fish had to rest on the bottom or swim constantly. To counteract the rather heavy head and body by providing sufficient 'lift', the end of the vertebral column is bent upwards and the tail is developed from its lower edge (heterocercal tail). This condition arose from even more primitive fishes in which the vertebral column is not bent upwards and a lobe of the tail is present both above and below (protocercal tail). In the modern bony fishes the tail appears to be symmetrical but in fact the end of the vertebral column is still bent upwards and a series of bony plates (hypurals) square-off the end of the body and provide the base for the attachment of the rays supporting the usually equal upper and lower lobes of the tail (homocercal tail). The great range in tail shapes found in bony fishes is due to variations in the size, number and shape of the hypurals supporting the tail.

The vertical fins, the dorsal and anal, are basically stabilizers that prevent rolling, especially during turns. The more primitive of

Rock goby *Gobius poganellus* showing united pelvic fins which act as a sucker with which the fish clings to rocks.

Pectoral fins (top left) of Frilled shark, Australian lungfish and cod, caudal fins (top right) of sturgeon and tenpounder, and skeleton (below) of a typical bony fish.

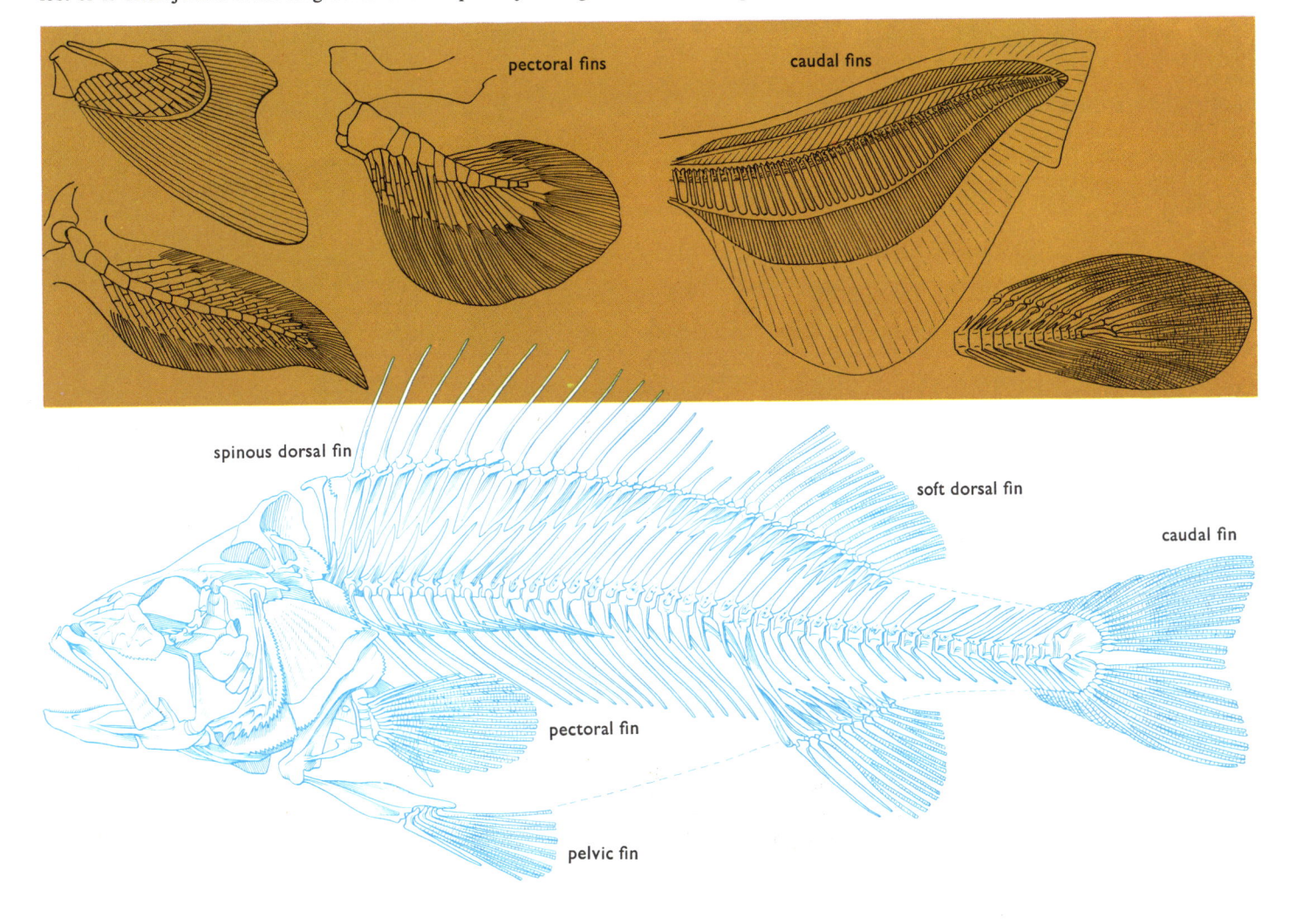

Fin whales

the modern fishes, such as the salmon and herring, have the short-based dorsal and anal fins set close behind the centre of gravity. In lurking predators, such as the pike, in which a sudden thrust of speed is required, the dorsal and anal fins are set well back on the body. In the more advanced perch-like fishes the dorsal fin is long-based and often separated into two distinct parts, the first part supported by spiny rays and the second by soft and flexible rays. The spiny rays appear to act as 'cut-waters' and were perhaps only secondarily adapted for defence. In some fishes, for example members of the salmon family, there is a small and fleshy adipose fin behind the main dorsal fin. Its function may be the adjustment of eddies along the back to reduce drag. A similar function can be supposed for the line of small finlets behind the dorsal fin in mackerels and tuna.

In sharks and primitive bony fishes which lack a swimbladder the pectoral fins act as hydrofoils which lift the front half of the body as the fish swims through the water. With the evolution of a swimbladder the pectorals were able to take on other functions. They were then chiefly used as brakes or, if only one pectoral is extended, for steering. In perch-like fishes, which hover in the water, the pectorals are gently back-paddled to prevent the fish moving forward by the force of the stream of water pumped out of the gill chamber. The pelvic fins in primitive fishes are set back on the body somewhere below the dorsal fin (herring, trout). In the more advanced bony fishes they are brought forward to below or even in front of the pectoral fins. In this position they can work in conjunction with the pectorals in braking and turning, counteracting the lift of the pectorals with a downward drag so that the fish does not tend to shoot upwards every time it stops.

Slow swimming movements are achieved in some fishes by undulations of the dorsal fin (Sea horse, eels, pike when cruising) or by sculling movements of the pectoral fins (Ocean sunfish). The pectoral fins can be adapted for gliding (flyingfishes) or flapping flight (Flying characins), for crawling on the bottom (some gurnards) or for progress on land (mudskippers). The pelvic fins have been adapted as suckers (gobies). The dorsal fin has become a means of defence (spines, sometimes with venom glands), a sucking disc (remoras), a 'sail' (sailfish), a fishing rod (anglerfishes) or a factor in sexual display (Fighting fishes). The anal fin has sometimes become modified into a copulatory organ in those fishes which are live-bearers. The tail may be used for digging (some eels) or may be modified into an extraordinary variety of shapes. In certain groups of fishes some or all of the fins may be reduced and certain fins lost.

The greatest impetus to the evolution of fins was the development of a swimbladder. Once buoyancy was achieved, the fins could be used for functions other than swimming.

FIN WHALES, alternative name for the rorquals or Finback whales, but more usually the use of Fin whale is restricted to the Common rorqual *Balaenoptera physalus*. See rorquals.

FIREBRAT *Thermobia domestica,* an insect belonging to the group known as *bristletails, sometimes found in bakeries and other warm places.

FIREFLIES, 1,100 species of nocturnal beetles famous for their ability to produce light. They are rather elongated, with nearly parallel sides and flexible wing cases. Although most species are tropical, about 60 occur in North America, but only two, one of which is the Glow worm, occur in Britain. In many species the male is fully winged and has huge compound eyes, whereas the female is commonly without wings, has small eyes and resembles a segmented larva. The adults feed very little, but the larvae are carnivores preying on snails and slugs.

The photogenic organs of the firefly are situated in certain segments of the abdomen, sometimes the thorax, and emit a yellow-green light or luminescence. Light is produced instantaneously when the substance luciferin in the photogenic organs is oxidized to oxyluciferin by atmospheric oxygen in the presence of water and the enzyme luciferase. This remarkable system of light production is extremely efficient as about 95% of the energy released when luciferin is oxidized to oxyluciferin is in the form of light rays. In contrast, the sun produces about 35% light and an electric lamp only gives out 10% of its energy as light. Some fireflies emit a continuous glow, whereas others show periodic flashes. The light mutually attracts the sexes for mating. FAMILY: Lampyridae, ORDER: Coleoptera, CLASS: Insecta, PHYLUM: Arthropoda.   M.J.P.

FIREFLY LIGHTS. It is not surprising to find that fireflies have been used in many parts of the world as a cheap form of illumination. The light is not very bright, the brightest firefly producing no more than $\frac{1}{40}$ candle-power, but it is of wavelengths to which the human eye is particularly sensitive. Fireflies have been kept in special lanterns or even worn in the hair and around the ankles. More decorative than functional is the 'Railway worm' of South America, the larva of a glow worm, with a red 'headlight' and two rows of green lights.

FIREMOUTH, a common name for a rather distinctive cichlid fish. See cichlids.

FISHER, R.A., 1890–1962, British geneticist. Suffering from extreme myopia in childhood, one of his early teachers had him work out statistical problems in his head. This doubtless was one of the influences in the development of possibly the most important of all statistical biologists. His works include Statistical Methods for Research Workers (1925), The Design of Experiments (1935) and Statistical Methods and Scientific Inference (1956).

Fisher graduated from Cambridge and

The lionfish or scorpionfish *Pterois* has elaborate fins used to warn off potential attackers.

Above: Conger eel *Conger conger* stranded at low tide. Below: Mediterranean seahorse *Hippocampus guttulatus*.

studied statistical mechanics and quantum theory under Jeans and Stratton. His interest in genetics developed gradually, culminating in his very important book The Genetical Theory of Natural Selection, published in 1929 while he was at Rothamsted Agricultural Research Station, by which time he had been elected a Fellow of the Royal Society. In this book he demonstrates the compatibility of Darwin's theory of evolution and Mendelian genetics, and in the light of natural selection goes on to consider the problems of man and society. Eventually returning to Cambridge where, in 1956, he was made President of his old College, he received many honours, including the Darwin, Copley, and Royal Medals of the Royal Society. He was knighted in 1955.

FISHES, a large group of cold-blooded aquatic vertebrates that breathe by means of gills, the bodies of which bear a vertical tail fin. Most fishes fall within this definition, but a few breathe atmospheric air by means of a lung or lung-like organ (see air-breathing fishes), some species have a body temperature slightly above that of the surrounding water (see tunas) and in certain fishes the tail may be missing (see Ocean sunfish) or reduced to a filament (see grenadiers). The definition does exclude, however, whales, dolphins, seals and porpoises which are warm-blooded, have lungs and have a tail that is horizontal, not vertical. The question *What is a fish?* is complicated by the fact that there are four classes of fish-like vertebrate, (see table of classification) which differ from each other in so many fundamental ways that it is as misleading to lump them together as it would be to place all mammals, birds and reptiles in a single group 'land animals'. This is discussed more fully under fossil fishes. For this reason, the jawless

Fishes

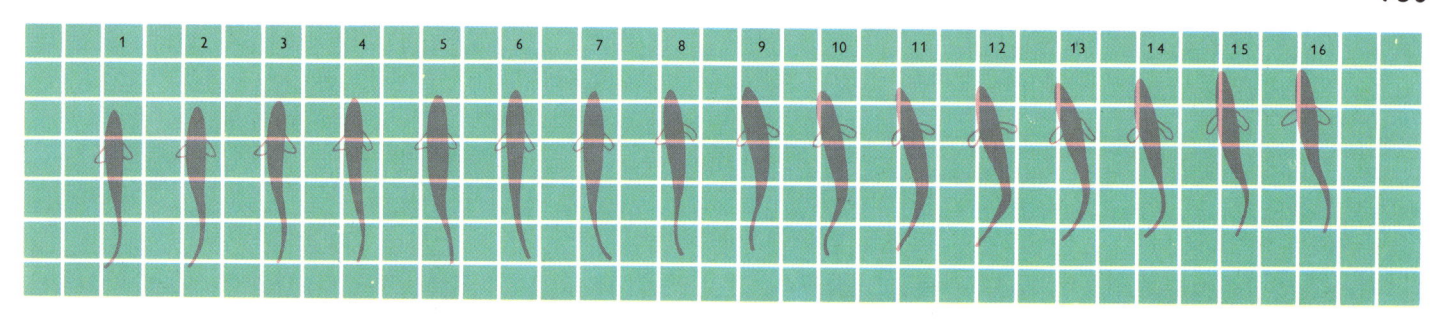

Most fishes swim by lateral undulations of the body, a wave passing from the head of the fish back along the body. Shown are 16 successive undulations.

fishes (Agnatha), the placoderms (Placodermi) and the cartilaginous fishes (Chondrichthyes) are described under separate headings and only the fourth class, the Pisces Osteichthyes or bony fishes are considered here.

The class of bony fishes includes three rather distinct subclasses. Of these, the extinct Acanthodii are dealt with under fossil fishes and the Sarcopterygii are discussed under the same heading and also under coelacanth and lungfishes. The remaining subclass, the Actinopterygii or ray-finned fishes, contains the chondrosteans (bichirs, sturgeons and one entirely fossil order), the holosteans (bowfins and five fossil orders) and finally the teleosteans. The overwhelming majority of present-day fishes are teleosts. There are at least 20,000 different species of teleosts and countless millions of individuals inhabiting the seas, lakes and rivers of the world. The teleosts represent the ultimate stage in the evolution of the Actinopterygii, a group that dates from the Devonian period. The teleosts first appear in Jurassic rocks and for the next 100 million years several evolutionary lines seem to have arisen from the more ancient holostean stock and to have attained what can now be recognized as the teleostean level of organization (form of fins, scales, skeleton, jaws and so on).

The teleosts show an amazing diversity of form. One has only to compare a perch with a frogfish, eel, Sea horse or Flounder flatfish to see the degree to which the teleostean organization has become adapted to particular living conditions. The classification of this huge group has always presented considerable difficulties and many problems still remain. For example, similarity between members of different families or orders may truly reflect a common ancestry; it may, however, be due to convergent evolution, similar features arising to meet similar needs (such as the elongated form in eels and blennies). Again, two or more families may have evolved independently along quite similar lines (parallel evolution). Until fairly recently, it was assumed that whenever a particularly advantageous feature arose radiation of species with this character followed and that it was from one of these that the next advantageous feature would appear (and thus the next radiation). The great radiation of the perch-like fishes (the largest of the teleost orders), for example, seemed to stem from the ability to protrude the jaw. It is now realized, however, that the freeing of the upper jaw to make protrusion possible must have occurred quite independently in a number of lineages. It is better, therefore, to regard some groups of fishes as representing a 'level of organization' rather than a homogeneous group descended from a single ancestor. A classification is, however, an essential tool to the study of a group, even if that study results in modifying the classification. The scheme adopted here is essentially that proposed by Dr Greenwood, Dr Rosen, Dr Weitzman and Dr Myers in the *Bulletin of the American Museum of Natural History* (vol 131, pp 339–456). (The interested student should also consult the work of Dr Rosen and Dr Patterson in the same journal—vol 141, article 3—in which certain changes are made.) These two papers have brought up to date the earlier classifications of C. Tate Regan and later L. S. Berg, and they probably mark a new era in our understanding of the way in which the teleost fishes have evolved. It should be stressed, however, that considerable work yet remains to be done before a really satisfactory classification of this difficult group can be achieved.

The diversity of the teleost fishes makes

Diagram of a fish. A. organs for feeding, blood circulation, breeding and secretion: 1. mouth, 2. gills, 3. heart, 4. alimentary canal, 5. swimbladder, connected with the gullet by a small tube, 6. liver, 7. gallbladder, 8. ovary, 9. kidney, 10. capillaries. B. cross-section through the centre of the body: 11. dorsal fin, 12. vertebra, 13. muscles, 14. pectoral fin. C. cross-section through tail (caudal peduncle): 15. caudal fin.

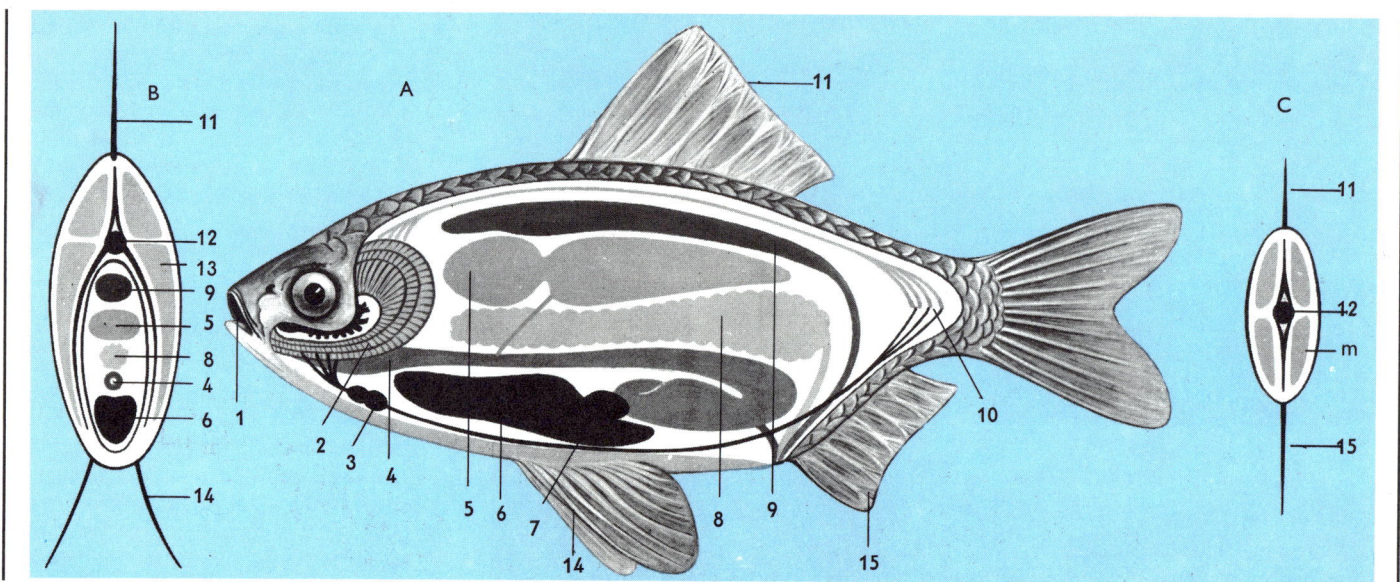

731 Fishes

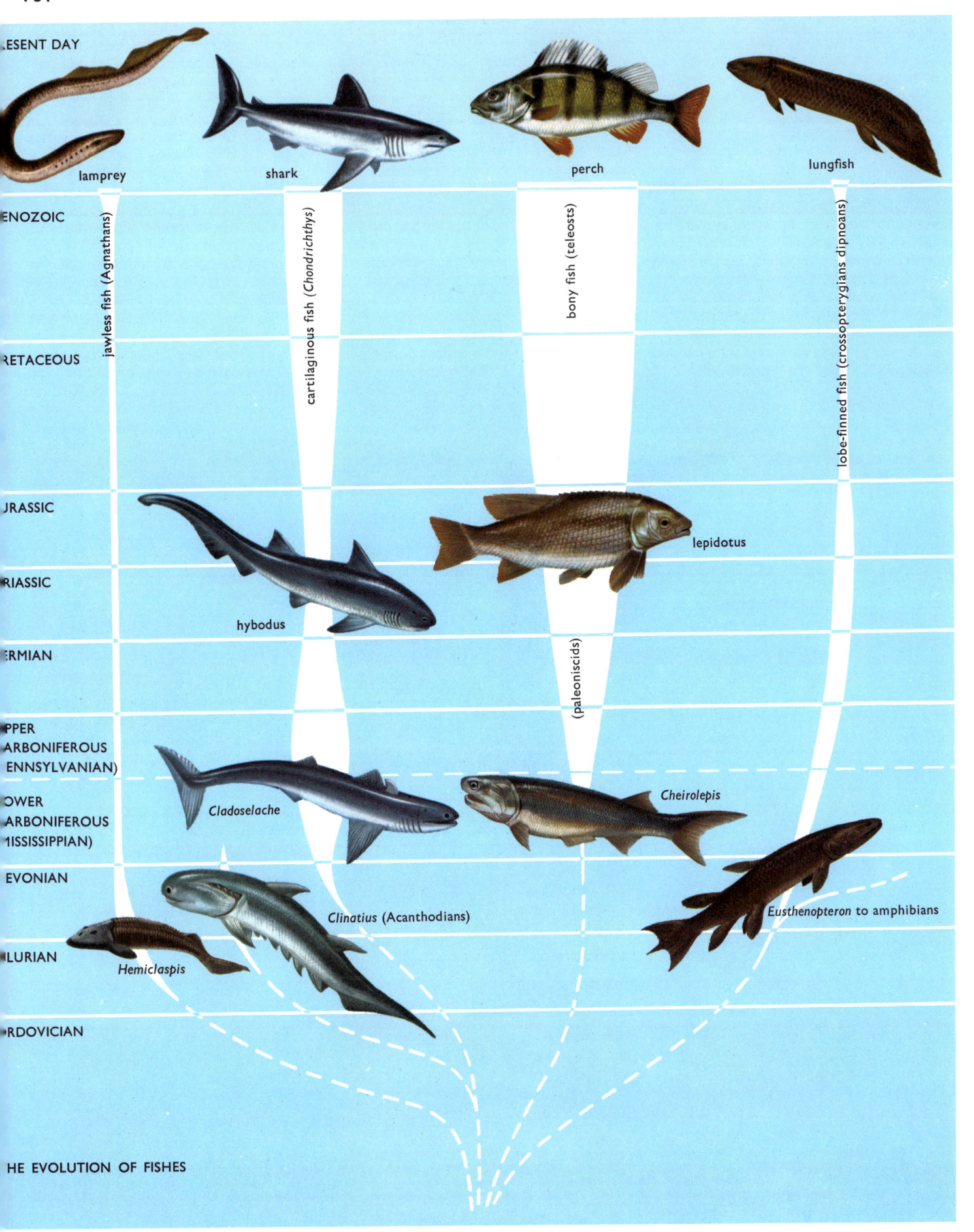

PRESENT DAY

lamprey · shark · perch · lungfish

CENOZOIC

CRETACEOUS

jawless fish (Agnathans) · cartilaginous fish (Chondrichthys) · bony fish (teleosts) · lobe-finned fish (crossopterygians dipnoans)

JURASSIC

TRIASSIC

lepidotus

hybodus

PERMIAN

(paleoniscids)

UPPER CARBONIFEROUS (PENNSYLVANIAN)

LOWER CARBONIFEROUS (MISSISSIPPIAN)

Cladoselache · *Cheirolepis*

DEVONIAN

Clinatius (Acanthodians) · *Eusthenopteron* to amphibians

SILURIAN

Hemiclaspis

ORDOVICIAN

THE EVOLUTION OF FISHES

Fishes

description of a 'typical' member difficult. They range in size from a total length of over 20 ft (6 m) in certain sturgeons and the oarfish and a weight of over 2 tons in the case of the Ocean sunfish, to an adult length of only $\frac{1}{2}$ in (1·2 cm) in a Philippine goby *(Paudaka pygmaea)*, the latter qualifying as the smallest of all vertebrates. Typically, the body is streamlined, rising smoothly from the head and tapering gently to the tail, but the body shape clearly reflects the mode of life of the fish. The torpedo-shaped tunas show streamlining taken to extreme lengths for fast and sustained swimming. The disc-like body of the Angel fishes *(Pterophyllum)* is an adaptation to a life camouflaged amongst weeds, the fish darting out to catch its food. The spherical or box-like pufferfishes and boxfishes leisurely 'row' themselves about the coral reefs, while the cylindrical pipefishes hide away among the leathery strands of seaweeds. In most fishes swimming is achieved by throwing the body into a series of lateral undulations which travel along the length of the body growing in amplitude towards the tail (marine mammals undulate *vertically*, so that 'sea serpents' can be identified as mammals or fishes from their mode of swimming). The tail provides the final thrust and evens out the oscillations of the body (amputate the tail and the fish can still swim but the body vibrates more rapidly while progress is slower). The tail is stiffened along the upper and lower borders and the larger the tail the greater the thrust but also the greater the turbulence created (and thus the greater the drag). For fast but sustained speeds, fishes such as tunas have a crescentic tail with stiff edges and reduced central rays; its small surface area keeps drag to a minimum, but it also reduces the rate of acceleration. In a pike, on the other hand, the large blunt tail can give tremendous thrust for sudden spurts towards a prey but would be exhausting for sustained speeds. The article on fins describes in more detail the modifications of the tail and other fins to various modes of life. In general the fins are used as stabilizers, brakes, hydrofoils, occasionally as paddles or as sensory appendages (see gurnards), as means of defence (see poisonous fishes), rarely as wings or aerofoils (see flight in fishes), and possibly as sails (see sailfish), sometimes as copulatory organs (see live bearers) and in a few fishes to assist in terrestrial locomotion. The variation in shape, number and position of fins provides

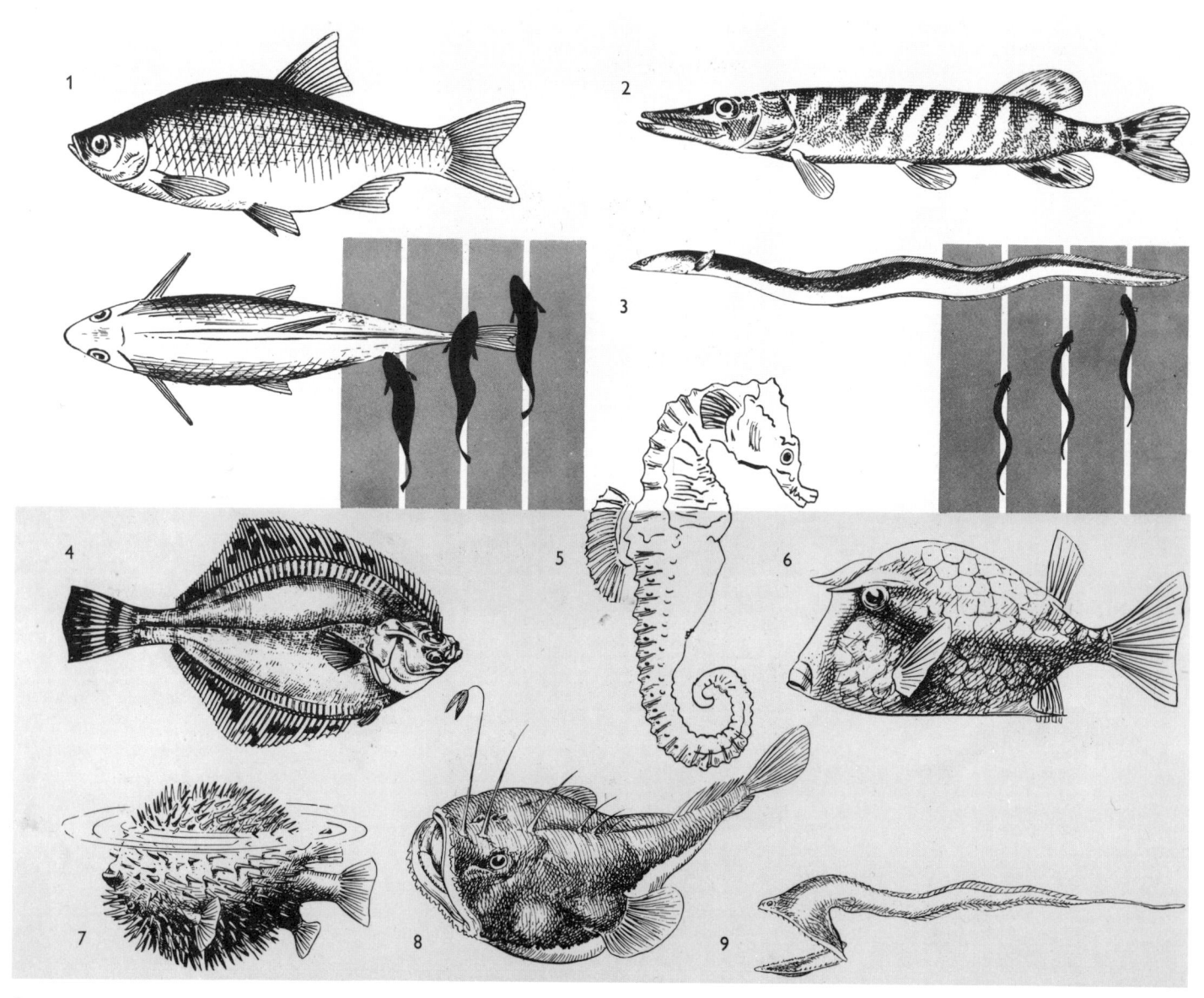

Contrary to popular belief fishes do not move by using fins but by lateral undulations of the entire body except those with armoured bodies such as 5–7. Fins are used for steering and braking and keeping the fish upright. Most fishes have a flattened torpedo shape (1). Arrowlike fishes like the pike *Esox lucius* (2) are able to move short distances at great speed. The undulations are most noticeable in eel-like fishes (3). Strongly differing shapes are: 4. flat-fish, 5. seahorse, 6. boxfish *Ostracion quadricornis*, 7. puffer-fish *Diodon hystrix*, 8. anglerfish *Lophius piscatorius*, and deep-sea fishes like 9. the gulper *Eupharynx pelicanoides*.

a useful clue to the identity of a fish and was widely used to classify fishes by early ichthyologists until it was realized that the same pattern had often evolved in quite unrelated groups. Even so, the late Professor J. L. B. Smith devised a useful key to all the marine fishes of southern Africa based simply on the numbers of hard and soft rays in the fins.

The more primitive teleost fishes, such as the tarpon, herring, salmon and Bony tongues, are long-bodied and have soft-rayed fins with the pelvic fins set well back from the pectorals. Although some of these fishes are fairly fast swimmers, they lack the manoeuverability of the more advanced perch-like fishes grouped in the super order Acanthopterygii. One has only to watch the fishes of a coral reef to see that some structural change has occurred to enable these lightning-fast twists and turns around the coral. Typically, the acanthopterygians have rather short and deep, compressed bodies which results in fewer undulations along the body during swimming but gives a much tighter and more direct control of movement. The pectoral fins lie higher on the body and the pelvic fins have now moved forward to lie below the pectorals. The combined effect of the four fins enables the fish to stop or turn with great rapidity and the deeper and more compressed body helps to prevent rolling. The dorsal fin is now much longer and the rays in the anterior part of the fin are no longer soft but spiny. The spiny portion of the fin can be raised and lowered at will and when erected provides a further means of stabilizing the body during sudden turns.

Although all these advanced features are found in the acanthopterygians, it should be remembered that they are essentially adaptations to a life in which manoeuverability is important. In many cases these spiny-finned fishes have adopted a mode of life in which reduction of fin spines or the evolution of a long body has been of greater advantage than the ability to make sudden turns. As shown in the table, a second advanced group of teleost fishes, the Paracanthopterygii, appears to have evolved independently of the acanthopterygians. They share many common features with the latter, as well as a number of features of their own, and they provide a good example of parallel evolution.

One characteristic (but not invariable) feature of fishes is the presence of scales on the body. The smooth *cycloid* scales typical of the more primitive teleosts (tenpounder, tarpon, herring, etc) represent a tremendous reduction from the thick scales of their palaeoniscid ancestors (see fishes, fossil). In the perch-like fishes the hind margin of the scale is often roughened by little comb-like projections, a fact that is immediately apparent if the fish is stroked the 'wrong way'. Such scales are referred to as *ctenoid*. In a

Two Sarcastic fringeheads *Neoclinus blanchardi* 'kissing'. These Californian fishes have unusually large mouths.

The rare scorpionfish *Taenionothus triacanthus* of the Pacific, swims like a piece of seaweed, oscillating from side to side as if swayed by the current.

number of fishes (anglerfish, some catfishes) scales are absent or greatly reduced and the skin is leathery. In the pipefishes and Sea horses the body is covered by bony rings, while the trunk- or boxfishes are the tortoises of the fish world with a hard carapace of bony plates. Even in normally scaled fishes, such as the carp, varieties occur with few scales (Mirror carp) or none at all (Leather carp). The scales are essentially a means of protection.

A very great diversity is found in the form and placing of teeth in the mouth of teleosts. In a number of filter-feeding species (e.g. some of the shads) there are no teeth at all. In other teleosts, teeth may be present along the jaws, on the tongue, on various bones that roof the cavity of the mouth, along the gill arches and in the gullet. Unlike mammals, fishes usually have teeth of a similar shape along the jaw, but in the wolf-fish and some Sea breams the teeth in the front of the jaw are canine-like while those behind are grinding molars. The teeth are normally used to hold the prey during swallowing but in the bluefish and the piranha the jaw teeth are actually used to bite chunks out of the prey. Fine comb-like jaw teeth are found in species that browse on algae, while fang-like jaw teeth are characteristic of predators. The teeth are usually kept throughout life but are occasionally replaced by subsequent rows (some catfishes).

In the more primitive teleosts, the premaxillary bones are rather small and most of the upper jaw is made up by the maxilla. In the more advanced members, however, the pre-maxilla elongates and excludes the maxilla from the biting edge of the jaw, the maxilla then playing a part in the complex mechanics of jaw protrusion. The ability to protrude the jaw led to the development of a variety of nibbling, seizing and sucking mouths. The John Dory can protrude the mouth a remarkable distance. In the Elephant-snout fishes the small mouth is at the end of a long tube which can be probed into the mud. The tube-like snouts of the pipefishes and Sea horses are used like a pipette to suck up minute organisms. In the catfishes there are species with expanded lips which act as suckers to attach the fish to rocks while the teeth rasp away at algae. In certain deep-sea fishes the jaws can be unhinged to allow the entrance of prey much larger than its captor.

The diversity in the form of jaws and teeth is rivalled by the diversity of foods eaten by teleosts. It is, indeed, difficult to think of any organic matter that is not eaten by some teleost fish, including such unlikely diets as coral (parrotfishes), gill parasites (Cleaner

The parrotfish *Scarus* sp. Note the parrot-like beak with which this fish feeds on corals.

Fishes

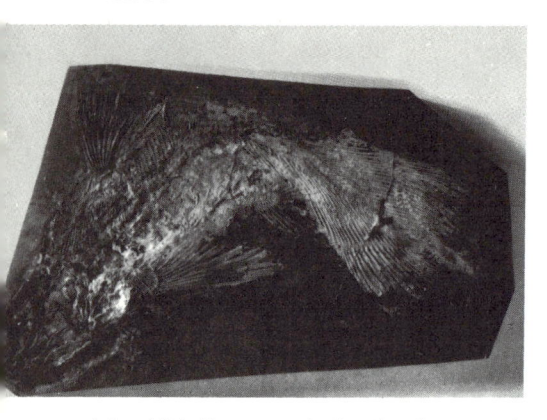

A fossil fish illustrating the fine detail preserved, enabling scientists to reconstruct the anatomy of extinct fishes particularly well.

fishes), and the fins and scales of other fishes (certain African cichlid fishes). An equal diversity is found in the methods used to capture food. Usually the food is seized, nibbled or sucked in, but this may follow a long chase, a sudden lunge, a placid filtration process or a cunning use of some form of lure (see anglerfishes). One of the more bizarre methods of capturing prey is the shooting of insects by the archerfish.

The development of the various sense organs in teleosts clearly reflects their way of life. Eyes are well developed in those that rely mainly on sight for feeding and the avoidance of predators, but the eyes are regressed or absent in some deep-sea and cave fishes, such fishes relying more on information from their lateral line system. This system is used for positioning by shoaling fishes in the well-lit surface waters but it is reduced in fishes such as sticklebacks in which sight and smell are of more importance. Smell is particularly important in scavenging fishes and it plays a critical role in the homing of salmon. Hearing is well developed in most fishes and especially in those that produce sound. The echo-location system in electric fishes is without parallel among vertebrates (bats use sound and not electric pulses). Luminous organs are found in many deep-sea fishes and these provide means for species and sex recognition, for producing a form of obliterative shading and for illuminating the environment. Communication between fishes (by sound, light, colour changes, behaviour, etc) is a subject that requires much more study, as do many aspects of the ways in which fishes perceive elements in their surroundings.

The teleosts have evolved a wide range of breeding habits. The vast majority lay eggs. In species that do not exhibit any form of parental care the number of eggs laid by a female may reach several millions (cod, ling, etc), of which an average of only two survive to adulthood if the species is not increasing. Such eggs may float freely at the surface or adhere to stones or plants. Fishes which show some form of parental care usually lay fewer eggs and may build a crude nest (salmon) or a very well constructed nest (sticklebacks) in which the eggs are deposited and hatch. In some species of *Tilapia* the nest is used merely to deposit the eggs, the latter then being picked up by one of the parents and incubated in the mouth, as in the Sea catfishes. In the pipefishes the eggs are incubated by the male in a special pouch on the abdomen and in the Sea horses the eggs are also nourished in a pouch. One characin lays its eggs out of water and keeps them moist by splashing. In the Annual fishes the eggs are drought resistant and will survive desiccation until the next rains. In several groups of teleosts the eggs are retained in the ovary and hatch there, the larvae later being born (see redfish and live bearers). In certain of these viviparous fishes the embryos and larvae are nourished by secretions from the mother and some form of connection between the two may develop (a pseudoplacenta). The young may be variously guarded and in the mouth-brooding species of *Tilapia* the fry are taken into the mouth in times of danger. In the discusfish the young feed on a mucous secretion from the body of the parents.

An entire chapter could be written on the

A ray, one of the flattened bottom-living fishes related to sharks.

John dory *Zeus faber* seizes small fishes with a sudden protrusion of its telescopic jaws.

ways of teleost fishes and the vast range of habitats into which they have penetrated. They are found in the seas, from the shallows to the abyssal depths, in lakes and rivers, in caves, hot soda springs (some *Tilapia*), artesian wells (some catfishes), in torrential streams (Capitane catfish), in the gill chambers of other fishes (candiru) and in water just above freezing (icefishes). Some tropical lakes support a high density of fishes and will yield a standing crop of 300–500 lb

Wreckfish or Stone bass *Polyprion americanum*.

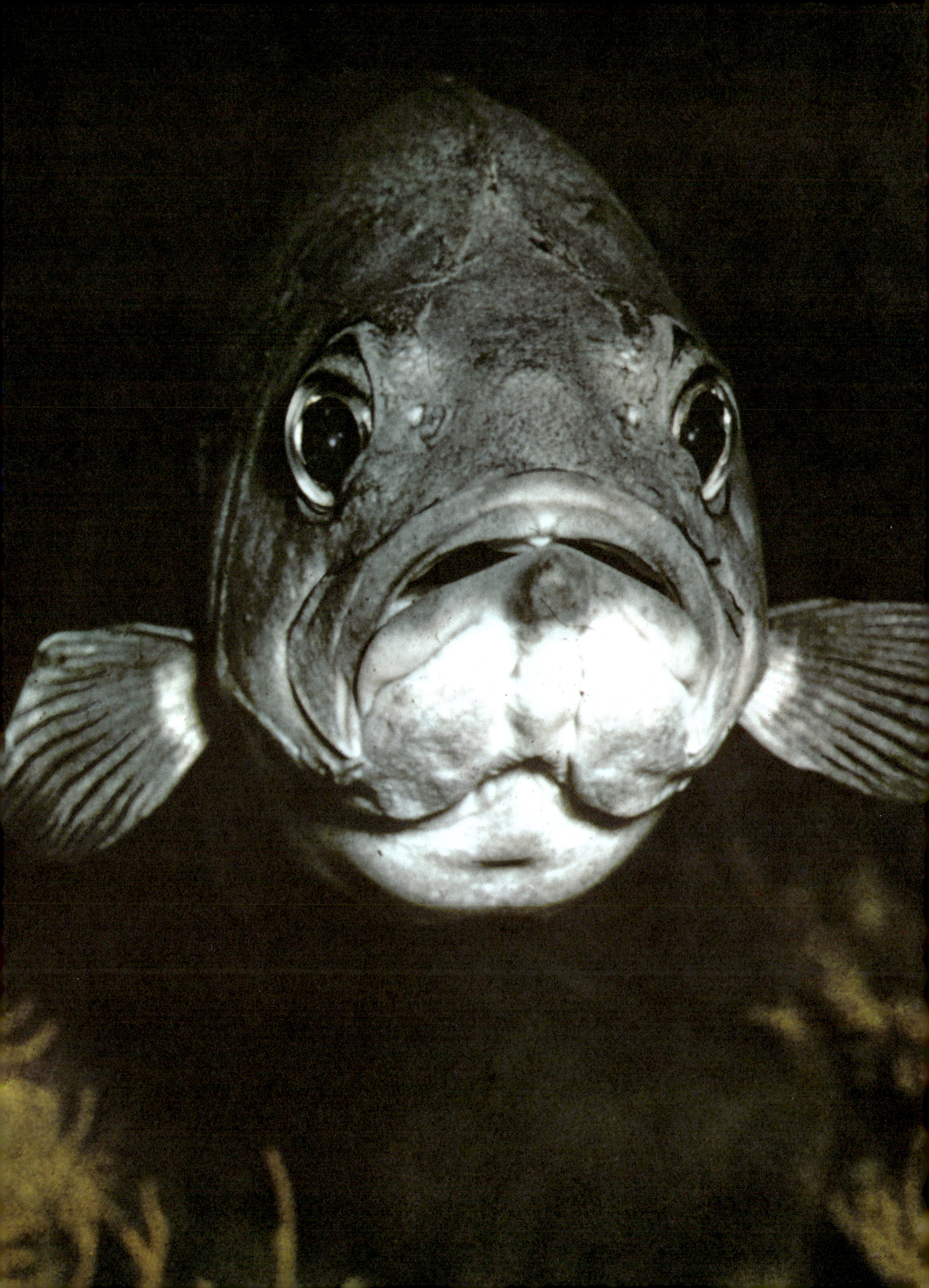

Fishes, fossil

The dab Limanda limanda, which lies on its left side, the left eye moving around the body to lie alongside the right.

(135–225 kg) per acre (per 0·4 ha). In the deep parts of the oceans food is so scarce that only one fish per cu mile can be supported. Some species are so numerous that several million tons can be caught every year without any appreciable effect on the stocks (see anchovies), while others are so rare (or depleted by man) that only a few hundred individuals are known. One of the most curious modes of existence is that of the adult male deep-sea anglerfish, which becomes totally parasitic on the female, but closer inspection shows that in its way each species is very beautifully adapted to its own living conditions. What appears to be a rather uniform environment—water—is quite as varied as any land surface and has resulted in an extraordinary range of adaptations. The teleost fishes have shown a basic plasticity in their form, physiology and behaviour which has enabled them to conquer habitats denied to their ancestors. The number and diversity of present-day species is an indication of the great evolutionary success of this group.

FISHES FOSSIL provide the essential clue to the classification of both the recent and the extinct fish-like vertebrates and a true reading of the fossil record shows the steps by which these forms evolved and eventually gave rise to the ancestors of the modern land vertebrates. For this reason a complete classification, including both recent and fossil groups, is given here and not in the article entitled 'Fishes'. Because of the large gaps in the fossil record and the still considerable amount of work needed on the recent forms, no classification meets the criticism of all authorities. That given here, based on a classification by A. S. Romer (1967), is sufficient for ordinary use. The latest based on more recent research is given in full in the classification tables in our final volume.

The inclusion of such a complex classification in a book designed for the general reader might be questioned. It must be borne in mind, however, that the animals grouped loosely together as 'fishes' have no more right to be merely lumped together than have all the terrestrial vertebrates. Thus, there are

---

CLASSIFICATION OF FISHES
(+ all members of group now extinct)

1. Class AGNATHA – jawless fishes
   a. Subclass Monorhina – one nostril
      + Order Osteostraci
      + Order Anaspida
      Order Cyclostomata – living jawless fishes (lampreys and hagfishes)

   b. Subclass Diplorhina – two nostrils
      + Order Heterostraci
      + Order Coelolepida

2. Class PLACODERMI – jaws present
   + Order Macropetalichthyidae
   + Order Rhenanida
   + Order Arthrodira
   + Order Phyllolepida
   + Order Ptyctodontida
   + Order Antiarchi

3. Class CHONDRICHTHYES or Selachii – cartilaginous fishes
   a. Subclass Elasmobranchii – shark-like fishes
      + Order Cladoselachii
      + Order Pleuracanthodii
      Order Pleurotremata – living sharks
      Order Hypotremata – living skates and rays

   b. Subclass Bradyodonti (= Holocephali) – chimaeras or rabbitfishes
      Order Chimaeriformes

4. Class PISCES or Osteichtyes – bony fishes
   a. Subclass Acanthodii
      + Order Climatiformes
      + Order Ischnacanthiformes
      + Order Acanthodiformes

   b. Subclass Sarcopterygii
      Order Crossopterygii (= Actinistia) – coelocanth and rhipidistians
      Order Dipnoi – lungfishes

   c. Subclass Actinopterygii – ray-finned fishes
      i. Infraclass Chondrostei
         + Order Palaeonisciformes
         Order Polypteriformes – bichirs
         Order Acipenseriformes – sturgeons
      ii. Infraclass Holostei
         + Order Semionotiformes
         + Order Pycnodontiformes
         Order Amiiformes – bowfins and garpikes

         + Order Aspidorhynchiformes
         + Order Pholidophoriformes
         + Order Leptolepiformes – place uncertain

      iii. Infraclass Teleostei – modern bony fishes

Division I

Superorder Elopomorpha
   Order Elopiformes – tenpounders and tarpons
   Order Anguilliformes – eels, Gulper eels
   Order Notacanthiformes – Spiny eels
Superorder Clupeomorpha
   Order Clupeiformes – herrings, shads, anchovies, Round herrings

Division II

Superorder Osteoglossomorpha
   Order Osteoglossiformes – Bony tongues, African butterflyfish
   Order Mormyriformes – Elephant-snout fishes

Division III

Superorder Protacanthopterygii
   Order Salmoniformes – salmon and salmon-like fishes
   Order Cetomimiformes – whalefishes
   Order Ctenothrissiformes
   Order Gonorhynchiformes – Beaked salmon, milkfish
Superorder Ostariophysi
   Order Cypriniformes – carps, characins, loaches
   Order Siluriformes

four classes of fish-like vertebrates (Agnatha, Placodermi, Chondrichthyes and Osteichthyes or Pisces) which are in many ways as different from each other structurally as are the four much better known classes of land vertebrates (Amphibia, Reptilia, Aves and Mammalia).

Even now, the relationships and origins of the four classes of fishes are not fully understood. Their fossils appear very early in the geological timescale and something over 300 million years ago the four classes were already established. A tentative scheme of linking the groups in an evolutionary sequence is given in the picture on p. 731. The amphibians certainly arose from the Sarcopterygii. The inclusion of the subclass Acanthodii within the class Pisces (the bony fishes) is conjectural as also is the placement of the Leptolepiformes. The latter group seems to have been ancestral to the Teleostei or modern bony fishes but their more advanced members are little different from some of the more primitive teleosts. In the past, the classes and subclasses were thought

Superorder Paracanthopterygii
    Order Percopsiformes – Trout perches
    Order Batrachoidiformes – toadfishes
    Order Gobiesociformes – clingfishes
    Order Lophiiformes – angelfishes, frogfishes
    Order Gadiformes – cods and relatives

Superorder Atherinomorpha
    Order Atheriniformes – Flying fishes, garpikes, toothcarps, guppies

Superorder Acanthopterygii
    Order Beryciformes – squirrelfishes
    Order Zeiformes – John Dories, boarfishes
    Order Lampridiformes – opah, dealfishes, oarfish
    Order Gasterosteiformes – sticklebacks, Sea horses, pipefishes
    Order Channiformes – snakeheads
    Order Synbranchiformes
    Order Scorpaeniformes – scorpionfishes, gurnards, bullheads
    Order Dactylopteriformes – Flying gurnards
    Order Pegasiformes – Sea moths
    Order Perciformes – perches and perch-like fishes
    Order Pleuronectiformes – flatfishes
    Order Tetraodontiformes – triggerfishes filefishes, boxfishes, pufferfishes, porcupinefish

of as rigid divisions, so that a particular fish was obliged to fit into one category or another or, failing this the category had to be re-defined. Modern experts tend to regard these higher categories rather as 'levels of organization' representing a particular evolutionary achievement (in structure, habits, etc.). At each of these levels a group of animals sharing the characteristic structures or habits of that level will exploit the new environmental conditions now available to them. In doing so they will evolve even more specialized structures, habits etc., until at a certain point a new level of organization can be recognized. Because the fishes at the original level started with the same kind of specialization, it is very possible that mo e than one species, genus or even family will arrive at the new level of organization. This means that it is often useless to look for a single ancestor to a major group.

The four classes of fish-like vertebrates will be discussed, with examples of some of the more important forms.

1 **Agnatha** or jawless fishes are represented nowadays by the lampreys and hagfishes placed here in the order Cyclostomata. Lacking true jaws and with the gills contained in pouches, the earliest of the Agnatha are the pteraspids from the Ordovician strata, the best known genus being *Pteraspis* of the Devonian. These were flattened forms with an armoured head and trunk which suggests a sluggish life on the bottom grubbing for food. The order Osteostraci, contains small flattened fishes, with a bony shield over the head which was rounded in front and drawn into points behind. Through the work of Professor Stensiö, these fishes are now the best known of all fossil fishes. Patient grinding of sections of the head has revealed the pattern of the nerves and blood vessels. The order Anaspida contained rather different fishes having slender bodies covered with small, scale-like bony plates which suggests that these forms were fairly good swimmers. Although the evolution of jaw mechanisms is now fairly well understood, the actual group of jawless fishes that gave rise to the jawed vertebrates is still not known. See also jawless fishes.

2 **Placodermi** is a class of rather varied fishes that extend from the Upper Silurian to Lower Carboniferous times. Most of the placoderms were marine and generally the head and chest were covered in bony plates with hinges between the two regions to allow movement. In many species the rest of the body was naked and one can see a general trend towards the reduction of armour as the group evolved. Among the best known of the placoderms are the Arthrodira, represented by such generalized forms as *Coccosteus,* a streamlined fish from the Devonian of Scotland. *Arctolepis,* a freshwater species known from Spitzbergen, had heavy chest armour which was not hinged to the head and clearly this restricted swimming movements. These heavily armoured forms were mostly small, but in late Devonian times one finds larger fishes with less armour which were predators and probably active swimmers. The late Devonian *Dunkleosteus* reached 10 ft (3 m) in length and the aptly named *Titanichthys* of North America grew to 30 ft (9 m). No teeth were present in the jaws of arthrodires but some had bony serrations along the jaw and others had plates in the mouth for crushing shellfishes.

Very little is known about the presence of paired (pectoral and pelvic) fins. In *Arctolepis* the chest armour is produced into curved and immovable pectoral spines and possibly in later forms, in which the spine has become progressively reduced, some fleshy movable fins had developed. The ptyctodonts, the crushing jaw-plates of which are fairly commonly found, had reduced armour and in some species a dorsal spine is present. The petalichthyids were flattened, bottom-living forms some of which had a rather shark-like skin covering. *Cratoselache* does in fact strongly resemble a shark but is too late in time to have been ancestral to that group. The rhenanids, on the other hand, strongly resemble skates in their expanded pectoral fins but the resemblance is only superficial.

Antiarchs were small and rather grotesque freshwater forms that flourished for a while in the Middle and Upper Devonian. These fishes, which were something of an evolutionary experiment, had jointed arms and an external body covering that gave them the appearance of crabs. In the last century a Scottish quarryman, Hugh Miller, collected fossils of the antiarch genus *Pterichthyodes* and although quite untrained in paleontology succeeded in reconstructing some of the fishes. One of his original paper models is now exhibited in the British Museum (Natural History) in London beside more modern reconstructions. His work was excellent and it is fitting that a species should be named after him, *Pterichthyodes milleri*.

One of the best known of the antiarchs is *Bothriolepis* of North America. Specimens of this fish died by suffocation in muddy water and through this lucky chance it has been possible to learn a great deal about the internal organs of the antiarchs. The fine mud particles penetrated into the alimentary canal and a perfect cast was formed before the soft parts decomposed. The fish also became embedded in a rather coarser-grained mud and the contrast between the two muds now makes it possible to reconstruct the internal organs. A spiral valve is present in the intestine, foreshadowing that

Fishes, fossil

found in the sharks, but more important perhaps was a pair of sacs developing from the ventral surface of the pharynx which might well have been lungs.

The origins of all these placoderm fishes are obscure, but they are amongst the oldest of the jawed vertebrates, and their ancestors must have existed long before, probably in the Silurian. Included here amongst the placoderms is *Palaeospondylus,* a small fish found in quantities in some quarries in Scotland. The fossils are all rather similar but although reconstructions of the head have been made it has not yet proved possible to understand the structure of the jaws. The affinities of this fish remain a mystery.

3 **Chondrichthyes** or cartilaginous fishes such as the modern sharks, skates and rays were once thought to represent a very primitive stage in evolution from which fishes with bony skeletons evolved. The fossil evidence shows, however, that the Chondrichthyes appeared after the bony fishes and that a cartilaginous skeleton may be a degeneration from a bony one. The earliest evidence that we have of the Chondrichthyes are isolated spines, teeth and scales from the Upper Silurian and Lower Devonian beds. Even these show considerable diversity, suggesting that we have a group already launched on its 300 million year career. Devonian strata yield ancestral sharks such as *Cladoselache,* one of the most primitive sharks yet discovered. *Xenacanthus,* from late Devonian to Triassic times, possesses claspers, an indication that internal fertilization took place. These early sharks share many primitive features in the form of the skull, jaws, fin skeleton and teeth, and as a group are said to represent the 'cladodont' level of organization. The hybodonts, or 'hybodont' level, appear in the Permian. They are much nearer to modern sharks in general appearance. Some have sharp teeth in the front of the jaws and flat, crushing teeth at the rear, an arrangement which links them with the modern Port Jackson sharks. The Carboniferous was the heyday of the sharks, their zenith before competition from the bony fishes forced them into their present position. Our present day sharks have a long lineage and, apart from the Grey sharks, all the remaining families contain genera that occur as fossils in rocks dating back to the Cretaceous or even the Jurassic, The sharks and their flattened relatives the rays became bypassed by the rest of vertebrate evolution and they have lingered on as a relict of what was once the dominant vertebrate group in the oceans.

4 **Pisces** or bony fishes are now the most successful of the four classes judging by the number of different species (about 25,000) and the diversity of habitats in which they now live. The earliest members of this class are thought by some to be the Acanthodii of the Silurian, although other authorities link the acanthodians with the shark-like fishes. The name acanthodian means 'spiny shark' and these fishes do indeed have a shark-like appearance, particularly in the heterocercal tail (having the upper lobe larger than the lower). The acanthodians more closely resemble the modern fishes than do the placoderms. They were small fishes with the fins supported by a massive spine along the leading edge and in many cases there was also a row of spines, possibly supporting membranous flaps, along the body between the pectoral and pelvic fins (e.g. *Climatius* of the Lower Devonian). This arrangement was taken as evidence of the 'fin-fold' theory which postulated that the earliest fishes had a continuous fin-fold and that the acanthodians show the first stage in the division of the fold into discrete pectoral and pelvic fins. These fins appear to have been immovable, however, and probably acted as hydroplanes. Unlike the placoderms, the internal skeleton seems to have been fairly well ossified and there was an elaborate armour of denticles on the body in the form of minute diamond-shaped ganoid scales. There is no evidence of claspers (modifications of the pelvic fins in male sharks and rays for effecting internal fertilization). If related to the shark-like fishes, the acanthodians may have diverged from the main stem of evolution before the appearance of the true chondrichthyans.

The third subclass of the Pisces is the Actinopterygii or 'ray-finned' fishes. The evolution within this group, from the primitive Palaeonisciformes to the modern and highly specialized Teleostei, is described in the article on fishes. The palaeoniscids, which appeared in the Devonian, are now extinct. They were small fishes with heavy, shiny ganoid scales and most appear to have been fast swimmers with one dorsal and one anal fin. Most of the internal skeleton was of bone but the centra of the vertebrae were unossified and were composed of cartilage. They survived through, comparatively unchanged, until the Triassic, when several lines of palaeoniscids achieved what can be referred to as the holostean level or grade. The first palaeoniscids appeared in the Middle Devonian and are represented by such rare forms as *Cheirolepis,* a freshwater fish. By the end of the Devonian the palaeoniscids were much more common and were found all over the world in both the sea and freshwater. Although generalized types such as *Cheirolepis* and *Palaeoniscus* persisted, certain aberrant forms evolved to meet specialized environments. *Tarrassius* developed a single long median fin and lost the pelvic fins and most of its scales. *Carboreles* was almost entirely naked and deep-bodied forms such as *Platysomus* and *Chirodus* appeared. The last few palaeoniscids lingered on into the Lower Cretaceous.

The only surviving members of the Chondrostei, the infraclass in which the palaeoniscids are placed, are the sturgeons and the bichirs. The sturgeons are linked to the palaeoniscids through the Jurassic fish, *Chondrosteus.* The sturgeons are much larger fishes than their palaeoniscid relatives and have lost all their bone and have inferior, suctorial mouths. Were it not for the connecting link *Chondrosteus,* only the heterocercal tail of the sturgeons would point to their primitiveness. The bichirs have no connecting link, but the retention of ganoid scales hints at their primitive origins. The pectoral fins have fleshy lobes at the base, a characteristic of the Sarcopterygii (see below), but at least one palaeoniscid (*Cornyboniscus*) also possessed such structures.

The second infraclass, the Holostei or holostean level of organization is characterized by the tail becoming symmetrical and by certain structural modifications in the jaws. These changes, and a general reduction in the density of scales on the body, enabled the holosteans to exploit new ecological niches. The typical holostean form, as in the palaeoniscids, is a compressed streamlined body adapted to fairly fast swimming, although even the early holosteans were capable of producing such variants as the long-snouted and pike-like *Saurichthys* (which some authorities place with the sturgeons).

The earliest of the holosteans are the Semionotiformes, heavily-built fishes whose armour of heavy scales probably limited their mobility and led to their failure to compete by Cretaceous times with the more agile teleosts. *Lepidotus* from the Jurassic had crushing teeth for eating shellfishes, as also did the deep-bodied *Dapedius.* It is considered that the modern garpike may possibly be related to the semionotids. Although its body-form and way of life are very different, there are certain similarities in the skull that suggest such a link.

The Pycnodontiformes were small, compressed, almost circular fishes that lived in quiet waters from the Jurassic to early Eocene times. The scales were modified into elongated rods that formed a network over the body and the teeth and mouth suggest that these fishes browsed on corals. They may have evolved as an independent line from the palaeoniscids. The Aspidorhynchiformes were more elongated, with the upper jaw produced into a beak.

The Amiiformes are now represented by the bowfins. The fossil forms had a fusiform body and there was generally some reduction in the scales. Some resembled the bowfin (*Amia*) but *Caturus* was a fast-swimming, predacious fish with a mackeral-like body and strong teeth in the jaws. The Amiidae, the family containing the modern bowfins, of North America, has a long history, dating back to Jurassic times.

The final order at the holostean level is the Pholidophoriformes, the more advanced members of which clearly approach the teleosts, *Leptolepis* from the Jurassic is so close to that group that many authorities consider it to be the first real teleost. Structurally, it is only slightly more primitive than the ten-pounder.

The third infraclass of actinopterygians is the Teleostei, the group that contains the modern bony fishes. Throughout the Mesozoic the holosteans had radiated into numerous forms and possibly three independent lines evolved to the teleostean level. From these have stemmed the overwhelming majority of living fishes. The teleosts have left a fairly complete fossil record, at least in some groups, so that it is possible to deduce that the most succesful of all the teleost groups, the huge order of perch-like fishes, Perciformes, evolved from the squirrelfishes (Beryciformes). In some groups, such as the modern sticklebacks and their relatives, however, the earliest fossils from the Eocene are almost identical to the modern forms. The evolution and classification of the teleosts is outlined under 'fishes'.

The second subclass within the overall grouping of the Pisces is the Sarcopterygii, which contains the coelacanths and lungfishes. The sarcopterygians are of immense interest because it was from them that the first land vertebrates evolved, leading eventually to the appearance of man. The first sarcopterygian fishes appeared in the Devonian. Numerous species arose and for a while they were more common than the actinopterygii or ray-finned fishes. The latter, however, gradually gained supremacy, at least in water, and the sarcopterygians are now represented only by three genera of lungfish and the rare coelacanth. The early sarcopterygians had a curious hinged skull, the two parts separated by a layer of cartilage, which apparently prevented jarring of the brain when the jaws snapped shut. The early forms also had two dorsal fins (as in the coelacanth) whereas only a single dorsal was present in the early ray-finned fishes.

The sarcopterygian fishes are grouped in two orders. The first of these, the Crossopterygii or lobe-finned fishes, contains the coelacanth and its ancestors (for its evolution see coelacanth) and the Rhipidistia. The rhipidistian fishes survived up to the Carboniferous period and it was from this group that the first tetrapods or four-legged land vertebrates arose. These are the only fishes with true internal nostrils. The fins had fleshy lobes at their bases and the internal bones of these lobes were those which were destined to evolve into the limb bones of the tetrapods. In *Eusthenopteron* from the Upper Devonian the fin skeleton is already very like that of a miniature arm. The bone arrangement in the skull, as well as the complicated structure of the teeth, point to the condition found in the early amphibians. *Osteolepis,* an early rhipidistian, grew to 9 in (23 cm) in length, but *Holoptychus* of the late Devonian reached 6 ft (1·8 m) and *Rhizodus,* a Carboniferous descendant of *Osteolepis,* grew to 13 ft (4 m). Most were freshwater forms but by the late Devonian some had moved into the sea. At an early stage in their evolution, the rhipidistians took their first steps on land and in this new environment radiated into the lines which were to give rise to the amphibians, reptiles, birds and mammals of today.

The second order of the sarcopterygian fishes is the Dipnoi or lungfishes, the evolution of which is described in detail in the article devoted to the living forms. Whereas the coelacanths and the rhipidistians seem to have had a common ancestor in the Devonian, the lungfishes apparently split off from this stock in the Silurian, many million years earlier. That a few forms should have survived down to the present is remarkable.

Fishing snake of Asia and Australia.

FISH DEFINED. Before the days of John Ray, Linnaeus and others who started to classify animals systematically on their anatomical characters, there were some strange ideas about the relationships of animals. Several animals were classed as fishes although they had no gills, did not bear scales and often did not look in the slightest way like fish. Included in this list were the whales and dolphins which do at least look like fish, Barnacle geese, which were supposed to arise from barnacles, otters and penguins. We now know that these animals are either mammals or birds and, zoologically, very different from fish. Common English, however, often fails to follow scientific classification or definition and 'fish' was often used to denote any aquatic mammal. Therefore it would be quite correct to speak of whales and otters as fish. Such a definition had practical advantages to Roman Catholics forbidden to eat meat on Fridays or during Lent and, until the end of the 19th century, Barnacle geese were considered to be fish rather than meat.

FISHING SNAKE *Herpeton tentaculum*, one of the rear-fanged snakes of the subfamily Homalopsinae, members of which inhabit ponds, rivers and estuaries from China to

Fish louse

New Guinea and northern Australia. They appear to be at home in both fresh and salt water. Their valvular nostrils are situated on top of the snout and a forward extension of the glottis plugs into the internal opening of the nostrils, thus preventing water entering the lungs via the mouth.

The Fishing snake, otherwise known as the Board snake, Tentacled snake or Siamese swamp snake is the most aquatic member of the subfamily and has much reduced, keeled ventral and subcaudal plates. It can readily be distinguished from its relatives by the presence of two leaf-like scaly tentacles on its snout. It attains a length of about $2\frac{1}{2}$ ft (77 cm) and is usually reddish-brown with white-edged dark cross-bars although lighter coloured individuals with longitudinal stripes are also encountered. It inhabits streams and swamps in Thailand, Cambodia and South Vietnam where its colour pattern forms an excellent camouflage against a background of aquatic vegetation. It has a remarkable habit of anchoring itself to some stem or root with its prehensile tail and adopting a rigid, board-like posture which greatly increases its plant-like appearance and consequently its concealment, not only from predators, but also from unwary fish and aquatic amphibians upon which it feeds. This rigid posture is maintained even when the snake is removed from the water. Although equipped with venom injecting apparatus it is not dangerous to man.

It has long been thought that the tentacles, which are muscular and movable, act as a lure to passing fish, but recent observations on captive Fishing snakes have shown that this is not the case. However, it is now believed that their only purpose is to enhance the snake's plant-like appearance.

The young are born alive, there being between seven and 13 in each brood. FAMILY: Colubridae, ORDER: Squamata, CLASS: Reptilia. A.F.S.

FISH LOUSE, not a louse, but a crustacean parasitic on fishes and remarkable for its disc-like body and a pair of large adhesive suckers with which it clings to host fishes. The head bears a pair of sessile compound eyes and the underside of the front part bears numerous triangular spinules. These spinules point backwards and help the louse in adhering to the host. Members of the genus *Argulus* align themselves so that the head points in the same direction as that of the host and the spinules catch firmly in the fish's skin.

The Fish louse has four pairs of swimming legs, so that it can swim actively to seek out its host. Once on the host the louse clings by means of its suckers and spines and pierces the skin with its narrow mandibles, which are housed in a proboscis on the underside of the head. The physical damage inflicted by the mandibles is probably not very great, but the small wounds sometimes become infected by bacteria or fungi and these may eventually kill the fish.

The genus *Argulus* is widespread throughout the world on both marine and freshwater fishes. The largest species is *Argulus scutiformis* which reaches a length of over 1 in ($2\frac{1}{2}$ cm), but most species are about $\frac{1}{4}$ in ($\frac{1}{2}$ cm) in length.

The Fish louse does not lay its eggs on its host, instead it lays them in clusters which are stuck in flat layers and parallel rows on the surfaces of hard objects. There is considerable variation in the time taken for the eggs to hatch. Several species have been

Fish louse *Argulus foliaceus*.

observed to take about 35 days from laying to hatching, but others have taken as little as 18 days and others again as long as 80 days. The young emerging from the eggs vary in their degree of development in different species. The general form resembles that of the adult, but there are variations in the development of the swimming legs, and none of the species has suckers when it first hatches. Instead all have stout limbs with claws. The young Fish louse moults for the first time four or five days after hatching, and then moults at three or four day intervals, so that by the time it is 20 days old it has moulted five times. During this series of moults the stout limb with claws is replaced by a sucker.

The genus *Dolops,* which is abundant on freshwater fish in Africa and South America, does not have suckers but retains the larval claws throughout life. *Dolops* is also of interest because its blood is often red with the respiratory pigment haemoglobin. This appears to be an adaptation to living on fishes which inhabit poorly aerated water. Species of this genus have also been found attached to frog tadpoles.

The young of the genus *Chonopeltis* hatch with an enormous pair of pincers in place of each sucker, but as the larva moults and grows the pincers diminish and a sucker develops. FAMILY: Argulidae, ORDER: Branchiura, CLASS: Crustacea, PHYLUM: Arthropoda. Ja.G.

FLAGELLATE, the common name applied to a large superclass of single-celled animals with flagella. See dinoflagellates, phytoflagellates, *Trypanosoma* and *Leishmania*. PHYLUM: Protozoa.

FLAME CELLS, probably have an excretory and osmoregulatory function and are found in many acoelomate animals such as rotifers, flukes, flatworms and tapeworms. They are found at the tips of ducts and from them bundles of cilia project into the ducts. The cilia beat continuously, giving the appearance, under the microscope, of a flickering flame, hence the name flame cell, and it is thought that they drive fluids down the duct. See excretion and excretory organs.

FLAMINGO PINK. When flamingos were first kept in captivity it was found that they gradually lost their beautiful pink colouration. The same happened to captive Roseate spoonbills and Scarlet ibises. The pink colour in the feathers and bare skin of these birds is caused by pigments called carotenoids, very similar to the substance that gives carrots their colour. The carotenoids come from their food, such as Brine shrimps, and when captive flamingos are fed on artificial food lacking carotenoids the colour slowly fades. Nowadays flamingos in zoos are given carotenoids, sometimes in the form of carrot oil, in their food and the plumage colour is preserved.

FLAMINGOS, a family of large, brilliantly coloured, aquatic birds which inhabit alkaline and saline lakes and lagoons of the Old World (except Australia), North and South America and some Oceanic islands, including the Galapagos. They prefer to live in hot, dry regions, avoiding cool, moist forested areas; but in the Andes they are found on freezing alkaline lakes at 14,000 ft (4,250 m).

All flamingos are large, 3-6 ft (1-2 m) in length, with long sinuous necks, long legs and webbed feet. The bill is highly specialized for filter-feeding, sharply bent in the middle, with the lower mandible large and trough-like and the upper one small and lid-like. The plumage is pink, red and black, often brilliant. No other large gregarious birds are quite so colourful. The enormous flocks of Lesser flamingos *Phoeniconaias*

American greater flamingo in characteristic pose.

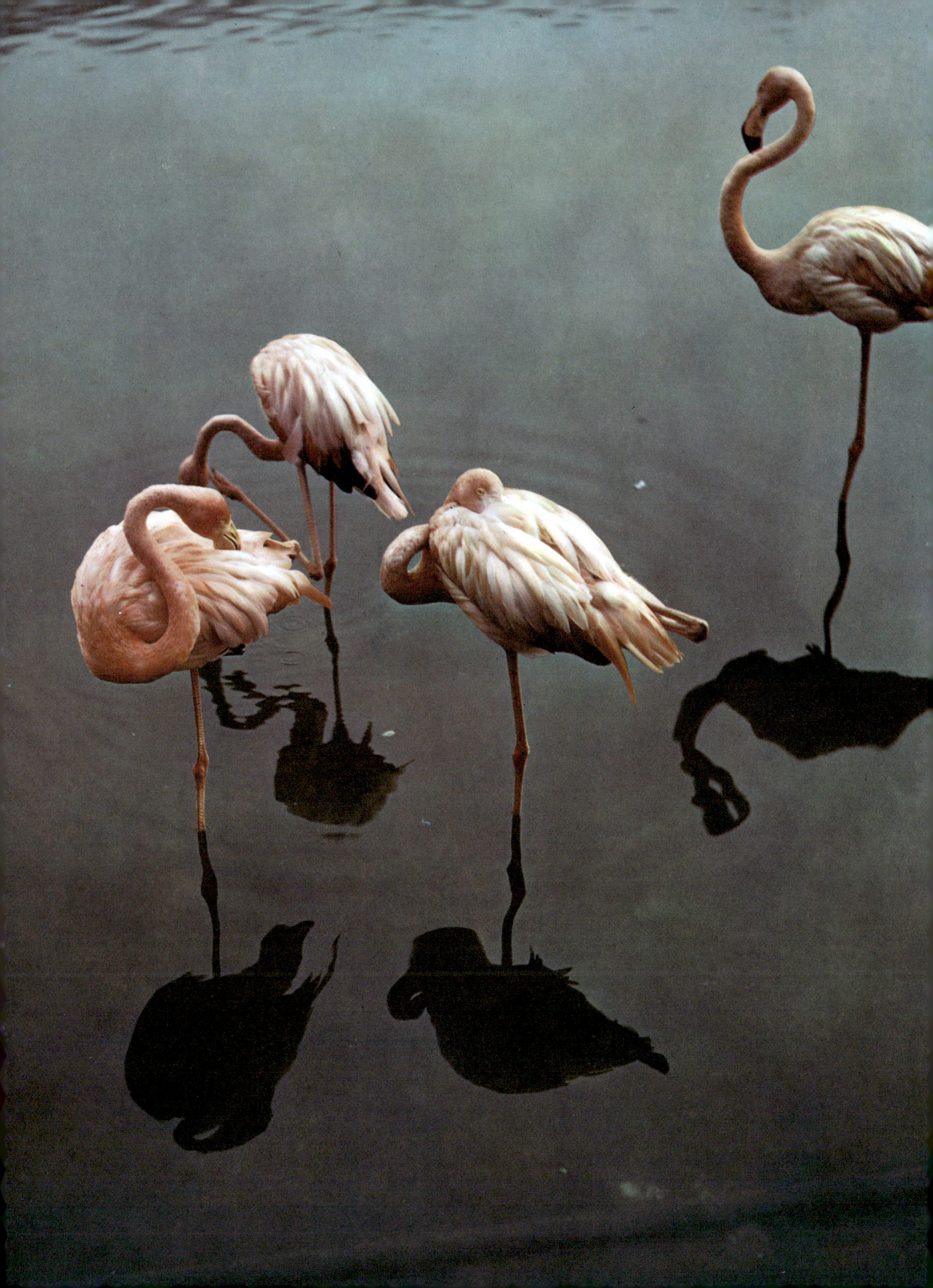

Flamingos

minor seen at some East African alkaline lakes, are probably the most remarkable of the world's bird spectacles.

The exact systematic position of flamingos is obscure, though it is clear that they are an old, specialized group, unlike any other present-day birds. On the basis of their field habits, feather lice, calls, webbed feet and wing-moult they appear most nearly allied to ducks and geese. They sometimes moult *en masse* into a flightless condition, as do ducks and geese. Some anatomical evidence indicates relationships with ibises and storks, while analysis of their egg-white proteins suggests that they may be allied to herons. Whatever their relationships, they are quite unique, intensely specialized for a particular environment.

Flamingos are placed in three genera, *Phoenicopterus* with one to three species, *Phoeniconaias* with one species and *Phoenicoparrus* with two.

Phoenicopterus, the Greater flamingo, differs from the other two genera in its much larger size (large individuals standing nearly 6 ft (2 m) tall) and in the structure of the bill. In *Phoenicopterus* the upper mandible has a shallow internal keel, quite different from the deep triangular keel of *Phoeniconaias* and *Phoenicoparrus*. *Phoenicopterus* is adapted for feeding upon relatively large organisms on the bottom and in deep water, whereas the deep-keeled species are adapted for feeding on the surface or in shallow water.

Depending on the classification followed, there are one, two or three species of Greater flamingos. They are the American greater flamingo *Ph. ruber* (or *Ph. r. ruber* if it is regarded as a race), the European greater flamingo *Ph. roseus* (or *Ph. ruber roseus*) and the Chilean flamingo *Ph. chilensis* (or *Ph. ruber chilensis*). All have a similar bill structure, differing mainly in their colour and size. The American greater flamingo is the darkest red, but otherwise almost exactly resembles the European greater flamingo in size and habits. The Chilean flamingo is much smaller, paler pink and the grey legs have a red ring round the tarsal joint. In zoos the American and European greater flamingos readily consort together, but the Chilean species is apt to keep apart. Thus, even if the Chilean is regarded as only a race of the species *Ph. ruber,* because of its bill structure, it is the most distinct race. A possible compromise is to regard the Chilean flamingo as a full species, *Ph. chilensis* and the European and American greater flamingos as two races of another species, *Ph. ruber.*

Phoeniconaias contains only the Lesser flamingo *Ph. minor* which is mainly African but does also occur in Asia. It is the smallest, least brilliantly coloured, but by far the most numerous of all flamingos. There may be as many as 4–5 million Lesser flamingos, of which about 3–3½ million inhabit East Africa. Lesser flamingos live on alkaline lakes and are not seen on fresh waters unless they are sick, or have strayed. In India they are found on highly saline lagoons in such areas as the Rann of Kutch, where their status as a nesting or visiting species is still rather obscure.

The Andean flamingo *Phoenicoparrus andinus* and James' flamingo *Ph. jamesi* inhabit alkaline or saline lakes at high altitudes in Peru and Bolivia. They breed only on these highland lakes. The Andean flamingo is relatively common, totalling perhaps 100,000, but James' flamingo is by far the rarest of all flamingos. It was not heard of between 1924 and 1957, but since then has been re-discovered in the Andes. Probably there are not less than 15,000, so that it is in no immediate danger of extinction.

All flamingos feed by filtering small animals or microscopic plant life from the mud or water. The bill structure is fundamental to their method of feeding. In all species it is sharply bent in the middle, so that when the flamingo is walking and feeding in the water, the upper mandible is underneath and the lower uppermost. In the James' and Andean flamingos the lower mandible is bulbous and full of cellular bone

Opposite page bottom: Lesser flamingos on Lake Nakuru, Kenya, and above: American greater flamingos with their nests.

and may actually act as a float, helping the bird to feed steadily in choppy water. In all species the basic filter feeding method is similar. Water and mud are sucked into the bill and special structures within the bill catch the small organisms on which the flamingos feed, while unwanted material is rejected.

In the Greater flamingos, including the Chilean flamingo, the bill is 'shallow-keeled'. The upper mandible is not deeply triangular in section and covers a large space within the bill like the lid of a box. When the Greater flamingo is feeding the bill is opened and closed very rapidly, like that of a duck. As it is closed, water and mud containing small animals is squirted out and stiff hairs on the edges of the mandibles catch the small animals and the tongue, which runs in a groove of the lower mandible like a piston in a pump, collects these with the aid of fleshy processes and pulls them back to the gullet. Inside the bill there are also areas of laminae, lines of fine hair-like processes, which lie down as water is sucked in, and are erected when it is ejected. These are probably used to extract microscopic suspended matter in the water, so that the Greater flamingo has a relatively varied diet.

In the Lesser flamingo and the two Andean species, the bill is 'deep-keeled'. The upper mandible is triangular in section and fits closely into the lower mandible; there is no large space in the bill. The inner surfaces of both mandibles are covered with many lines of fine down-like laminae, which in the Lesser flamingo number about 45–50 per cm, in James' flamingo 22–25 per cm and in the Andean flamingo about 15 per cm. The areas of similar laminae inside the bill of the Greater flamingo are at about 12–15 per cm. Thus the Lesser flamingo's bill is adapted to feed on the finest particles. In fact, it cannot feed on large particles or such small mud-living animals as Brine shrimps, copepods and chironomid larvae, which are the favourite food of the Greater flamingo.

The method of feeding also differs. Greater flamingos normally feed on the bottom, their long legs and necks enabling them to feed in 3 ft (1 m) of water or more. Lesser flamingos feed on the surface 1–2 in (2½–5 cm) and can feed equally well when swimming or walking as long as the water is calm; they do not feed in rough water. Greater flamingos are thus confined for feeding to the shoreline or shallow water, while Lesser flamingos can feed on the surface layers in any depth of water.

When a Lesser flamingo is feeding, whether swimming or walking, it swings the bill from side to side with a scything motion. The bill does not perceptibly open and shut, as in the Greater flamingo, but at close range a rapid pulse of water can be seen to be flowing from it. The tongue, working like a piston in the groove of the lower mandible, sucks in and ejects water. As water is sucked in and ejected, the laminae of hairs alternately lie down and are erected, to catch the minute plant life in the water. By working the two mandibles together like a pair of wool-carders, the flamingo moves the accumulated masses of algae on to the tongue, where backward pointing processes automatically collect the food and draw it into the gullet, with the same motion used in pumping water in and out. The process is both highly specialized and very efficient. Lesser flamingos extract very large quantities of green matter from the waters of the lakes in which they live and, in doing so, they also extract and reject nearly all of the water itself which, being alkaline, could be harmful to the kidneys and other excretory organs.

Flamingos occur in spectacular flocks where conditions are suitable. The Lesser flamingo outnumbers all other species together. The next most numerous, and by far the most widespread, is the Greater fla-

Flamingos

mingo, which may number 1 million or more. Its great stronghold is the Rann of Kutch, in northwest India, where at least 500,000 breed, but there are many smaller colonies in Africa, Asia, Europe and North and South America. The best known colonies are those in the Rhône Delta and in the West Indies, where the species has been studied in great detail. Even James' flamingo, about 300 times as rare as the Lesser flamingo, is still common enough to occur in spectacular flocks.

Flamingo populations have been reduced in several parts of the world. In Europe they were formerly persecuted, but are now protected. The numbers of the brilliant West Indian greater flamingos have been reduced in about a century from at least 95,000 to about 25,000. These are now protected, so should increase. In the Andes colonies of all flamingos (Andean, James' and Chilean) are exploited by local populations for their eggs. It appears, however, that this is an ancient practice, and that numbers are not decreasing through this exploitation.

Flamingos are strong fliers and are migratory or nomadic. They readily leave one feeding ground and fly to another. In flight their long necks are stretched out in front and the legs trail behind, so that the bird resembles a flying spear, as one observer put it. The brilliant colours are even more evident in flight than on the ground, especially in the Greater flamingo. Being long-legged, rather spindly birds, they are vulnerable to avian predators in flight by day, so migrate mainly by night. However, they fly freely about the shores of the lakes they inhabit by day and at dusk often fly from one feeding place to another, almost like ducks and geese. They call to one another when moving from place to place at night. The call of the Greater flamingo is a brassy goose-like honking; that of the Lesser flamingo a high pitched, still goose-like, chirrup.

Many animals and birds prey upon flamingos. In Africa known predators include large mammals from the lion to the jackal, several species of eagles and vultures and the Marabou stork. The tight-packed flocks of Lesser flamingos are especially vulnerable, since they are so massed that they cannot all take off at once. A predator can easily knock over flamingos by a quick dash out on to the mud. The flamingos are defenceless, having weak, thin legs and light fragile bones. They especially fear Marabou storks and panic at any sudden scare. In African breeding colonies of Greater flamingos over 4,000 pairs have been known to desert their eggs because of the advent of less than 20 Marabous and a single Marabou walking along the shore will put tens of thousands of Lesser flamingos to flight.

Being so vulnerable, flamingos usually breed in places which are inaccessible to predators. Their nesting sites long remained unknown in most countries and it was those of the Greater flamingo in Europe, the Rann of Kutch and in the West Indies, that were found first. The first good account of the breeding of Lesser flamingos was published in 1954 and the nesting of James' flamingos was unknown until 1957. In the last ten years, however, most of these mysteries have been solved.

All flamingos breed colonially on remote salt or alkaline lakes and lagoons, sometimes in staggering numbers. The largest recorded colony was of 1,100,000 pairs of Lesser flamingos at Lake Magadi, Tanzania, in 1962; but huge colonies of Greater flamingos have also been recorded in the Rann of Kutch. The enormous colonies are composed of smaller groups and may take several weeks to develop fully from first egg-laying. In such places as the Galapagos Islands the flamingos are too scarce to breed

Nesting colony of Lesser flamingos.

in large colonies and small groups must here be able to reproduce the species.

Before breeding, though there is no change in the essential plumage patterns, flamingos usually become much more brightly coloured, through a moult. Mass moult to flightlessness, occurring in ducks and geese after breeding, may occur in flamingos before, during or after breeding, or even in years when no breeding occurs. In some years when flamingos breed they do not moult to flightlessness.

The breeding cycle begins with nuptial display, often very striking and long. In the Greater and Lesser flamingos, the displays are essentially similar, differing only in detail. Greater flamingos congregate in certain areas, usually, but not always, at the breeding ground. They gather into a loose-packed flock and perform ritualized movements of the head, neck and wings. Standing bolt upright, with long neck up-stretched to its limit, the flamingo first wags its head from side to side. Then, as the intensity of the display increases, some of the birds rigidly point their beaks at the sky and suddenly open their wings, holding them out to the side for a few seconds, then smartly closing them again; this gesture is known as 'wing-salute'. It is followed by preening movements along the back and by a forward bow, in which the wings are part-opened to expose the upper-wing coverts. All these movements display the brilliant red and black plumage of the wings, in a series of arresting signals. Finally, and rather rarely, a group of the birds may rush together with an outburst of calling, with heads and necks held in a crook-like posture; this appears to precede copulation, and is known as 'hooking'. Both sexes perform all these display movements and can be recognized by their relative height, females standing about 1 ft (30 cm) lower than males.

In the Lesser flamingo the wing movements, wing-salute, bow and preening are also performed, but are not the most important or striking part of the display. The main feature appears to develop from a movement akin to 'hooking'. Ten birds or more suddenly rush together and, packed so closely that their bodies touch and the breast of one bird overlaps the back of the one in front, they trot through the flock of other flamingos, attracting more and more as they go, till the displaying group may number several hundred. The moving mass, resembling some curious multi-legged monster, creates a dark red blotch in the paler pink of resting flocks and can be seen from afar. Within the flock they are too tight-packed to perform any of the wing movements of the Greater flamingo, but wag their heads from side to side, bicker with one another bill to bill, bob, or double the head and neck into a posture making it look as if the neck was broken. Display can continue for weeks and months, and while it may be a necessary preliminary, it does not always mean that the birds will breed. Lesser flamingos do not normally display close to their breeding ground, but at certain places, which are traditional. They seem to display only when large numbers are gathered on one lake. Both Greater and Lesser flamingos call more loudly and continuously than normal in display.

Flamingos prefer to breed on soft mud, in which they build characteristic mounds, usually 6–18 in (15–46 cm) high, shaped like truncated cones with a hollow on top. The density varies according to species, site and size. In Greater flamingos the nests are usually 1–2 per sq yd (0.9 sq m); but in Lesser flamingos, 4–5 per sq yd. Lesser flamingos excavate about 45 lb (20 kg) of mud per nest, Greater flamingos about 75 lb (35 kg). In Africa and South America Greater flamingos sometimes nest not on mudflats, but on rocky islands. They then make a slight nest of feathers, gravel and straws, or may lay virtually on the bare rock.

Normally one egg is laid in the hollow on top of the nest mound; about one in 300 nests contains two eggs, and two females may lay in the same nest. Eggs are large, elongated, pale blue, with a thick chalky layer which soon becomes stained. The yolk is blood red, like the fat stored in the adults' bodies.

Both sexes incubate, in all observed cases. The flamingo does not incubate, as in old travellers' tales, with the long legs hanging down beside the mud mound nest, but with them doubled under the bird and projecting behind like red drumsticks. The incubating flamingo continually bickers with its neighbours, picks up pieces of nest material, or may threaten a passing bird with a territorial display in which the feathers are raised so that the bird resembles a huge chrysanthemum. From time to time it will rise from the egg, move round the nest, then settle to incubate again. Incubation takes about 28 days in both the Greater and the Lesser flamingos, despite the difference in size.

The parent bird may actively assist the hatch by dragging the egg-shell from the emerging chick. When the shell cracks the parent continually lowers its head to the hatching chick and calls, perhaps imprinting its voice on the emerging chick's memory. The newly-hatched chicks are clad in soft,

Left: Lesser flamingos in flight.

Below: flamingo feeding chick on nest.

silky, grey down; occasionally albinos occur. The legs are swollen, soft and bright red. For the first few days the chick does not leave the nest mound; it may be unable to climb back onto it if disturbed. The legs harden and become blackish in four or five days and the chick then becomes more active.

Chicks are fed on liquid regurgitated matter containing (at least in the Greater flamingos) blood from the parent's crop. The chick and the parent both face forwards, but the adult's bill points backwards and is upside down. Tipping the upper mandible provides a channel of delivery. Very small chicks are often fed while being brooded under the parent's wing, but as soon as they become active they are normally fed standing. Both adults feed the chicks, at long intervals in the later stages of the fledging period. Each parent feeds only its own chick

Flat-backed millipedes

and not the chicks of other birds that beg. Each chick knows its parent's voice and when a calling adult alights, a particular chick will run to meet it.

After 10–12 days the chicks gather in herds, attended by a few adults. They may swim from island to island, or move about the colony, trampling everything in their path and gobbling fragments of egg-shell or membrane. In the Lesser flamingo the herds reach enormous numbers, but move away from the breeding ground and collect several miles away in a huge mass that may cover acres. Here they remain till almost ready to fly. In the Greater flamingo the herds of active young are never so large, but large enough to overrun and trample smaller chicks, or even force adults off their nests.

At one month the flamingo chick is the proverbial ugly duckling, with ungainly heavy legs, a bent black beak and dirty brown down through which the dull brown immature feathers emerge. It is difficult to believe it will ever develop the beauty of the adult. It is still fed by its parents, but is left more and more to itself in the company of other chicks in herds. The adults with these crèches become fewer as the chicks grow. The parents may have to forage far afield and will usually return to feed their chicks only at dusk or at night. The chicks are very vulnerable to avian predators, but are relatively safe from mammals on their inaccessible island or mudflat breeding grounds. Predation by vultures and eagles, however, normally accounts for less than 5% of the chicks hatched. Disease may sometimes decimate apparently healthy herds.

By 60 days old the chicks of both Lesser and Greater flamingos are feathered, have acquired the bent bills of the adults, and are increasingly feeding themselves. They make their first flights at 65–70 days, sometimes longer. Once they can fly, they quickly leave the breeding colonies and travel to other lakes, or to different parts of the same lake. As soon as they can feed themselves they become independent of the adults and usually keep to themselves in flocks.

The whole breeding cycle, from nest-building to the free flight of the young, takes about 100 days. Flamingos do not breed every year; and several years may pass without breeding, or they may breed several times in one year. Once they start to breed they are intensely gregarious; thousands of pairs will lay almost on the same day ensuring synchronization of all subsequent stages. In the Lesser flamingo, which apparently has only one or two main breeding grounds (the largest being at Lake Natron), a population of about 3,000,000 adults produces about 130,000 young per year on average. At this rate the mean age of adults must be over 20 years and probably individual flamingos live to a great age. Very little natural mortality is noticed, even where large flocks congregate, which tends to support the view that flamingos are very long-lived. FAMILY: Phoenicopteridae, ORDER: Anseriformes, CLASS: Aves.   L.B.

FLAT-BACKED MILLIPEDES, also known as polydesmoids, have the dorsal, lateral and ventral shields of each body ring fused into a rigid cylinder. In this respect they are like the Snake millipedes but, in contrast to the smooth outlines of the Snake millipedes, the posterior part of each ring spreads into a pair of wing-like keels. Most Flat-backed millipedes have 30 or 31 pairs of legs but some have 19, 21 or 22.

No polydesmoid has eyes but there are other millipedes belonging to the order Nematophora, Silk-spinning millipedes, which are also called Flat-backed millipedes and differ from the polydesmoids in having 30 rings and also eyes.

There are nearly 3,000 species in the order Polydesmoidea, which is the largest order of millipedes. All are blind and the stink glands secrete hydrocyanic acid. The South American *Platyrrhacus pictus* is nearly 6 in (15 cm) long and just less than 1 in (2·5 cm) wide. *Oxidus gracilis* is probably the most widely spread millipede. It is present throughout the tropical regions and its range has been extended into the temperate zones by its being introduced into hot-houses. Some polydesmoids are luminescent, for example, the appropriately named *Luminodesmus* of California. ORDER: Polydesmoidea, CLASS: Diplopoda, PHYLUM: Arthropoda.   J.G.B.

FLATFISHES, bottom-living fishes characterized by their highly flattened body-form and the extraordinary development which results in both eyes being on the same side of the head. They are grouped in the order Pleuronectiformes, Whereas a skate or an anglerfish is depressed, that is to say flattened from top to bottom, the flatfishes are compressed or flattened from side to side. The larva of a flatfish, however, is a perfectly normal symmetrical animal, much like the larval forms of other fishes, and it swims at the surface. During its development it undergoes a remarkable metamorphosis, the body gradually changing shape and becoming flattened, one eye moving across to the other side of the head and the mouth becoming, to varying degrees, asymmetrical also. By the time that both eyes are on the same side of the head, the small flatfish has settled on the bottom. Flatfishes lie on the 'blind' side, which in some groups is the right and in others is the left. The upper side of the body becomes pigmented but the blind side remains white. Occasionally freaks are found in which the lower surface is partially or even fully pigmented and, conversely, albinos have also been recorded. Normally, all members of a species lie on the same side, but in certain primitive flatfishes, such as the members of the Indian Ocean genus *Psettodes,* equal numbers are found lying on one as on the other side. In all flatfishes, except the primitive family Psettodidae, the dorsal fin is extremely long, extending not only the length of the body but forwards above the head. The anal fin is also very long indeed, the small pelvic fins lying just in front of it. One pectoral fin is on the upper side of the body while the other is on the blind side. In the soles (Soleidae) and the Tongue soles (Cynoglossidae) the pectoral fins are absent. The general body shape of the flatfishes varies considerably, from being almost disc-like to being quite elongated. Thus, the turbot and its relatives are almost as broad as they are long, while the little Tongue soles, as their name suggests, are rather long and narrow.

Most flatfishes are predators, spending much of their time on the bottom. For most of them, camouflage is important. In some this is achieved by covering the edges or even the whole body, except for the eyes,

Disturbed flamingos taking off.

Flatfishes

Plaice *Pleuronectes platessa* swimming. Its normal habit is to lie inconspicuously on the seabed.

Flounders *Platichthys flesus*, on pebbles, their colours changed to blend with the seabed.

with sand which they flick over themselves by a wriggling movement of the fins. Most flatfishes are predominantly brown in colour on the dorsal surface and only a few have any very striking colour-patterns, although a few species have strong black bars on the body. If a pattern is present, it is more usually made up of spots and blotches, The Peacock flounder *Bothus lunatus* of the American tropical Atlantic has purple rings and spots on a brown background while the plaice has well-marked orange spots. A number of flatfishes have the ability to change colour to match their background. In some fish, such as the Mediterranean *Bothus podas,* the ability to match a background is carried to such an extent that the fish will make a remarkably good attempt to produce a black and white pattern if layed on a chess board. Some American species of flounders of the genus *Paralichthys* can produce an effective camouflage on coloured backgrounds, although they are not very accurate in matching red backgrounds.

The halibut *Hippoglossus hippoglossus,* one of the largest of the flatfishes, reaching a length of 9 ft (2·7 m), is a very active swimmer that hunts for its prey. Other species make rather elegant flutterings after small crustaceans that come within their reach.

For the most part the flatfishes are marine, but a few species, including the flounder, can live either in the sea or in freshwaters. The small American flatfish *Achirus* is a freshwater species that is often imported into Europe as an aquarium fish. It provides a splendid example of certain uncharacteristic but revealing uses to which the flattened body can be put. Small *Achirus,* for example, have such a relatively large surface area to body weight ratio that they can suspend themselves from the surface of the water solely by surface tension. They are also able to form a vacuum with the underside of the body and can then adhere to rocks, leaves, or the glass sides of the tank.

Flatfishes are egg-layers and in most cases the sexes are similar in appearance. In *Bothus podas,* however, the eyes are much further apart in the males than in the females, while in *Arnoglossus imperialis* the first few rays of the dorsal fin in the male are elongated into a plume.

The flatfishes appear to be a very successful group judging from their wide distribution, They are found from the Antarctic Circle to beyond the Arctic Circle and they range from freshwater forms living in a few inches of water to marine species adapted to life at considerable depths. Even the halibut has been caught at depths of 3,000 ft (about 1,000 m). In temperate seas some species are represented by enormous numbers of indi-

Dab *Limanda limanda* half-hidden under sand it has flipped over itself with its fins.

Flatfishes

Flatfish with its head raised waiting for prey, such as a marine Bristle worm, to show its head above the sand.

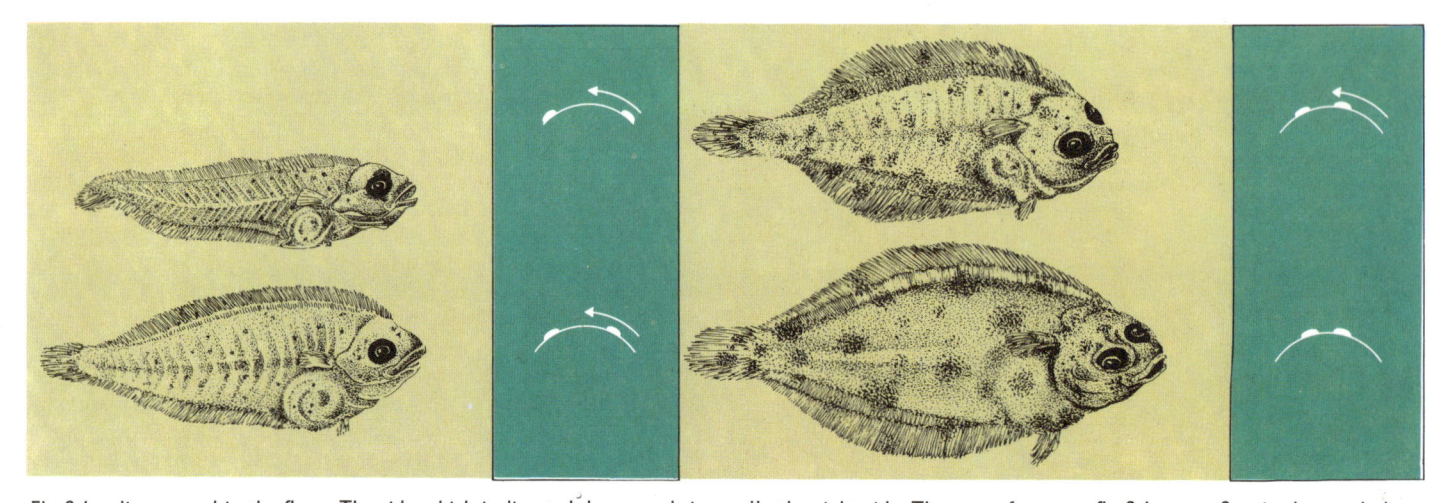

Flatfishes live on and in the floor. The side which is directed downwards is usually the right side. The eyes of a young flatfish are at first in the usual place, but one of the eyes soon moves to the top of the head and over to the other side. This migration lasts 45 days.

viduals and the flatfishes rank high amongst the commercially exploited fishes of the world. In the North Atlantic, species such as the plaice have been intensively fished and the demand seems at times to outstrip the natural rate of replacement of stocks. Since the pelagic stage of the larval life is the most vulnerable to predators, large scale experiments have been conducted in an attempt to maintain the larvae in tanks until they have metamorphosed and can safely rely on their camouflage at the bottom of the sea. The young are then transported to areas which are known to provide good growing conditions. The flesh of flatfishes is firm and white and they have long been regarded as amongst the most desirable of table fishes.

Flatfishes are regularly caught by trawl. Normally, a trawl net would merely pass over the fishes as it skims across the bottom, but by means of chains hung from a rope in front of the trawl the fishes are disturbed, swim up and are scooped up into the net.

The flatfishes form a very distinctive group, the characteristic flattened form and complicated metamorphosis apparently having proved sufficiently advantageous for numerous species to have evolved in this manner. The origin of the flatfishes is, however, a little obscure, although they are clearly derived from perch-like ancestors. The primitive genus *Psettodes* has pectoral and pelvic fins which are essentially perch-like in form and it is only the eyes and long dorsal fin that distinguish it superficially from the Sea perches. Certain perch-like fishes tend to rest on the bottom lying on one side, and the advantages that this gives in concealing the fish may have led to the evolution of the true flatfishes. The earliest fossil flatfishes, however, are already just as specialized as the modern forms.

Species of flatfishes are also described elsewhere under their common names. ORDER: Pleuronectiformes, CLASS: Pisces.

FLATHEADS, marine bottom-living shore fishes belonging to the group known as the Mailcheeked fishes. The head is flattened and the rather drab body colours provide camouflage for fishes which probably lie in wait for their prey. They are found in the Indo-Pacific region and some species are important to fisheries. The principal genus is *Platycephalus* (meaning 'flat-head'). FAMILY: Platycephalidae, ORDER: Scorpaeniformes, CLASS: Pisces.

FLATWORM, the common name applied to members of the phylum Platyhelminthes, a grouping of invertebrates which includes the free-living turbellarian worms and the parasitic flukes and tapeworms. See turbellarians, flukes and tapeworms.

FLEAS, comprising the insect order Siphonaptera (*siphon*—sucking-tube, *apteros*—wingless), appear to be related to the scorpionflies (Mecoptera) as is suggested by similarities in the structure of the gizzard and the sperm flagellum.

Fleas are small wingless insects with streamlined, laterally flattened, bodies which are hairy and shiny and varying in colour from yellowish brown to almost black. Fleas that live on animals having dense fine fur are sleeker and more streamlined than those living on coarse-coated hosts. Other fleas that spend most of their adult life in the nest of the host (nest fleas) may lack eyes or have reduced powers of jumping. In 'body fleas' the eyes are usually well developed, unless these fleas are parasites of wholly nocturnal hosts, such as bats, or of subterranean hosts. The short antennae lie in deep grooves, one on each side of the head, and are erectile in the male only (their function, in nearly all species, includes grasping the female during copulation). The mouthparts consist of two pairs of palps while three stiletto-shaped parts together form the piercing-sucking tube. Each of the three thoracic segments bears a pair of legs which are modified for clinging and, especially the hindlegs, for jumping.

Being parasites of warm-blooded animals (94% of the known species on non-marine mammals, 6% on birds), fleas are found wherever such hosts occur, even in Arctic and Antarctic areas; but temperate regions are the richest in flea species. Some 2,000 different kinds of fleas, grouped into some 200 genera and—at present—15 families, are known and probably another 400 await description.

The cycle of development from egg through larval and pupal stages, normally takes place in the nest or dwelling-place of the host. A female may produce several hundred eggs or more; a cat-flea, for instance, can under optimal conditions lay about 25 eggs a day for at least three or four weeks, or 800–1,000 eggs during its lifetime. Most eggs are laid during the female's sojourn on the host or in the latter's nest or lair and the majority will therefore land in the right places for the development of the elongate, pale, legless and eyeless larvae which hatch after a period of about five days, in the case of human- and cat-fleas. The larvae feed on organic debris present in the nest or dwelling place of the host. Blood is a nutritional requirement for larvae of many species. It is supplied by the feeding adult fleas ejecting faeces which consist of the remnants of digested blood of a previous meal followed by droplets of virtually undigested blood (these mark the underwear or bed linen of flea-infested persons). Some larvae can even prod adult fleas to produce faecal blood which they then suck up. Moreover, larvae are predators and scavengers and they attack, kill and devour weak and small arthropods present in the nest material, including adults of their own species. After two or three weeks, during which it moults twice, the larva is fully grown and spins a cocoon of silk produced by the salivary glands. The viscosity of freshly spun silk causes dust and other fine particles to adhere to the cocoon which will thus be camouflaged. Two or three days later the cocooned larva, or prepupa, sheds its skin and is transformed into a pupa. The duration of the pupal stage depends on the ambient temperature but is usually one or two weeks.

The adult flea, after emerging from the pupal case, requires a stimulus (usually vibration) to induce it to leave the cocoon and in the absence of this stimulus can remain alive, but inactive, within the cocoon for long periods. This peculiarity explains why the first person or animal to enter a dwelling or nest which had been uninhabited for a long time, may suddenly be attacked by innumerable fleas.

The adults of a number of species can copulate immediately after their emergence from the cocoon and egg-production may then begin after one or a few days; the females require nourishment before a batch of eggs is laid. In such species there is often no apparent linkage between the breeding season of the host and that of the flea. In other species the pattern of behaviour and development may be more or less completely interwoven with that of the host species. For instance, in the European rabbit-flea *Spilopsyllus cuniculi* both sexes undergo a period of maturation whilst feeding on a pregnant doe, influenced by an increase of hormones in her blood, and impregnation can only be effected after feeding on new-born rabbits.

Fleas can fast for long periods and this enables them to spend a considerable time searching for a host after their original host has died or has vacated its nest, or to await patiently the return of a host to the nest.

The males of all and the females of most species visit a host only temporarily, although repeatedly, for obtaining food. Such well-known species as the human-flea *Pulex irritans* (equally at home on badger and pig), cat-flea *Ctenocephalides felix*, dog/fox-flea *Ctenocephalides canis*, hedgehog-flea *Archaeopsylla erinacei* and chicken-flea *Ceratophyllus gallinae* (also very common in dry types of birds' nests) belong to this category. However, the females of the 30 species of the family Vermipsyllidae are more sedentary and remain on the host for most of their adult life in the cold season of the year. As they suck blood fairly continuously they may cause anaemia in host animals (mostly Carnivora); a heavy infestation with vermipsyllid fleas is called vermipsyllosis. In Central Asia the so-called alakurts cause vermipsyllosis in sheep and other large mammals. The abdomen of a gravid female alakurt expands enormously and may reach $\frac{5}{8}$ in (16 mm) in length and $\frac{4}{5}$ in (20 mm) in girth.

Excellent examples of modification, structurally and habitually, in response to a close association with the body of the host are found in the family Pulicidae. Two kinds of sedentary fleas can be distinguished here: (*a*) stick-fast fleas (species of *Echidnophaga* and *Hectopsylla*) which attach themselves with powerful mouthparts to the skin of the host (mammals and birds) and remain on the chosen safe spot till the end of their egg-

Flea, caught on man but probably of the species characteristically living on a cat or a dog.

The plague-flea *Xenopsylla cheopsis*.

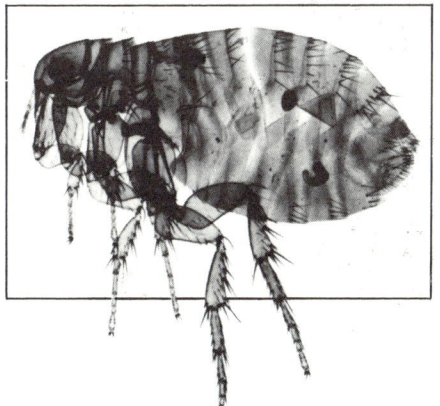

Flea circus

producing period, (b) jiggers or sand-fleas (species of *Tunga* and *Neotunga*), the females of which bury themselves under the skin of the host with the aid of strongly developed mouthparts, the abdominal tip, through which several thousand eggs are expelled, remaining just outside the surface of the skin. The abdomen of an embedded *Tunga penetrans*, the notorious jigger of Central and South America and tropical Africa, distends to reach the size and shape of a small pea. The presence of the common jigger in some part of the human skin often leads to inflammations (tungosis) while neglected jigger-lesions have in the past been responsible for the loss of toes or even a whole foot or leg.

Most fleas regularly commute between the bloodstream of one host and that of another, not necessarily related, animal. Consequently they are potential carriers (vectors) of micro-organisms that may be present in the blood of mammals and birds. From a medical point of view a number of fleas are highly important as vectors of plague, which is primarily a disease of rodents. The plague bacillus is transmitted from one animal to another by rodent-fleas and when a rodent dies of the disease its infected fleas will leave to attack other available animals, including man. The bubonic form of plague is transmitted either by regurgitation of some of the mass of bacilli contained in the digestive system of fleas which have become 'blocked' after being infected for some time, or by direct contamination from the flea's mouthparts. Plague has been a great killer in the past and is said to have influenced the course of history in various regions at various times. Fleas have thus left their mark on world history. They certainly have been effective indirect population-density regulators. The last great epidemic occurred in India between 1898 and 1918 when over ten million people died of plague.

Among other diseases spread by fleas are tularaemia (a plague-like disease of rodents and hares), murine typhus (a form of the louse-borne 'European' typhus, affecting many wild rodents) and myxomatosis (a highly lethal virus disease of the European rabbit). Fleas can also act as intermediate hosts for certain parasitic worms such as the common tapeworm of dogs and cats. Not infrequently mites are found on the abdomen of fleas, especially of nest-fleas, but they are usually there for transport only.

The fantastic agility of the fleas encountered by man and their liaison between the sexes of the host has made these insects almost symbols of frivolity and jollity and they inspired numerous popular stories, often of a jocular or amorous character. Around 1600, well before he was ordained Dean of St Paul's Cathedral in London, John Donne wrote the immortal lines:

'Marke but this flea, and marke in this,
How little that which thou deny'st me is;
It suck'd me first, and now sucks thee,
And in this flea, our two bloods mingled bee;
Thou know'st that this cannot be said
A sinne, nor shame, nor losse of maidenhead,
...'

ORDER: Siphonaptera, CLASS: Insecta, PHYLUM: Arthropoda. F.A.G.M.S.

FLEA CIRCUS. There seems to be no particular advantage to having fleas rather than any other insect as entertainers, except for their small size, which makes their acts more impressive. The flea circus was never a common form of entertainment, even in the days when fleas were more abundant on man and his domestic animals, as considerable time and patience was needed to produce the acts. Only human-fleas were suitable, and the best were said to be those imported from Russia. On joining the circus a flea was first given a collar made from a silk thread so that it could be easily handled. It was then taught to walk rather than hop, a process taking two weeks, and was then ready to be put to various acts. Some fleas towed carriages or model ships up to 240 times their own weight. Others played in orchestras, being tied down to chairs with instruments fixed to their legs. When stimulated, they waved their legs, and hence the instruments, apparently in time to a tune from a musical box. In return for this hard work the fleas were cossetted. They were given individual boxes for the night and allowed to feed, morning and evening, on their trainer's hand.

FLEDGING, the process of the development of a young bird's first true feathers. Birds are either hatched naked or clothed in down but they must have an efficient plumage when they leave the nest or the parents. When this plumage is fully developed the bird is considered to be fully fledged. The development of the feathers, from hatching to fledging, may take from a few days to many months, according to species.

FLEDGLING, a young bird as it reaches the final stage of development of its first true feathers and for a short period afterwards.

FLICKERS, North American woodpeckers of the genus *Colaptes*. They are medium-sized; the plumage dull brown and grey, heavily spotted and barred, but showing vivid yellow and red on the undersides of the wings and tail when in flight. Like the Green woodpecker *Picus viridis* they frequently feed on the ground, taking ants. FAMILY: Picidae, ORDER: Piciformes, CLASS: Aves.

FLIES, a word restricted by entomologists to insects of the order Diptera, the two-winged or true flies. In everyday speech, 'fly' is likely to be used for any winged insect, and through long-established usage this word forms part of the English names of a miscellany of insects from many different orders.

True flies are characterized by having the hind pair of wings modified into balancing organs known as halteres, which vibrate in time with the forewings. The halteres act as gyroscopes indicating to the fly any change in direction during flight, the principle being the same as that of the automatic pilot of an aeroplane. Many adult flies have lost their wings, and some of these have also lost the

Hover fly *Volucella* on a scabious flower.

The life-history of a blowfly. Top left: an adult female blowfly, attracted by the odour, seeks out dead or decaying flesh upon which to lay her eggs. Top right: blowfly larvae. Bottom left: blowfly pupae. Bottom right: adult blowflies.

halteres. To recognize these as flies requires expert knowledge of the detailed structure of head and thorax.

Diptera are related to scorpionflies, Caddis flies, butterflies and moths and fleas and together with these form the 'Panorpoid Complex', so called from *Panorpa* the common scorpionfly of the hedgerows. It is believed that the entire group originated from ancestors which bred in damp moss, from which some members, notably the butterflies and moths, became terrestrial, while others, notably the Caddis flies, became aquatic. Diptera show this divergence in evolution within the one order. A single family Tipulidae, which includes the craneflies, or Daddy long legs and many smaller relatives, has members which breed in moss, in decaying wood, in water and in soil. Most are vegetarian, some are carnivorous, as larvae. A recent Russian work recognizes 120 families of Diptera, although more conservative authors accept 30–40. None is quite so varied as the Tipulidae. Diptera are usually grouped into three suborders: Nematocera, Brachycera and Cyclorrhapha. Nematocera consist of Tipulidae plus two main groups of families. One group has aquatic larvae and adult females which characteristically suck blood: mosquitoes (Culicidae), blackflies (Simuliidae), sandflies (Phlebotomidae) and biting midges (Ceratopogonidae). To this group also belong the non-biting midges (Chironomidae), which are believed to be descended from biting ancestors. The other group of Nematocera have terrestrial larvae, and harmless, non-biting adults. They include the fungus-gnats (Mycetophilidae and Sciaridae), the March flies (Bibionidae) and the Gall midges (Cecidomyiidae), as well as certain other families of small midges. Brachycera include the Horse flies (Tabanidae) and several families of distinctive, though less familiar flies: the Soldier flies (Stratiomyidae), Sniper flies (Rhagionidae), Robber flies (Asilidae), Bee flies (Bombyliidae) and others. Transitional between these and the rest are the Dance flies (Empididae), the Long-legged flies (Dolichopodidae) and the Coffin flies (Phoridae). The large suborder Cyclorrhapha includes the Hover flies (Syrphidae) and a few close relatives, as well as two very large groups of families known as the 'calyptrates' and the 'acalyptrates' respectively. The calyptrates include very bristly flies such as the bluebottle and the House fly, while the acalyptrates are mostly small, less bristly flies like the Fruit fly *Drosophila* widely used in genetic experiments. Pupipara are a small group of flies that feed entirely on the blood of mammals, birds and bats.

When a fly 'bites' it really pierces the skin of its victim and sucks up the blood that flows. Most blood-sucking flies use stylets formed from the mandibles and maxillae, and blood-sucking is confined to the female. Males of these families have no mandibles and feed only from flowers. A few families have adopted the habit of sucking blood

Flies

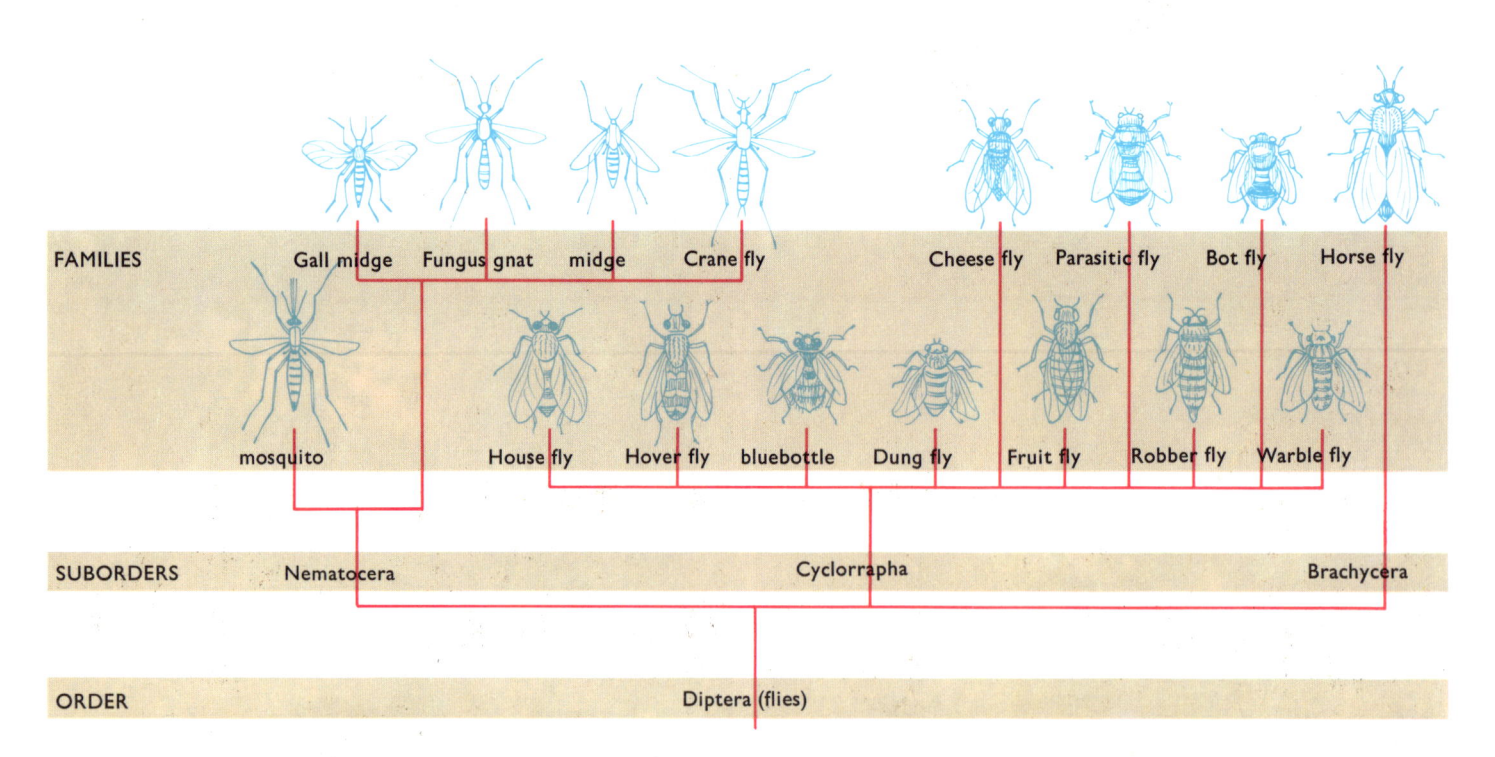

FAMILIES	Gall midge	Fungus gnat	midge	Crane fly		Cheese fly	Parasitic fly	Bot fly	Horse fly
	mosquito	House fly	Hover fly	bluebottle	Dung fly	Fruit fly	Robber fly	Warble fly	

SUBORDERS	Nematocera	Cyclorrapha	Brachycera

ORDER	Diptera (flies)

although they have lost the mandibles, so they have developed other methods of piercing. Robber flies (Asilidae) and Dance flies (Empididae) pierce the cuticle of other insects by means of the hypopharynx, suck them dry, and discard the empty skin. Tsetse flies, the Stable fly *Stomoxys*, and the Pupipara use the labium which, instead of being soft and spongy as it is in most flies, has become hard and tipped with teeth like a miniature oil-drill. A few other families of flies either crush small insect prey between their labella (lobes of the labium) or rasp the skin with specially hardened 'teeth'. Whenever a special method of piercing has been evolved it is common to both sexes. Many, perhaps most flies, also take nectar and pollen from flowers, the pollen providing a protein diet similar to but less concentrated than blood.

Flies are found in every part of the world, from the tropics to the arctic tundra, and from the tops of high mountains down to caves and mines. The biggest flies are tropical: some Robber flies in Madagascar are over 3 in (7·5 cm) long, and nearly 4 in (10 cm) in wing-span, and other huge flies occur in Australia and in South America. The smallest flies are little more than $\frac{1}{25}$ in (1 mm) long and occur in every region, though they are seldom seen unless they happen to be biting midges, which have a bite quite out of proportion to their small size. In inhospitable situations—towards the poles, high on mountains, or on remote islands—the number of species is low, but the number of individuals may be very large. In Alaska, Northern Canada or Northern Europe mosquitoes, Horse flies and blackflies can make human life almost unbearable during the short arctic summer. Flies found around mountain tops are often there for the purpose of flying in mating swarms, or have been carried up there by air-currents, but a few, notably the Snow fly *Chionea* (Tipulidae) may be found on the ground right up to the snowline. In the equatorial rain-forest the forest canopy forms a special habitat, in which many insects and other animals live, including flies which feed on the flowers of the forest trees, and others which bite the monkeys living in the tree-tops.

Flies normally pass through four stages during their lives: egg, larva, pupa and adult fly. This life-history may be telescoped at any point. Thus some Blow flies habitually hatch their eggs internally, and drop young larvae. Tsetse flies and the parasitic Hippoboscidae, Streblidae and Nycteribiidae nurture their young internally and do not drop the larva until it is ready to pass into the pupal stage: hence these latter three families are classed as Pupipara. The cecidomyiid *Miastor* can reproduce while still a larva, producing 'daughter larvae', and thus cutting out both pupa and adult stages. Most flies, however, pass the greater part of their lives as larvae and there is some ground for considering that, biologically, the larval stage is the real life of the insect and the adult, though more familiar to us, is biologically a short reproductive stage.

The larvae of the blood-sucking Nematocera (including those of the non-biting midges, Chironomidae, which are related) are aquatic, and are often highly modified for life in water by having various types of gills, for extracting oxygen from the water, or siphon-tubes through which they can reach to the surface and take in air. Some can pierce the stems of underwater plants, which often contain bubbles of oxygen formed by the process of photosynthesis. Larvae of blackflies anchor themselves, either to a submerged plant or to some underwater creature such as a crab or prawn, and capture minute fragments of plant or animal matter by sweeping it into their mouths with mouthbrushes. A few aquatic larvae feed on plant material, such as diatoms or algae, but many are carnivorous, living on single-celled animals and plants, on minute Crustacea, and any other water creatures small enough for the larvae to capture.

The larvae of many families live in decaying plant material or in the tissues of living plants. Thus there are two families called 'Fruit flies', one of which, the large Fruit flies (Trypetidae), live as larvae in growing fruit or in stems, or form galls on the leaves, while the other, the small Fruit flies (Drosophilidae) feed as larvae in decaying fruit and vegetable material. *Drosophila melanogaster* is the most famous insect of all, since it is used in experiments on genetics, partly because it is easy to breed in bottles with a mash of banana or other decaying fruit. Larvae of Cecidomyiidae form galls on many plants. A plant gall is formed when a larva feeds in the tissue of a leaf or stem, and its activity causes the plant to produce a mass of extra cells which form a swelling, the gall. A mine, on the other hand, is formed when a larva eats away the internal tissue, leaving only a thin, transparent skin. Leaves of trees and shrubs can often be seen bearing either a twisting pale pattern ('serpentine mine') or a pale blotch ('blotch mine'). The acalyptrate family Agromyzidae is the one most often associated with leaf-mines though sometimes flies from other families have this habit.

The versatile maggots of Cyclorrhapha participate in all these habits and some of them have become parasites, using the sharp mouth-hooks to penetrate the flesh of warm-blooded animals. Some only do this occasionally, living normally on decaying meat, or in dung, but others, such as the Screw-worm flies (Cuterebridae) burrow into the flesh and form a sort of boil, with a central hole through which the larva is able to obtain oxygen by means of its posterior spiracles. Such larvae are natural parasites of rats and other rodents, but may infest cattle and people, with disastrous results. Blow flies of various kinds, which normally lay their eggs in dead bodies, may sometimes lay them in the nose, throat or other natural orifices, or in wounds or sores, and the larvae may eat away at the living flesh. Some which always live internally are no longer pointed at the front end, but are blunt-ended larvae called bots or warbles, for example, the Horse botfly *Gasterophilus*, which lives as a larva in the stomachs of horses and related animals, a single host animal having perhaps hundreds of them at once. The larva of the Warble fly *Hypoderma* enters the skin of a cow on the legs and burrows up to the back, by way of the throat. When the larvae lie beneath the skin of the back they make breathing-holes which cause serious flaws in the leather made from the skin.

Flies affect man in three principal ways. First, perhaps, they are pre-eminent in their sheer annoyance. They are very persistent when trying to settle and suck blood, sweat or tears. The 'Sweat flies' of the genus *Hydrotaea* (Muscidae) are the ones which appear round one's head and face in summer, particularly under or near trees. They are among the many flies that gather in hundreds round the eyes and mouths of pasturing cattle, causing these animals continual disturbance. Out in the open cattle are much bothered by *Musca autumnalis,* a relative of the House fly. Until recently this fly was confined to the Old World, but in 1952 it appeared in North America and has increased so rapidly there that it has been given the name of the 'Face fly', and many pages of technical journals are devoted to articles about how to combat it. The House fly *Musca domestica* is well-named because it really follows man and has spread through human agency to all parts of the world. There are two main reasons for this, one being that the larvae can live in a wide variety of food materials, including most waste substances left lying about by man, and secondly because the adult fly likes to suck the same sort of sweet things that man likes. The House fly used to breed extensively in heaps of stable manure, but this food-supply has greatly diminished except in areas where horse-riding is a growing pastime. Modern living, however, relies more and more on packaged foods, which results in a growing pile of used packets and tins being dumped everywhere. If these are not most carefully disposed of, they provide new larval breeding-places, not only for the House fly, but also for many mosquitoes which can breed in the water that collects in tins and other containers every time it rains.

Secondly, flies of certain families are carriers of dangerous diseases. The mosquitoes are by far the most important of these, carrying malaria, Yellow fever, dengue, elephantiasis and many virus diseases that are only now beginning to be understood. Sand flies carry 'sandfly fever' and oriental sore, while Tsetse flies carry the deadly sleeping sickness to man, as well as nagana, a fatal disease of cattle and horses. The latter is believed to have been a principal cause of the slow development of parts of Africa until the railway, motor lorry and aeroplane replaced the horse as means of transport. Blackflies carry *Onchocerca*, a parasitic worm which can cause blindness. The House fly, besides being a nuisance, helps to spread a number of diseases of the intestine and the skin, particularly in overcrowded communities with poor sanitation.

Thirdly, the larvae of many flies attack growing plants and can cause damage to commercial crops. The Onion fly, the Cabbage root fly, and many kinds of Fruit flies, can all cause heavy financial loss to growers, who are tempted to try to control these flies with powerful insecticides which have harmful residual effects, and which themselves have to be controlled by legislation. ORDER: Diptera, CLASS: Insecta, PHYLUM: Arthropoda. H.O.

FLIGHT IN BIRDS. The bird is uniquely adapted for flying. In all birds, except those which have become secondarily flightless, the whole structure is so modified that the forelimbs can be utilized for flight and the hindlimbs for locomotion on land or in water.

The birds are one of the few groups of animals that have developed true flight, that is, the ability to move through the air with some continuing means of self-propulsion. Insects, pterosaurs and bats share this ability, the insects and bats with great and continuing success. But it is the birds which show this ability in its most highly developed

The mouthparts of the fly. Left: head in side view with mouthparts in section to show the complex tube, shown also in the cross-section bottom right, through which liquid food is sucked up through the tongue (labellum) into the mouth. Top right: mouthparts in front view.

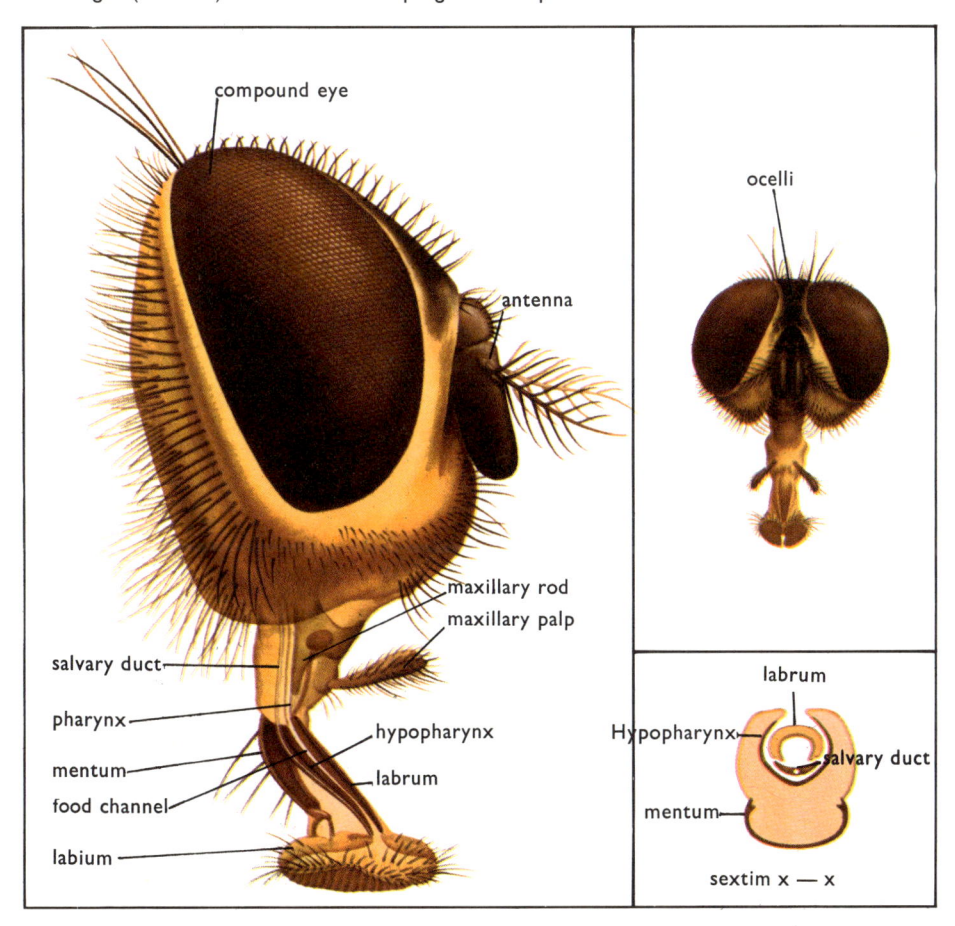

Flight in birds

Left: redstart *Phoenicurus phoenicurus* hovering. Right: redstart coming in to alight. Note position of wings and tail and also the Rat-tailed maggot in bill.

form, for the bats are, for the most part, clumsy on the ground and the insects are evolutionarily restricted by their relatively primitive form—they cannot, for example grow larger than a certain size, and their powers of temperature regulation are severely limited. Birds on the other hand are masters of both air and land, or water, and sometimes of all three.

A number of other isolated examples of animals developing the ability to move through the air are known, for example the 'flying' fishes, frog, lizard, snake, opossum and squirrel—and even the 'flying' squid. But these animals do not really fly, they glide, using a preliminary leap from an eminence or acceleration through water to launch them into the air, having negligible propulsive power in the 'wings'.

Adaptations for flight. These affect the whole structure. They are, therefore, all interrelated, but for ease of understanding and explanation they must be classified in some way. We may therefore speak of structural adaptations and behavioural ones. The structural adaptations involve the propulsive and directional characteristics of wings and tail and streamlining, which are all brought about by the development of feathers and the nature of the skeletal and muscular systems beneath. Structural modifications have also been centred around the problem of weight, and birds have achieved lightness in a number of ways. Teeth are heavy structures and birds have long since lost them. But bone is also heavy and birds, therefore, have a skeletal structure which is so organized that, by pneumatization and sculpturing of the bones, strength has been allied to lightness. They also have an air-sac system connected with the lungs which increases their buoyancy. Other structural features will be detailed below.

Behavioural adaptations for flight go hand in hand with the structural features as all structural modifications necessitate behavioural modifications. But certain behavioural features of flying birds are not directly related to their structure. For example, it is not common for birds to congregate together in close physical contact with one another except, in some cases, when sleeping. The reason for this is probably the need for an unobstructed take-off in the event of attack by predators.

Skeletal adaptation. The axial skeleton is very highly modified as compared with the reptilian precursors of birds. The skull is unique in its bony bill and rounded brain case of thin, fused plates of bone giving

European starlings gathering at a roost.

The Common tern *Sterna hirundo*, of Europe, with its long wings, necessary for fast flight.

strength with lightness. The backbone is distinguished by the length and mobility of the neck, the fusion in the trunk region and the reduction in the tail. The neck features are the result of the wings being specialized for flight, mobility of the neck being essential for preening, accurate vision and balance during locomotion. The bones of the trunk region are fused to form a long, strong and rigid 'synsacrum' which provides a central base by means of which the legs and wings are able to function independently without impairing the other bodily functions. The reduced tail skeleton is connected with the fact that the bird's tail is largely feathers which only require a small armature for their support.

The bird's sternum is much enlarged for the support of the flight muscles, the keel or carina being developed for this purpose. The rib cage, connecting the sternum with the backbone, is strengthened by special uncinate processes which connect each pair of ribs with the pair behind.

To the rib cage and sternum is attached the pectoral girdle—almost entirely modified for flight. It consists of three pairs of bones. The clavicles, or collar bones, are fused to form the furcula or wishbone which supports some muscles and an air sac. The scapulae, or shoulder blades, are small and extend backwards over the rib cage. The most important bone by far is the coracoid. This bone, lost in mammals, extends up from the front of the sternum on each side and contributes to the articulation of the wing while acting as the main element of strength in the pectoral region. At its upper end the coracoid joins the clavicle and scapula and, at their shared point of articulation, they form a special pulley—the foramen triosseum. Through this foramen passes the tendon of the minor pectoral flight muscle. The significance of this is as follows. Both major and minor pectoral muscles have their origin on

Flight in birds

the sternum and their outer attachment on the humerus and they both contract in the same direction. Yet the major muscle pulls the wing down, while the minor pulls it up. This is achieved by the attachment of the minor muscle tendon to the upperside of the humerus via the foramen triosseum, so that when the muscle contracts it pulls on the upper side of the humerus and the wing is lifted. The three bones of the pectoral girdle on each side also serve for the attachment of muscles which control the twisting of the wings.

The skeleton of the wing is also much modified. The humerus, except in flightless birds, is strong and freely movable around its point of articulation. It is unusual in that its ventral surface faces outwards when the wing is folded. The forearm skeleton consists of the usual vertebrate radius and ulna, the latter being posterior and bearing a row of projections for the attachment of the secondary feathers of the wing. The wrist and 'hand' skeleton is much reduced and consists mainly of a few bones fused to form the carpo-metacarpus, which acts as a rigid attachment for the primary flight feathers. The second (first apparent) digit acts as the support for the small slot arrangement on the leading edge of the wing known as the alula or bastard wing. The first and fifth digits are entirely absent.

The possession of *feathers is, of course, a primary contributor to the success of birds as flying bipeds. Not only do they provide light, strong, and versatile flight surfaces but also an insulating body covering which makes possible a highly efficient temperature-regulating mechanism. Without this a high degree of muscular activity and nervous control would be impossible. The primary and secondary flight feathers of the wing (remiges) and the flight feathers of the tail (rectrices) can be controlled by the bird to give a highly variable flight surface. The folding of the wing is generally understood but one tends to forget that the tail can be fanned or closed, or its attitude may be changed. The bird is unique in the degree of control it has over its aerodynamic surfaces.

Like the skeleton and the feathers the air-sac system may be regarded as having a multiple function. The air sacs, in association with the lungs, give the bird a highly efficient respiratory system. Air is swept through the lungs from one set of sacs to another and thus there is no dead air space as there is in mammals. As well as providing buoyancy this makes for a highly efficient metabolism.

Lift and wing shape. The aerodynamic properties of the wing are far from clearly understood. Either the wing sets up far less drag than is possible in man-made aerofoils, or the pectoral muscles are more efficient than is thought possible, or both.

When a symmetrically streamlined object is moved through the air there is no difference in pressure or velocity of the air passing over upper and lower surfaces as long as the object is heading directly into the current. If, however, the upper surface of the object is more curved or the lower surface flatter then the air over the upper surface moves faster and the pressure is there decreased. An object shaped in this way, that is an aerofoil, therefore tends to rise in the air.

At the front of the aerofoil the air molecules are first displaced and then accelerated and the least pressure and greatest lift is therefore above the leading edge of a wing. This effect can be increased by raising the leading edge of the wing (increasing the 'angle of attack') or increasing the camber (the curving of the surface) of the wing. But each of these procedures has the disadvantage that sooner or later the smooth air flow over the aerofoil will become disturbed and turbulent and the wing will stall—the lifting force is lost and the object will fall. This effect can, however, be offset to a certain extent by the development of slots at the wing tip and leading edge which modify the air flow at high angles of attack. Stalling is therefore delayed, that is it occurs at a greater angle of attack than without the slots.

These aerodynamic principles were being utilized by bird ancestors from the earliest times—at least 80 million years ago—and since then they have elaborated their flight techniques in many ways, some of which we do not yet understand. However, much is known of the ways in which birds have become masters of the air by developing their wing mechanism. In order for a bird to be able to move through the air it must be able to develop sufficient speed to produce a lift force equal to its weight. This lift force comes largely from the secondary feathers on the arm, while the forward momentum comes from the primaries of the wing tip. Variations in wing shape therefore are concerned very much with the relative requirements of speed and manoeuvrability, birds with long narrow wings being faster, those with short rounded ones being more manoeuvrable. However, an albatross would stall badly and be quite unable to fly under conditions in which a heron or crow would be perfectly happy. Wing shape, therefore, is the result of the interaction of a complex of factors including the use made of up-currents, the aspect ratio of the wing (proportion of length to breadth), the wing area and the general wing outline, as well as camber and slotting.

At high speeds the drag of the wing is proportional to its area × speed^2. Fast-flying birds therefore have small wings to reduce drag. But the wings also provide propulsion so they must be moved fast—at least in those birds which normally use flapping flight. The somewhat exceptional examples of fast-flying birds which have long wings, such as the albatrosses, are in fact high-speed gliders making use of strong winds to generate the required lift.

Slow flight requires a large wing area—lift also is proportional to area × speed^2—and slow flyers tend to have broad rounded wings, as in storks, herons, vultures and crows. This is particularly important in the case of birds which habitually soar in thermals, as demonstrated by the vultures. The wings of these birds are both long and wide, giving them a large wing area with a low aspect ratio (length of wing divided by average width), which results in a low wing loading (weight divided by wing area). They also have very highly developed slots at the wing tips and a deep camber. The total effect is one of unusually good lift at low air speeds.

Wing loading varies considerably in birds and is complicated by the fact that the weight increases as the cube of the linear dimensions but wing area only as the square. We would expect the larger birds to have relatively larger wings, but in fact their wings are not as large as might be predicted. This is because there are inherent disadvantages in having very large wings, and they approach the safety margin much more closely. Some known wing loadings, in kg/m^2, are goldcrest 1, crow 3, duck 10, swan 20.

Aspect ratio is important in that it is inversely proportional to drag, and this is one of the reasons why birds with fast flapping flight have high aspect ratio wings. A high aspect ratio also allows a low rate of descent in gliding—as in albatrosses—but a high aspect ratio wing stalls at relatively high air speeds and so slow overland soarers have a low aspect ratio. In swifts, which have the highest aspect ratio of fast overland flyers, there are numerous devices for reducing drag and the upstroke of the wing, as well as the

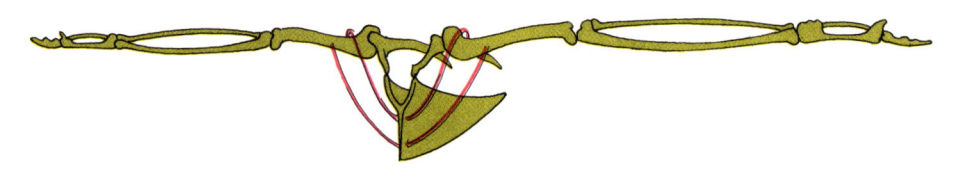

The two major muscles producing flapping of the wing run from the sternum to the humerus. The muscle pulling the wing down is much larger than that pulling the wing up.

Gulls against the setting sun.

downstroke, is powered, giving a double thrust.

General wing outline is important in that a pointed wing stalls first at the tip. Slow fliers, therefore, have low aspect ratio wings and have wing-tip slot devices for reducing turbulence. Stalling as a result of turbulence results from too low a speed or too great an angle of attack. The laminar flow of air over the wing is disturbed and it no longer functions efficiently as a support. But low aspect ratio wings and slow speeds go with high manoeuvrability and so in slow-flying birds the slots are particularly important. The primary feathers of such birds are emarginated in such a way that when they are spread slightly gaps are opened in the wing area at the tip. Air passes through these gaps with the result that the smooth air flow over the surface of the wing is maintained. A similar function is performed by the alula or bastard wing—the small group of feathers borne on the second (the apparent first) digit on the front of the wing. This, by reason of its physical characteristics is raised, not by muscular means, but by the pressure of the air current over the leading edge of the wing. At a certain angle of attack the alula automatically lifts and prevents stalling at that angle.

The slow-flying corvids and the soaring birds of prey have particularly well-developed slots and in the Californian condor they may occupy as much as 40% of the general wing area.

Wing action. Normal flapping flight is a complex procedure which is far from completely understood. The inner part of the wing moves less than the outer wing and operates more or less as if the bird were gliding. The wing as a whole is beaten rather rigidly downwards and forwards and then more quickly upwards and backwards, bent at the elbow and wrist. On the down stroke the wing tip has such a high angle of attack that it would stall if it were not for the fact that the tips of the primaries separate and each acts as an aerofoil, twisting up and back so that the resultant thrust is forwards. This is seen in a well-developed form in the pheasants and their relatives which have short broad wings developing a strong thrust.

In birds which hover in relatively still air the wing acts more in the horizontal plane, generating thrust on both 'up' and 'down' strokes. This is seen in its most highly developed form in the hummingbirds in which the wing acts essentially as a variable pitch propellor. The elbow and wrist joints are almost rigid but the wing is very freely moveable at the shoulder joint. The wing is mostly 'hand', the arm section being reduced, and is flat and pointed, without slots. Such an arrangement requires an enormous energy output, the hummingbird's pectoral muscles accounting for up to 30% of its body weight, and the metabolic rate is accordingly very high. So much energy is in fact used that hummingbirds often become torpid at night in order to conserve their reserves. Nevertheless this type of hovering

Flight in fishes

flight can be very successful, giving high manoeuvrability, as long as the bird has access to sufficient fuel of the right kind and has a high enough temperature in which to operate.

Take-off and landing are much more complex procedures than level flight. The smaller birds can obtain the necessary impetus by jumping into the air, but the larger ones often need to taxi considerable distances or fall from an eminence in order to become airborne. In still air an albatross on a ship's deck or a condor in a corral is grounded. It has been shown that in the pigeon's take-off the thrust is produced by a backward component of the upstroke while the lift comes from the very powerful downstroke in which the wings may meet above the body at the beginning of the stroke, to make the well-known clapping as they take off.

On landing the bird must lose speed in order to avoid crashing. This is usually achieved by stalling. When landing on a perch the bird prefers to approach it from below, losing speed as it gains height. In any case, the angle of attack is increased, a braking component is provided by the fanned tail, and the wings beat to counteract the forward movement to enable the bird to alight gently.

Many birds can fly at 50 mph (80 kmph) and some at 100 mph (160 kmph) or more. But it is not speed which makes birds masters of the air; it is the great range of aerial abilities which they display—individually and collectively—making them the most advanced of all flying ventures.   P.M.D.

FLIGHT IN FISHES has been evolved independently in several groups of bony fishes. The flight may be little more than a prolonged leap from the water in which the fish glides by means of expanded fins, or it may involve active flapping movements of the fins which serve to keep the fish airborne for half a minute or so. The most likely reason for the evolution of flight in certain groups is as a means of escape from predators.

The term flyingfish is most usually applied to the members of the marine family Exocoetidae. These fishes have streamlined bodies, large pectoral fins which can be spread like wings, and the lower lobe of the tail enlarged to provide the motive power for taxiing at the surface. It is interesting to note that in the related sauries and half-beaks the lower lobe of the tail is also larger than the upper although the pectoral fins are not greatly enlarged. Both the sauries and the half-beaks will skip along the surface, but the flyingfishes have taken this further and, having attained sufficient speed, will spread their 'wings' and glide. The species of *Cypselurus* have both enlarged pectorals and enlarged pelvic fins and they taxi at the surface and reach speeds of 35 mph (56 kph) before lifting themselves into the air. Species of *Exocoetus* have small pelvic fins and launch themselves straight from the water. The flight may last up to half a minute and the fishes can cover $\frac{1}{4}$ mile (400 m). Like some oceanic birds, the flyingfishes probably make use of the updraughts of air in the troughs of waves and in a stiff breeze may be lifted 20–30 ft (6–9 m) sometimes landing on the deck of a ship. Flyingfishes are hunted by the dolphins and many of the tuna-like fishes, and flight offers only temporary safety.

The so-called Flying gurnard *Dactylopterus volitans* also has very large pectoral fins which can be expanded horizontally as in the flyingfishes. It is a bottom-living fish found in the Mediterranean and the warmer parts of the Atlantic. No photographic evidence has been produced to show that this rather heavily-built fish ever flies. When disturbed, however, the Flying gurnard will suddenly spread its colourful pectoral fins and this flash of colour is startling and even a little menacing. It is quite possible that this is the true function of the 'wings'.

Flyingfish just before it leaves the water, showing that water is splashed before the fish breaks surface.

With head raised and forewings spread, the fish 'taxis' over the surface, the lower lobe of the tailfin still in the water.

There are also certain freshwater flyingfishes. In South American waters the little hatchetfishes belonging to the characin family, Gasteropelecidae, exhibit true flapping flight. Members of the genera *Gasteropelecus* and *Carnegiella* make little leaps out of the water while rapidly vibrating their sickle-shaped pectoral fins (causing a faint humming noise). The anterior part of the body is greatly deepened for the insertion of the relatively large muscles operating the pectoral fins. These fishes can fly for about 15 ft (4·5 m).

In Africa, the freshwater butterflyfish *Pantodon buchholtzi*, a relative of the Bony tongues, is also able to flap its large pectoral fins during flight. This species appears to require a short run before becoming airborne.

FLIGHT IN MAMMALS. Although many species of mammals are referred to as 'flying', such as Flying squirrels and the Flying lemur, they only take gliding flights from tree to tree. True flight in mammals, involving powered wingbeats, is confined to *bats. See also gliding in mammals.

FLIGHTLESS BIRDS, birds in which the powers of flight have been lost over a period of time as an accessory to the development of some other form of locomotion, or as the result of the lack of predatory pressure, or both.

Flying requires a great deal of energy, but all birds are derived from an originally flying stock. There must, therefore, have been—and still are—compelling reasons for birds to be able to fly and it is only when these reasons are outweighed by some stronger environmental factor that flight is lost. Principally, amongst recent birds at least, the loss of flight is seen in two major groups: the very large, running, 'ratite' birds such as the ostrich; and the penguins. The loss of flight has also occurred in some other groups scattered through the class Aves, and some further species either have poor powers of flight or are disinclined to take to the air.

Most of the ratites—the ostrich of South Africa, the rheas of South America, the cassowaries of Australia and New Guinea, the emu of Australia, and the recently extinct moas of New Zealand and Elephant birds of Madagascar—have specialized in a walking and running mode of life and large size. Thus their pelvic girdles and legs are very strong. The kiwis of New Zealand are exceptional among ratites in that they are not large and are nocturnal, hiding in burrows by day. Loss of flight in the ratites has been accompanied by a reduction in the structures associated with flight; thus the wings are reduced or lost and the sternum is not keeled for the attachment of flight muscles (hence the name for the group—from the Latin, 'ratis', a raft).

Adélie penguin *Pygoscelis adeliae* in the South Orkneys. Penguins are not only flightless, they have become fully adapted to an aquatic life while still remaining mobile on land.

In the highly successful penguins, however, the wings are not really reduced but modified, becoming flippers; the penguins, as it were, 'fly' through the water.

One other recent group of birds seems to have been entirely flightless; the dodo and solitaires of the Mascarine islands, comprising the family Raphidae. In the absence of any significant predators these birds became strong-legged ground-dwellers like the ratites, but, again like the ratites, suffered from man and his introduced animals later. They became extinct in the 17th and 18th centuries.

Madagascar still contains other flightless birds—some or all of the three species of mesites, which are ground-dwelling pheasant-like birds allied to the cranes. Another bird presumed to be flightless is the unusual kagu of New Caledonia, a grey, long-legged walking bird that hides in crevices during the day.

In the rail family, Rallidae, there are a number of flightless species and other recently-extinct ones, again living on what were previously uninhabited islands. These include the takahe and the wekas of New Zealand and the very small Inaccessible Island rail which has peculiar hair-like plumage.

Flightless cormorant *Nannopterum harrisi* and marine iguanas. Its wings, although entire, are ridiculously small, one-third of the bird's length. They can, however, be used for shading chicks.

Flight of insects

There are also flightless species of cormorant, on the Galapagos Islands; of grebe, on Lake Titicaca; of Steamer ducks, in the Falkland Islands; and of Owl parrots (the kakapo) in New Zealand.

Perhaps the most interesting example of a flightless species in an otherwise fully-winged group is the Great auk *Alca impennis*, which became extinct in the 19th century and showed a number of structural convergences with the penguins. It was a large bird and an expert swimmer. But it was helpless on land and was finally exterminated by man. See also dodo, ducks, Elephant bird, Great auk, kagu, penguins, rails, ratite birds, solitaire.

P.M.D.

Magellanic flightless Steamer duck *Tachyeres pteneres*, of the Falkland Islands. It is a marine Diving duck of very heavy build.

FLIGHT OF INSECTS. For an insect to fly, it must produce forces which lift it off the ground and propel it through the air. The forces are produced by flapping the wings and the aerodynamic principles involved are fundamentally the same as for other animals using this method of locomotion. What does differ is the way in which the wings are moved.

The wings of insects are flat folds of cuticle supported by hollow struts called veins. These are usually concentrated towards the front edge of the wing so that this remains stiff and straight as the wing moves up and down, while the back part bends more or less passively so as to offer as little resistance as possible to the movement. Basically insects have four wings, but only dragonflies seem to have become really efficient fliers by using the four wings independently of each other. In most other insects the fore- and hindwings of each side are linked so that they work together as a single unit. In many moths a spine on the hindwing hooks on to a catch at

Flight response

the base of the forewing, while bees have the two wings joined by a row of hooks along the front edge of the hindwing. Sometimes the wings are joined together so well that it is difficult to see that there are two wings on each side, but there always are, except in one big group of insects, the Diptera or two-winged flies. These have only one pair of proper wings, their hindwings being reduced to small knobbed structures, called halteres, which beat up and down, but are too small to add much to the forces produced by the forewings. The hindwings in this case have become special sense organs which play a big part in enabling the *flies to carry out their complex manoeuvres in the air.

With a few exceptions, the wings of insects are not moved up and down by muscles attached directly to them, as is the case with bats and birds. Instead, they are moved indirectly by muscles which change the shape of the thorax. The thorax contains many muscles, but two sets are of the greatest importance in flight. These are a set of vertical muscles running from top to bottom of the thorax and a set of horizontal muscles running from front to back. When the vertical muscles contract they pull down the top of the thorax and the articulation of the wings with the thorax is such that when this happens they flip up. The horizontal muscles have the opposite effect. By pulling on the two ends of the thorax they cause the top to bow up and the wings to flick down. Hence by the alternating contractions of these two sets of muscles the wings will move rhythmically up and down.

Normally a muscle contracts whenever it is stimulated by an electrical impulse carried along a nerve and in the slow flapping flight of butterflies and locusts, which flap their wings about 20 times per sec, the muscles are stimulated alternately and they contract each time they are stimulated. But bees and flies flap their wings very much faster, about 100 times per sec and here this simple explanation will not do because the muscles just do not work properly if they are stimulated too often, too quickly.

If, in an experiment, a muscle is stimulated with an electrical impulse 100 times a sec it contracts, but it does not relax, it simply stays contracted as long as we go on stimulating it. So how does an insect like the bee manage to beat its wings so rapidly? It can do this because it has special muscles, quite different from any found in other animals, which when stimulated by a nerve impulse contract, not once, but several times. This property depends on the elastic nature of the cuticle of the thorax and the precise rate of contraction and relaxation is determined by the resonance of the thorax. Stimulation by the nerve is only necessary to keep the muscle active and so need only occur at relatively infrequent intervals.

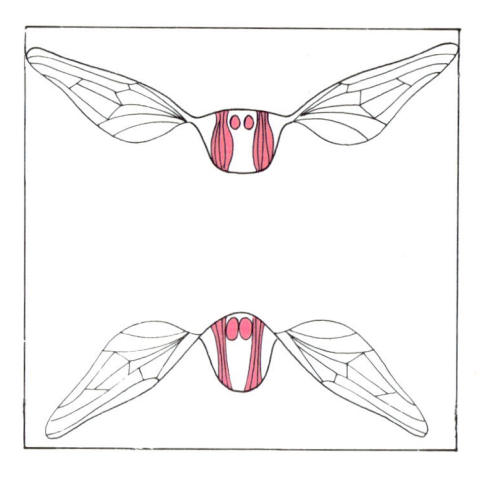

Movement of the wings in insects works upon a principle quite different to that of birds. The muscles are not attached to the wings but to the body wall. When the vertical muscles contract, the tergum flattens and the wings snap upwards; when the longitudinal muscles contract, the tergum arches and the wings snap upwards.

Just flapping the wings up and down does not produce flight; the movements must be modified so that the greatest forces are produced on the downbeat to push the insect into the air. This is achieved by twisting the wing so that on the downbeat its whole surface is used to press against the air, while on the upstroke only a small surface is presented. It is rather like feathering an oar while rowing. In flies this twisting is brought about automatically by the wing articulation, but in many insects there are special muscles attached directly to the base of the wing which cause the twist.

The speed of flight depends on the insect. Locusts fly at about 10 mph (16 kph) and can keep this up for hours. Flies, probably, usually fly at about half this speed, but can go faster in short bursts. They cannot fly for long because they use up all the energy necessary to make the muscles work. Locusts and butterflies which fly for long periods have big stores of fuel for providing energy and this is mostly in the form of fat instead of sugar as in insects which make only short flights.

Sometimes the whole character of insect flight changes. Many insects make short flitting flights from flower to flower or in pursuit of a mate. These are called trivial flights in contrast to the sustained flight which is characteristic of migration. On migratory flights insects seem to fly just for the sake of flying. They do not stop if they encounter a mate and are not deflected by obstacles in their paths, they simply fly over and on. Migration is not always as obvious as this and it is not easy to say where trivial flights end and migration begins.

Insects are the only invertebrates which can fly and their success as terrestrial animals is due in large part to the ease with which they can disperse through a habitat and spread from one habitat to another by flying. R.F.C.

FLIGHT RESPONSE, the reaction of a wild animal to approaching danger and its function is to put as great a distance as possible between the animal and the threat to its safety. Most animals capable of rapid movement show a flight response. Everyone is familiar with the way in which a House fly *Musca domestica* takes to rapid flight when it is chased and is attracted towards the light so that the possibility of escape is greater. The prawn *Palaemon elegans* has a flight reaction which consists of a rapid flicking of the abdomen which causes the animal to move swiftly backwards. The Common octopus *Octopus vulgaris* also moves backwards to escape from danger by rapidly ejecting a stream of water from its respiratory funnel. In addition to this form of jet propulsion the octopus also relies on camouflage and confusion of its enemy. During flight, the octopus may emit a dense cloud of ink and, as this emerges, it changes direction and may simultaneously change colour.

Wild mammals and birds usually allow a potentially dangerous animal to approach to within a certain distance before taking to flight. This distance has been termed the 'flight distance' and it varies for each species and different kinds of danger. It also varies within a species according to experience. For example, a Wood pigeon living in a town allows human beings to approach closer than one living in the country. A wild giraffe *Giraffa camelopardalis* allows a human being on foot to approach to within 150 yd (137 m) but a man in a car may approach to within 25 ft (7.6 m) of it, whilst a Herring gull *Larus argentatus* allows a man to approach to within 15–20 yd (14–18 m) but takes flight if a large dog *Canis familiaris* approaches to within 30 yd (27 m).

Wild animals may also show a flight response towards members of their own species: when a territorial animal is trespassing in a neighbour's territory or if a social animal is threatened by a higher ranking individual.

The flight response is usually a violent and vigorous reaction and is accompanied by the secretion of the hormone adrenalin which mobilizes the body's resources for violent action. During the flight response the animal may leap over a barrier which previously it had seemed incapable of surmounting.

Under some environmental conditions, especially if a clear escape route is not apparent, the flight response may be accompanied by a panic. The famous incident of the Munich elephant panic of 1888 is a well-documented case. A group of well trained circus elephants *Elephas indicus* were taking part in an orderly procession through the streets of Munich when a traction engine, disguised as a dragon, suddenly began to move and let off steam. The eight elephants alongside the engine panicked and fled, charging into the watching crowd. In this case a sudden shock induced the flight reaction in animals which were normally docile and well-behaved.

Most domesticated and tamed animals show no flight response towards man; this is also true of some birds which live on oceanic islands. See fear and panic. T.B.P.

FLIGHT RECORDS. The wingbeats of insects range from 5–9 per sec in large butterflies of the genus *Papilio* to about 1,000 per sec in the hairy-winged midge *Forcipomyia*, which has extraordinarily large flight muscles for its size. The number of wingbeats per sec is about 600 in mosquitoes, about 200 in honeybees and House flies, 130–240 in bumblebees and around 20 in dragonflies. Insects making short flights rely on sugar as a fuel and honeybees may have over 10% sugar in the blood, although the normal level is nearer 2½%. In man, by comparison, the sugar level in the blood is 0·1%. A honeybee's 'fuel tank' holds about 2·5 mgm of sugar and lasts about 15 min. This enables it to fly just over 3 miles (4½ km). The flight range of a honeybee limits the distance at which it can collect pollen and nectar. A Fruit fly carries sufficient reserves for a five hour flight and if flown to exhaustion it can take off again within 30 sec of a glucose meal.

FLOUNDER *Platichthys flesus,* one of the best known of European flatfishes. It can be distinguished from other inshore flatfishes by the opaque, mother-of-pearl whiteness of the underside. The upperside (right) is brownish-green with some faint orange marks which are similar to those found in the plaice, but soon disappear once the fish is out of water. The body is lozenge-shaped, there is a strong spine in front of the anal fin and the scales are small and embedded except along the bases of the dorsal and anal fins, behind the eyes and behind the gill cover, where they are firmly attached and rough.

Most flatfishes live their entire lives in the sea, but the flounder migrates up rivers to feed. Anglers are sometimes surprised to catch flounders 40 miles (65 km) or so from the coast. They spend most of the summer in rivers feeding and then in late autumn they make their way down the rivers, without feeding, to spawn in fairly deep water off the coast. Unlike the salmon, the flounder does not necessarily go back to the same river when it returns to feed in the spring. When in the sea, moderate migrations of several miles take place and one marked individual was found to have travelled 70 miles (112 km) in 18 days.

The flounder is common in the Mediterranean and is found in the eastern Atlantic as far north as Iceland. These fishes, the flesh of which is not particularly pleasing, reach 12–15 in (30–38 cm) and a weight of 6 lb (2·7 kg) although a 2 lb (0·9 kg) fish is considered a fair size. FAMILY: Pleuronectidae, ORDER: Pleuronectiformes, CLASS: Pisces.

FLOUR BEETLES, some of the many species of beetles occurring as pests in flour and associated products. The true Flour beetles are exclusively members of the family Tenebrionidae. Those of the genus *Tribolium* are reddish-brown or blackish, rather flat insects, ranging from 3–6 mm and may be found wherever flour and cereal products are manufactured or stored. The larvae are yellowish mobile grubs which burrow into flour, damaged grains, cereals, dried fruits, ground-nuts or spices. The Confused flour beetle *Tribolium confusum* is perhaps the most widespread species, being tolerant of wide temperature extremes. The Horned flour beetle *Gnathocerus* closely resembles *Tribolium*, but the males have large upward curving mandibles. FAMILY: Tenebrionidae, ORDER: Coleoptera, CLASS: Insecta, PHYLUM: Arthropoda.

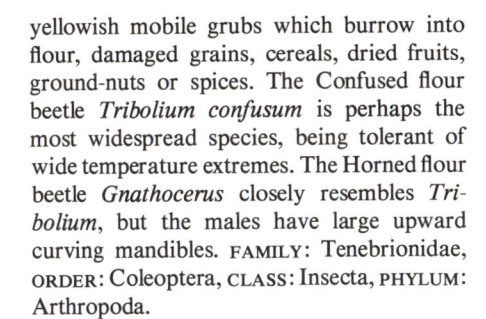

FLOUR BEETLE STUDIES. The Confused flour beetle *Tribolium confusum,* so called because of its similarity to a near relative, *T. castaneum,* has been the subject of many experiments on the growth and limitations of animal populations. Its particular value is that it lives in a homogeneous, simple environment, namely flour. When a small number of Flour beetles are placed in a box of flour there is an initial rapid increase followed by a tailing off to a steady maximum population. This is known as a sigmoid growth curve and the rate of increase and maximum numbers can be altered by varying temperature, humidity and so on. Experimental populations of other animals, such as Fruit flies and *Paramoecium* behave in a similar manner, as do natural populations, even of man, if they are in a simple environment.

FLOUR MITES, one of the many tiny arachnids, normally found in collections of debris, such as dry leaves, stubble and animals' nests, which are attracted to man's food stores. The so-called Flour mite *Acarus siro* shows a preference for the germ of wheat but can only attack damaged grain. Mechanical processes produce a good deal of this and so the protection of bulk stored grain, flour and similar substances presents a very real problem.

Associated with *Acarus siro*, are found *Tyrophagus* spp and glycyphagid mites. All these like a high relative humidity and, in fact, thrive in culture at relative humidities in the region of 80% at temperatures of 64–68°F (18–20°C). Consequently, the most effective preventive of infestation is storage under dry conditions. Flour and grain stored at 13% or less moisture content remains free of mites for a long time, even for periods of several years. The use of plastic sacks helps limit infection. Mites are not equally in need of moisture, glycyphagids being more so than the others, with *Tyrophagus* needing the least. Stringent precautions to keep stores clean are also necessary as these mites will feed in organic dust and on the moulds that grow thereon. The mites occur in the growing areas of grain

Profile of a flounder, from left side.

Flowerpeckers

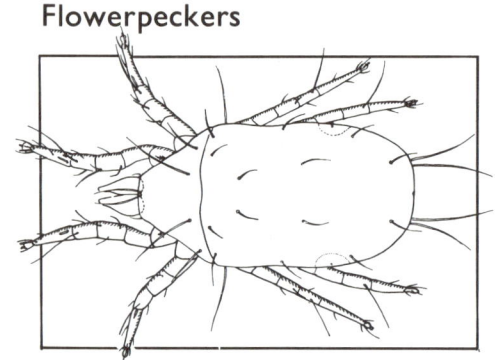

A Flour mite *Acarus siro*, female.

and may often be on the freshly harvested material; they can also be carried on clothing and on sacks, so that their introduction into stores is all too easy. The handling of quantities of mite-infested grain and flour can produce a dermatitis. This may be caused by some substance produced by the mite or by the sheer mechanical irritation caused by their minute bristles or setae. Flour infested by *Acarus siro* develops a typical musty smell. ORDER: Acari, CLASS: Arachnida, PHYLUM: Arthropoda. T.E.H.

FLOWERPECKERS, a family of small and often brightly coloured birds feeding on nectar or berries. There are 52 species occurring from India to China, and south through Indochina, Malaysia, the Philippines and Indonesia to Australasia and the Solomons. The typical flowerpeckers are small, 3–4 in (8–10 cm) long and rather short-tailed. They may be either dull green, with or without streaking below, or the males may be partly grey or black with areas of bright red, orange or yellow producing bold contrasting patterns. The bill may be slender and decurved like those of some sunbirds, or may be short and blunt. The slender type of bill is associated with nectar-feeding habits. Flowerpeckers have tongues deeply cleft at the tip, the two halves being rolled inwards at the edges to form a double tube used to suck up nectar, as in nectar-eating birds of other families. They feed on insects as well as nectar, many specializing in feeding on berries of various mistletoes which are swallowed rapidly and may pass through the bird very quickly, at times taking only a few minutes to do so. This is aided by a special structure of the stomach which allows the berries to pass rapidly but retains the less rapidly digestible food such as insects for more prolonged crushing and digesting. These species play an important part in dispersing the mistletoes by carrying the seeds to new sites.

The flowerpeckers are birds of forest and scrub. They are usually active in the upper foliage layers, being noisy, with sharp chipping calls, and constantly on the move. They usually occur singly or in pairs, except at temporarily rich food sources. Their nests are pendent domed structures suspended by a stalk of material from a support, and having an entrance high on one side, made of fine vegetable matter, bound with spiders' webs and lined with plant-down. In one species the material is felted together. The female appears to be responsible for nest-building and incubation, the male helping to feed the young.

The seven species of Australian pardalotes or diamond-birds (*Pardalotus*) are small and blunt-billed. The plumage is dull brown, black on head and flight feathers, with touches of white, red and yellow, and white spotting on head or dorsal plumage of some species. They feed on berries and insects and nest in holes in trees or in banks on the ground where they excavate tunnels, both members of the pair taking part. Domed nests are built in the cavities. The eggs are white. These species are more sociable than other flowerpeckers.

New Guinea has several genera of larger, dull-coloured flowerpeckers with short blunt bills or long slender ones, the former being berry-eaters. They build cup-shaped nests, in some cases finely-shaped closely-felted cups decorated with flakes of lichen. FAMILY: Dicaeidae, ORDER: Passeriformes, CLASS: Aves.

FLUKES, parasitic worms (Monogenea and Digenea) deriving their name from the Anglo-Saxon 'flok' meaning flat, referring to the fact that these worms, especially the monogeneans, often have flat, leaf-like bodies. The monogeneans are largely ectoparasites on fishes and have simple life-histories whilst the digeneans are endoparasites, having complex life-histories. The flukes usually have creamy, almost transparent bodies though the gut of blood-feeding forms may be conspicuously filled with dark brown haematin material, from the blood of the host. Most flukes are $\frac{1}{50}-\frac{2}{5}$ in (0.5–10 mm) long, so the Liver fluke *Fasciola hepatica*, which reaches just over 1 in (3 cm) in length, is a fairly large digenean,

Left: the Gill fluke of the Horse mackerel, living between the lamellae of the gills when adult. Right: the larval stages of digenean flukes.

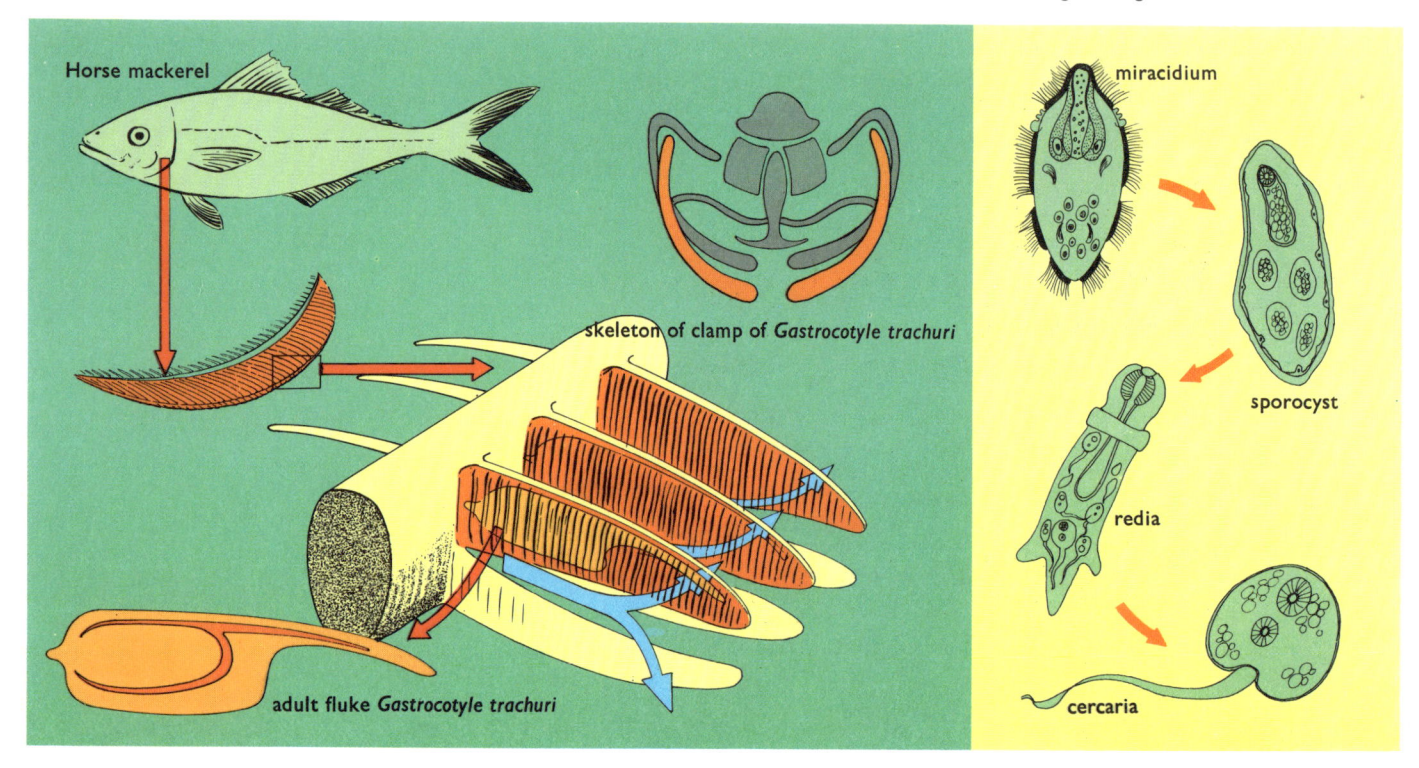

although the large American Liver fluke *Fascioloides magna* is said to reach a length of 4 in (10 cm) whilst an as yet un-named didymozoid digenean encysted in the sunfish *Mola mola* is said to measure 20-30 ft (6-9 m).

The flukes have the general characteristics of the phylum Platyhelminthes as well as the special features which adapt them to parasitism. Like all flatworms the flukes are acoelomate, bilaterally symmetrical and have a *flame cell or protonephridial type of excretory (or osmoregulatory) system. They have a gut (unlike the tapeworms) which is usually bifurcated and has a pumping pharynx. There is generally no anus and indigestible matter is regurgitated from the mouth. The region between the body wall and gut is packed with a cellular tissue termed parenchyma which may act as a transport system.

The body is limited by a kind of 'stretch girdle' of integumentary muscles which have circular, longitudinal and diagonal components. These muscles are particularly well developed in the regions of the often powerful adhesive suckers and the genital ducts. There is also a dorso-ventral muscle system. The nervous system consists of two cerebral ganglia (the brain) which give off three pairs of main nerves anteriorly and paired ventral and lateral (and a dorsal in the case of the digeneans) nerve cords and their transverse connectives, posteriorly. The submuscular nerve plexus is concentrated into these main nerve cords. Parasites are often mistakenly thought to have dispensed with sense organs; many monogeneans and digeneans have numerous sensory nerve bulbs sealed into the outer layer and these bear terminal cilia. Some of these sensillae (or small sense organs) probably act as tangoreceptors (specialized organs of touch) and others, the ciliated pits and sensillae composed of bunches of cilia, may be chemosensitive.

Like most platyhelminths the flukes are hermaphrodite and may have complex copulatory organs armed with sclerites or spines to ensure cross fertilization. They also produce an egg-shell of brown, quinone-tanned protein which prevents digestion of the egg by host enzymes in the case of the lung, liver and intestinal digeneans which use the host gut as an exit for their eggs; the tanned shell also protects eggs laid into water against bacterial attack. The egg-shell material, consisting of protein, phenols and phenolases, together with lipid-rich food reserves for the fertilized eggs is produced by the vitelline system which consists of a mass of vitelline follicles usually overlying the two caeca of the gut and joined by ducts which open into an ootype region with strong muscular walls. Here the egg-shell is moulded. From the ootype the egg passes through a uterus to the exterior. In digeneans the uterus may be used for insemination as well as acting as a passage for eggs, whilst monogeneans have separate vaginae for insemination. A special duct, termed Laurer's canal, is present in digeneans, which connects the ootype with the dorsal surface and may be used for insemination.

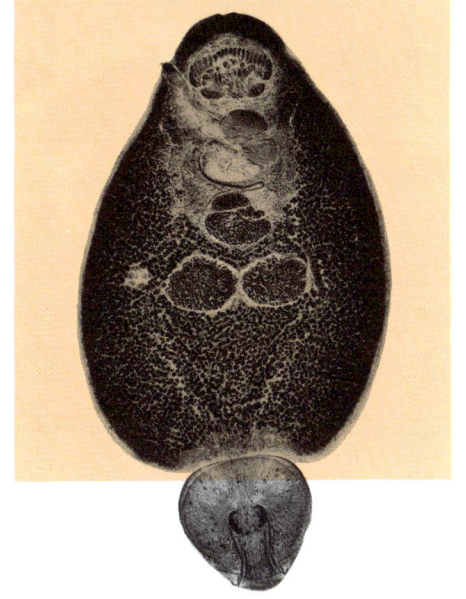

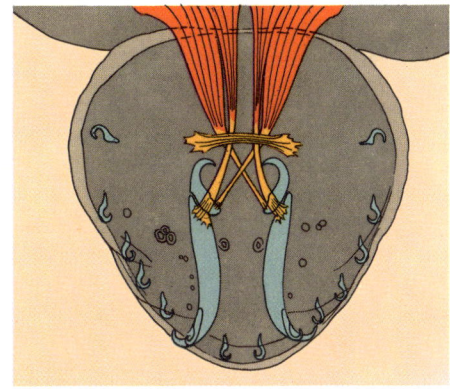

Above: *Entobdella soleae*, a fluke that parasitizes the skin of the Dover sole. Below: detailed structure of the posterior sucker of *Entobdella* showing large and small hooks.

Adaptations to parasitism. In addition to these general features the flukes have become modified in adaptation to a parasitic way of life. Their most noticeable feature is the presence of prominent muscular suckers, which in the monogeneans may be armed with hooks, spines and clamps for secure attachment to the host. The monogeneans have a single posterior adhesive organ (the haptor) whilst the digeneans typically have an oral and a ventral sucker (the acetabulum). Because adult flukes are largely sedentary, they no longer need a ciliated epidermis (for locomotion) of the kind found in the free-living turbellarians and indeed this is retained only in the free-swimming, host-locating fluke larvae, being shed when attachment to the host has occurred. The adult body covering of flukes is not an inert secreted cuticle, as was once thought, but a continuous layer of living cytoplasm uninterrupted by cell boundaries, which is not itself nucleated but is connected to cell bodies lying in the parenchyma beneath the muscle layers. The covering layer of flukes is therefore similar to that of tapeworms, although the cytoplasmic coat of the latter is greatly modified to absorb nutrients. The epidermis of many digeneans contains spines which may act as an accessory adhesive organ as well as perhaps helping to abrade tissues to be ingested, or to assist in burrowing and crawling.

In addition to muscular suckers, the monogeneans have anterior adhesive glands which assist in the leech-like, looping locomotion, performed by some skin parasites; the gill parasites being more sedentary. Adhesive glands are particularly important in the free-swimming larval stages of flukes because these have to locate and attach to a host. In addition to adhesive glands the miracidium larvae and cercaria larvae of digeneans have penetration glands containing enzymes which enable them to bore directly into their hosts.

The high reproductive rate of flukes compensates for the difficulties encountered in finding a suitable host. In digeneans also a process of larval multiplication by polyembryony, or subdivision of an embryo, occurs within the intermediate hosts. Thus a single digenean miracidium larva could give rise to many thousands of redia and cercaria larvae. Hermaphroditism is an obvious advantage to a parasite which might be isolated within the host, allowing self-fertilization. Cross fertilization is, however, usually the rule and the widespread occurrence of protandry, or the earlier maturation of the male gametes than female gametes, presumably encourages exchanges of sperm between different individuals before self-fertilization can occur. Two species of entobdellid monogeans have been found to produce spermatophores, or packets of sperm, which are apparently stuck to the skin of their respective fish hosts and then picked up by the muscular vagina of the partner, a way of transferring sperm efficiently without copulation.

Classification and evolution. It used to be customary to class the monogeneans and digeneans together as the class Trematoda, but there is now evidence that the monogeneans may be more closely related to the cestodes (tapeworms) than the digeneans and that they may also have a common origin. The term trematode is now used, therefore, to mean only digeneans and the Monogenea and Digenea have been made separate classes of equal importance to the class Cestoda.
Monogeneans. These are usually found on the gills and skin of marine fishes although some also occur on freshwater fishes. There are about 1,500 species, the majority of which occur on elasmobranchs (sharks and rays). Monogeneans not only parasitize fishes, some polystomes occur in reptiles and amphibians and an exceptional form *Oculotrema* occurs under the eyelids of the hippopotamus. Not

all monogeans are ectoparasites; some have migrated into the cloaca and oviducts of their hosts, for instance *Calicotyle* which occurs in rays, *Polystoma integerrimum* living in the bladder of frogs, and *Amphibdella torpedinis* living in the ventricle of the Electric ray as a juvenile and pushing out through the capillaries of the gills to become a gill-living ectoparasite as an adult. A dactylogyrid monogenean *Entogyrus cichlidarum* has actually been found living in the intestine of cichlid fishes. The tendency to endoparasitism of these contemporary monogeneans shows how cestode-like forms could have arisen from a monogenean-like ancestor.

There are two main types of monogeneans, skin parasites and gill parasites. The skin parasites have a single, usually undivided haptor, or posterior sucker, and this is typically armed with 12–16 small larval hooks arranged around its periphery. Towards the centre of the haptor are one or two pairs of large hooks or hamuli. Various kinds of accessory sclerites or connecting bars and plates may be associated with the hamuli and serve as areas for muscle attachment.

Entobdella soleae is a typical example of a skin parasite. It is about $\frac{1}{10}$ in (2·5 mm) long when mature and occurs on the skin of the sole *Solea solea*. Its haptor is a large circular sucker with around the periphery a valve-like flap of tissue and 14 tiny larval hooks which act like tent pegs keeping the haptor anchored around the edge. Two large hamuli occupy most of the centre of the sucker and there is also a pair of small hamuli. A pair of accessory sclerites lies at the anterior end of the large hamuli. It has been shown that once the sucker has become anchored around its edge the accessory sclerites are used to prop up the centre of the haptor creating a suction pressure. The roof of the sucker is supported by the long girder-like large hamuli which are operated by muscle-powered tendons and together with the small hamuli these gaff into the skin of the sole. *Entobdella* has prominent head glands which secrete an adhesive substance used to anchor the head whilst the haptor is detached during leech-like locomotion over the body of the host.

Some skin parasites have developed posterior accessory pads or suckers armed with spines, efficient attachment organs of prime importance to the monogeneans which, being ectoparasites, are subject to often quite powerful water currents tending to dislodge them from the host. The adhesive organs of the gill parasites are particularly specialized for here the haptor has become divided into separate adhesive units, or clamps, sometimes as many as 40–100, each of which grasps a secondary gill lamella of the host. So closely are these parasites adapted to their microhabitat on the gills of the host that their bodies have become asymmetrical to conform with the unilaterally incident gill currents of the host. Clamps are lost on the sheltered side of the body and are retained and may be increased in number on the side of the body that meets the gill current. Thus right- and left-footed gill parasites adapted to live on different sides of a gill occur in some species such as *Gastrocotyle trachuri* from the gills of the Horse mackerel *Trachurus trachurus*.

Monogeneans have a very simple life-history. Usually the egg hatches to liberate a ciliated larva, the oncomiracidium which is equipped with anterior adhesive glands and with a rudimentary haptor with a larval complement of attachment sclerites. The larvae locate the single host involved in the life-cycle, apparently by chemotaxis and attach to it by means of their adhesive organs. The ciliated epidermis is shed and the parasite remains attached to its host for the rest of its life. This cycle is termed monogenetic because only one kind of larva is involved. *Gyrodactylus*, which occurs on the skin and gills of carp and sticklebacks, does not produce a ciliated larva but is viviparous and reproduces by a kind of polyembryony, the adult enclosing an embryo which encloses three further embryos, one inside the other, like a Chinese puzzle box. Because this is a very efficient mode of reproduction and eliminates the hazards of a free-swimming stage, gyrodactyliasis builds up rapidly where fishes are kept in crowded conditions in aquaria or on fish farms and can cause the death of the hosts.

The fact that only one host is involved in the life-cycle has led to the development of a high degree of host specificity. This means that the parasites become so closely adapted to conditions on one host that they are unable to live on any other, also as the host evolves so the parasite adapts to meet the demands of its changing microhabitat. Thus a situation is eventually produced where related hosts bear parasites that are related to one another. Host specificity is particularly marked in gill parasitic monogeneans which may be physiologically adapted to imbibing a particular kind of blood from their hosts. It is so marked in this group that a particular species of monogenean is associated with only a single species of host. This high degree of physiological affinity that can be attained is particularly well demonstrated by the fact that development of the frog bladder parasite, *Polystoma*, is controlled by the hormones of the tadpole and frog host.

Digeneans or trematodes. The digeneans are endoparasites which live as adults in vertebrates occurring typically in the alimentary canal but also in the bile ducts and in the lungs. One group, the *schistosomes, occurs exclusively in the blood system. Less favoured sites are the coelom, urinogenital system, the swimbladder of fishes and various unusual sites such as the eye. There are about 5,000 species of digeneans and some of them are important parasites of man. The *Liver flukes *Clonorchis* and *Opisthorchis* infect people eating uncooked fish in Southeast Asia. *Schistosoma* causes a painful condition termed schistosomiasis, while *Paragonimus* causes lung fluke disease where infected raw freshwater crabs or crayfishes are eaten in Korea and Japan. Examples of digeneans infecting domestic animals of economic importance are *Fasciola hepatica* which causes 'liver rot' in sheep and cattle and *Paramphistomum* which parasitizes the rumen of sheep and cattle. See liver flukes.

The adult trematode characteristically has an oral and a ventral sucker but some groups such as the monostomes have only an oral sucker whilst the amphistomes have an oral and a posterior sucker. A group of trematodes, the strigeids, gut parasites of birds, have a special kind of oral holdfast organ which is formed from folds in the anterior body wall around the suckers. It secretes enzymes and is used in extracorporeal digestion.

These endoparasites develop through a series of larval stages which are unlike the adult with at least one and sometimes more changes of host, and are said to be digenetic. The first intermediate host is usually a mollusc, then the larvae emerging from this may penetrate into a second intermediate host which may be another mollusc, a crustacean or even a fish, before becoming adult in a vertebrate host. The digeneans show more specificity to the invertebrate intermediate hosts than to the definitive vertebrate host for a single species of digenean may become adult in several unrelated vertebrates which it enters more or less accidentally, due to the fact that these final hosts occur in the same area or eat the particular intermediate hosts used by the worm. It is therefore possible that digeneans are primarily and primitively parasites of invertebrates, whereas monogeneans and cestodes were probably primitively parasites of vertebrates. Digeneans are not confined to aquatic or amphibious hosts, as are most monogeneans, and have developed protective stages in the life-cycle, or ways of transmission that allow them to reach terrestrial hosts successfully.

A typical digenean life-cycle involves a free-swimming miracidium larva which penetrates, usually, a snail host by means of penetration glands. The ciliated coat is lost and the miracidium now becomes a sporocyst which feeds and grows actively within the snail's tissues. The sporocysts may be ovoid, cylindrical or branching. Germ cells in the miracidium grow and divide to form germ balls within the sporocyst and these develop into daughter sporocysts or into rediae. The rediae are cylindrical larvae with a collar just behind the head and two processes farther back known as lappets or procuscula. The rediae distend the sporocyst to the point of rupture and then migrate into the digestive gland of the snail. Each redia contains germ balls which produce either daughter rediae or cercaria larvae, so continuing the process of asexual reproduction started in the sporocyst. The cercaria is a tailed larva with a sucker pattern typical of the adult and a bifurcate gut as well as an excretory system.

The cercaria escapes from the redia through a pore immediately behind the collar and pushes through the tissues of the snail until it reaches the water in which the snail lives. Here, free-swimming, it uses its muscular tail to propel itself, or in some cases to attract a fish host which it will penetrate using its histolytic head glands. The next stage is one of encystment. The cercaria may encyst either freely, for instance on grass or on watercress in wet fields, as in *Fasciola*, or within the tissues of a second intermediate host, as in the case of some strigeids, the cercariae of which encyst in fishes, leeches and tadpoles. These are then eaten by the bird host. This cyst is known as a metacercaria, the layers of the cyst protecting the larval fluke against desiccation, in freely encysting forms, against host-immune reactions in the intermediate host and against host enzymes when the cyst is released in the gut of the host. CLASSES: Digenea, Monogenea, PHYLUM: Platyhelminthes. K.M.L.

FLUTEMOUTHS, small tropical marine fishes with elongated snouts, related to the trumpetfishes and Sea horses. They are placed in a small family containing only a single genus, *Fistularia*. The three or four species are found near the shore in tropical and subtropical parts of all oceans. They can be easily distinguished from the related trumpetfishes by the very long filament stemming from the centre of the tail, the filament often being as long as the fish itself (up to 6 ft or 1·8 m) in the case of the Red flutemouth *F. villosa*.

The flutemouths are long, cylindrical fishes with the dorsal and anal fins opposite each other and far back on the body. The most striking feature is the elongated snout, which is supported by the same series of bones as in other fishes but all are greatly elongated or distorted to produce a tube-like mouth with which the fish sucks in its food. The bones of the snout can be separated slightly while the jaws are closed. This has the effect of enlarging the cavity of the mouth so that when the jaws are opened small invertebrates are sucked in. To pass the food along to the throat waves of contractions can be set up along the snout. This feeding method is, in fact, highly successful judging by the size to which some species grow and the fact that specimens have been caught with whole fishes in their stomachs. The smaller flutemouths hug the reefs and are well camouflaged, but the larger fishes are found in open water. FAMILY: Fistulariidae, ORDER: Gasterosteiformes, CLASS: Pisces.

In common with the robin the spotted flycatcher will use almost any cavity for its nest.

FLYCATCHERS, term applied to certain perching birds of similar ecology but of two quite separate groups—one in the Old World and one in the New. Some members of each group capture insects by making short flights from a perch. The two groups are the Old World flycatchers, now placed in the subfamily Muscicapinae of the family Muscicapidae, and the New World flycatchers of the family Tyrannidae. The Old World flycatchers previously constituted the whole of the family Muscicapidae but recent reorganization and consideration of intermediate forms has united other forms, such as the thrushes and Old World warblers, in the same family. Certain of the species of Tyrannidae, a general name for which is 'Tyrant flycatchers', may be known under the name of 'tyrant', 'kingbird', 'phoebe' or 'pewee'—the last two arising from the bird's call.

The best-known of the Muscicapinae are the European species such as the Spotted flycatcher *Muscicapa striata,* an ashy-brown

Pied flycatcher at entrance to nest.

Flying dragons

Pied flycatcher in the act of seizing a fly in midair and hovering before turning to return to its perch.

bird with a creamy breast and the Pied flycatcher *Ficedula hypoleuca*, basically black above and white beneath; both birds being about 5 in (13 cm) long. There are over 300 other species, however, spread over the whole of the eastern hemisphere, except for the extreme north of Asia, and reaching New Zealand, the Marquesas and Hawaii in the Pacific. The species are very variable, some are dull-coloured, some very bright. A few are crested, others have face wattles. And the tail may be extremely long, as in the Paradise flycatchers of the genus *Terpsiphone* found around the Indian Ocean. In this species the males' central tail feathers may be elongated to give a total length of 21 in (53 cm).

The range of form in the Muscicapinae is well illustrated by the 50-odd species of the subfamily which live in New Guinea. These species are extremely diverse, within the limits defined by their basic insect-eating habit. They vary in bill shape, behaviour and tarsal length, so that some of them are more like warblers, chats or shrikes than flycatchers. Other species from elsewhere may be as well-built as a European blackbird or an American robin, or almost as slight as a kinglet, genus *Regulus*.

The Tyrant flycatchers—over 360 species, confined to North and South America—also show a considerable range of form. They vary from 3–16 in (7½–40 cm) including tail, in length, and from the grey of the Eastern phoebe *Sayornis phoebe* of North America, to the black, white, green, orange and scarlet of the Many-coloured tyrant *Tachuris rubrigastra* of South America. They also vary considerably in feeding habits, many being largely insectivorous, others taking small vertebrates as well as invertebrates, and others again eating fruits of various kinds.

The Tyrannidae cover a wide variety of habitats, from tropical rain-forest to desert and from coniferous forest to pampas. Most of the species, however, are neotropical. A wide variety of nest structure is seen in the family—open or domed, in bushes or trees, or in holes, or on the ground.

These two groups of flycatchers illustrate the advantages of being the primary occupants of a particular ecological niche complex. Each group has evolved many different forms to take advantage of the varied opportunities offered to flying insectivores in wooded terrain. See also Tyrant flycatchers. FAMILIES: Muscicapidae and Tyrannidae, ORDER: Passeriformes, CLASS: Aves. P.M.D.

FLYING DRAGONS, name commonly used for Flying lizards. They are among the most bizarre and gaudy members of the family Agamidae. 'Flying' is a misnomer, for unlike birds the 'wings' of these lizards are not supported by the forelimbs nor can they beat in flight. All four limbs are free for landing and for climbing on tree trunks but along the sides of the flattened body and between fore- and hindlegs are wings consisting of a thin membrane or skin stretched across greatly elongated and movable ribs. These ribs when extended provide the lizard with a taut patagium that can be opened and closed like a fan. When at rest on a tree the wings are closed; they open only when the lizard is displaying or when it is ready to launch itself from a trunk. As the lizard prepares to glide it turns, faces downwards, dives steeply, straightens out at an angle of about 22° and then as it is about to alight on another tree it banks so as to land in an upward position; the lizard then folds its wings. Although a few kinds of lizard can descend from the ground by parachuting, only the Flying dragon has the ability to glide and control the angle of descent.

Flying lizards have long dewlaps and wattles which in some species are vividly coloured, bright orange for instance in the large *Draco fimbriatus*, blue in the common *D. volans*. There is also sexual variation in the colour and length of these appendages. Over a dozen species are known, all restricted to the tropical forests of Southeast Asia and India and many feeding exclusively on ants. They reproduce throughout the year and one to four eggs, depending on species, are laid. None of the species attains a length of more than 12 in (30 cm). FAMILY: Agamidae, ORDER: Squamata, CLASS: Reptilia. A.G.C.G.

FLYING DRAGONS AS BABY FIRE EATERS. In the natural history books of the 15th and 16th centuries there were many accounts of dragons. In the *Serpentum et Draconum Historiae* written by Ulisse Aldrovandi in 1640 there is a charming picture of a two-legged dragon with bat's wings sprouting from its shoulder blades. This animal, described by other authors as well, was apparently on show in Paris as a baby dragon. From its size and general appearance it is not impossible that the baby dragon was a mutilated specimen of a Flying dragon *Draco volans* from the then newly discovered East Indies.

FLYINGFISHES, a term usually reserved for a family of marine fishes (Exocoetidae) with large pectoral fins adapted for gliding out of water. These fishes are discussed under flight in fishes.

FLYING FOXES, bats of the sub-order Megachiroptera, family Pteropidae, although sometimes restricted to the genus *Pteropus*. All are Old World fruit-eating bats which have dog-like faces, hence their name. Some species attain a large size and may be a nuisance to agriculture by raiding plantations. For further details see Bats.

FLYING GECKO *Ptychozoon homalocephalum*, also known as Fringed gecko or Parachute gecko, of Southeast Asia, has flaps of skin on its legs, tail and sides, those on the flanks being half as wide as the trunk. It is usually assumed that these flaps help to conceal the animal when it flattens itself, at rest, on a tree. Within recent years, however, tests have shown that they act as planing surfaces enabling the gecko to parachute at a steep angle to the ground. FAMILY: Gekkonidae, ORDER: Squamata, CLASS: Reptilia.

FLYING LEMUR *Cynocephalus volans*, also known as the colugo or kaguan, is neither a lemur nor does it fly. It is placed in an order on its own between the *Insectivora and the *bats. See gliding in mammals.

FLYING PHALANGERS or marsupial gliders, marsupials which glide from tree to tree and from tree to ground using a flap of skin which connects fore- and hindlimbs. The marsupial gliders range in size from the mouse-like Pigmy glider *Acrobates pygmaeus* to the lightly built but much larger Greater glider *Schoinobates volans* which may reach a length of over 3 ft (1 m). Gliders have soft fur, long tails, rounded heads and large eyes —conditions so exactly repeated in the true gliding squirrels that some of the first marsupial gliders described were included in the genera *Sciurus* and *Petaurista* along with the true squirrels of North America.

Three parallel evolutions of gliding membranes have occurred, apparently independently, amongst the gliding marsupials. The Pigmy glider has its nearest relatives amongst the Pigmy possums with which it shares common features of dentition, chromosome number and morphology. During gliding flights of a few yards the tail, fringed with hairs along each side, forms a featherlike rudder. The Sugar and Squirrel gliders *Petaurus* spp greatly resemble Leadbeater's possum *Gymnobelideus leadbeateri* which lacks only the gliding membrane. The membrane of Sugar and Squirrel gliders is attached to fore- and hindlimbs at the wrist and ankle while that of the Greater glider extends laterally only to the elbow and knee joints. The Greater glider has similar dentition to the Ringtail possums *Pseudocheirus* and like them has a restricted diet consisting almost entirely of leaves and blossoms. It has a very long, shallow gliding flight and near the ground may fall victim to a barbed wire fence.

The Flying phalangers have a generally eastern Australian largely coastal distribution. The Pigmy glider extends from Cape York, the extreme northern tip of the Australian continent, to the southern tip and westward to Spencer Gulf in South Australia. A single specimen recorded from New Guinea is thought to have been an introduction. The Greater glider has approximately the same distribution but is not found as far north or west and does not reach New Guinea. The Squirrel glider is of eastern Australian distribution and overlaps in range there with the Sugar glider which has a more extensive range extending to Tasmania (perhaps introduced), southeastern South Australia, Arnhem Land and other parts of the Northern Territory and neighbouring islands and New Guinea.

All, with the possible exception of the Pigmy glider, about which there is little information, produce young in winter which emerge from the pouch in spring and summer (August to February). The Pigmy glider produces about four young, the Squirrel and Sugar gliders two and the Greater glider one. Sugar gliders may produce two families in one breeding season. Their gestation period is 16 days and pouch life about three months. FAMILY: Phalangeridae, ORDER: Marsupialia, CLASS: Mammalia. G.B.S.

FLYING SNAKES, four species of Southeast Asian snakes, one of which is the oriental Golden tree snake *Chrysopelea ornata*. They live in trees and have developed a capacity both to leap from branch to branch and to descend over considerable distances to ground level in an inclined glide. The leaping ability is achieved by the sudden straightening of the body from a strongly coiled position. When gliding the body is held straight with the broad undersurface concave to form a 'parachute' surface. It is unlikely that these snakes have any ability to control the direction of the glide. FAMILY: Colubridae, ORDER: Squamata, CLASS: Reptilia.

FLYING SQUIRRELS, like all other 'flying' mammals except bats, do not really fly but they glide. They are true squirrels in that they belong to the same family of rodents, the Sciuridae, as the non-flying tree squirrels and the ground squirrels. There are about 30 species of flying squirrels, the great majority of them in the tropical forests of southeastern Asia, but with one species in temperate Eurasia and two in North America. Flying squirrels range in size from that of a small mouse, about 3 in (8 cm) without tail, e.g. the Pygmy flying squirrel *Petaurillus hosei* of Borneo, to that of a cat, e.g. the Giant flying squirrel *Petaurista petaurista* which is found throughout southeastern Asia.

The gliding is achieved by a membrane on each side of the body, stretching from the wrist to the ankle and in some species also between the hind legs and the tail. The membrane is furred on both sides and is supported in front by a rod of cartilage attached to the wrist. Although the membrane looks like only two layers of skin, it does in fact contain a thin layer of muscle by which its curvature can be altered to control the aerodynamic properties. The tail is generally about equal in length to the head and body and in most species the overall surface area is increased by the 'distichous' arrangement of hairs on the tail, the hairs spreading

The Sugar glider *Petaurus australis*; note the fold of skin between the legs, which is stretched out during gliding flight.

Foetus

Flying squirrel of the eastern United States.

sideways like the vanes of a feather. In most other details of structure flying squirrels closely resemble tree squirrels but, in keeping with their nocturnal habits, the eyes tend to be proportionally larger.

Flying squirrels usually nest in holes in trees and only emerge after dark, in contrast to the largely diurnal behaviour of most other squirrels. They tend to live entirely in the forest canopy and are therefore difficult to observe, and very little is known about many species. They glide from tree to tree, the larger species achieving glides of several hundred yards with very little loss of height. The gliding probably developed primarily as a means of escaping from predators, and they usually move by an extremely agile and rapid combination of running, climbing and leaping amongst the branches. The diet of flying squirrels probably does not differ much from that of other squirrels, being very varied with the emphasis on fruits, nuts and buds but including insects, birds' eggs and other items of animal origin.

Amongst the flying squirrels of southeastern Asia, one of the best known is the largest, *Petaurista petaurista,* which occurs, especially in montane forest, from the Himalayas and southern China through the Malaysia peninsula to Java and Borneo. It is a fairly uniform brown and the tail is very long and bushy, not flattened as in some other species.

In the coniferous forests of Siberia is found a small grey flying squirrel *Pteromys volans,* and two rather similar species occur in North America, a northern one *Glaucomys sabrinus* mainly in coniferous forest, and a southern one *Glaucomys volans* in deciduous forest throughout eastern USA. All these northern species are inactive in winter although they do not hibernate in the true sense. They nest in holes, sometimes using old woodpecker holes, and five or six may be found crowded together in one hole in cold winter weather.

Although both tree squirrels and ground squirrels are abundant in Africa, no members of the family Sciuridae in Africa have gliding membranes. However, there are flying squirrels in the rain-forests of West Africa which belong to a very different family of rodents, the Anomaluridae, generally known as Scaly-tailed squirrels. They show a range of size similar to that of the true flying squirrels and are superficially like them except for the tail, which is only densely haired at the tip. The most striking peculiarity is the presence of a double row of strong, sharply pointed scales under the basal half of the tail. These point backwards and enable the tail to act as a supporting limb when the squirrel is clinging to the vertical surface of a tree. The extremes of size are represented by the large *Anomalurus peli,* found in Ghana and the Ivory Coast, which measures about 18 in (45 cm) without the tail, and the tiny species of *Idiurus* of the Congo forest, measuring only 3 in (8 cm).
FAMILY: Sciuridae, ORDER: Rodentia, CLASS: Mammalia. G.B.C.

FOETUS, an *embryo in which the main features of the fully-formed animal are recognizable. The term is usually restricted to mammalian embryos.

FOLLICLE MITES, skin parasites which feed mainly on the products of the sebaceous glands, but probably also imbibe tissue fluid at times. This mode of life has led to profound modification in shape: the body is much elongated and annulated and the legs are very short. The life-cycle, on the other hand, is quite normal. The parasite spends its entire life in or on the skin and dissemination is by contact. In the species which infects man, the second nymphal stage leaves the follicles at times and is found on the surface; this is, presumably, the infective stage. Although probably universally present, it only rarely causes inconvenience in man. It is usually found round the root of the nose and on the eyelids and may spread to the scalp. In horses Follicle mites may cause loss of coat and skin eruptions but as in man and sheep, it can exist without clinical symptoms. On pigs, pustules are found on the more tender parts of the skin and on cattle, too, such nodules, which are sebaceous cysts, may be quite large, 1 in (2·5 cm) or more across; the mites are found inside the cheesy contents. In dogs, particularly thin-coated breeds like the dachsund, *Demodex canis* is a serious cause of mange, which usually starts on the head and ears, and can lead to loss of coat, thickening of the skin and formation of pustules, which become secondarily infected with staphylococci. This condition, which also occurs in cats, can become generalized. Since the mites are in the hair follicles, they are difficult to reach and until recently treatment was not very successful. Rotenone, benzyl benzoate, gammexane and selenium compounds have all now been used successfully. Benzyl benzoate is often toxic to cats. Some believe that the mites are transferred in dogs only during puppyhood. FAMILY: Demodicidae, ORDER: Astigmata, CLASS: Arachnida, PHYLUM: Arthropoda. T.E.H.

The Follicle mite *Demodex folliculorum* (male).

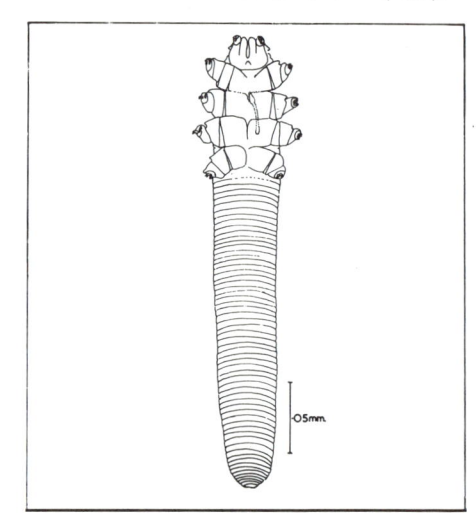